KING COBRA, *NAIA HANNAH*

The world's most dangerous serpent.   It ordinarily attains a length of twelve feet and has been recorded up to eighteen feet—the greatest known length of any poisonous snake.   Combined with its size is an insolent and at times aggressive disposition, powerful fangs and a proportionately great amount of the particularly lethal poison of the cobras.   It inhabits India, Indo-China, the Malay Peninsula, thence ranges through Malaysia including the Philippines.

SNAKES
OF THE WORLD

By RAYMOND L. DITMARS, Litt.D.

Curator of Mammals and Reptiles at the New York Zoological
Park; Fellow of the New York Academy of Sciences; Fellow
of the New York Zoological Society; Corresponding
Member of the Zoological Society of London

WITH ILLUSTRATIONS FROM LIFE

NEW YORK
THE MACMILLAN COMPANY
1943

NORWOOD PRESS LINOTYPE, INC.
NORWOOD, MASS., U. S. A.

To

GEORGE HURD

Who has accompanied the author
on many trips of investigation and adventure.

PREFACE

FROM numerous queries presented in person and by correspondence to the author, the need of a general book on snakes has been clearly indicated. Of the several groupings of reptiles, that of the serpents ranks far above the others in general interest. The principal reason for this is the fair portion of their numbers being poisonous, the bites of some species dramatically dangerous to man and the larger animals.

The preparation of this book has been largely guided by queries about snakes. Hence the thought has been to make it as practical as possible. The author has endeavoured to inject not only details to make interesting reading, but helpful information where the same is possible. The arrangement of the poisonous snakes of the world in zoogeographical chapters imparts particular significance to prospectors, exploring scientists or sportsmen going into various countries.

The photographic plates have undergone intensive thought and study. The captions on these plates alone are in excess of eight thousand words in elucidating characteristic points about the subjects figured. The text throughout carries reference to the respective plates, which are also to be found listed in the index.

R. L. D.

ACKNOWLEDGMENTS AND CREDITS

In the text of this work the author has drawn freely from scientific writings which he has in the near past prepared for publications of the New York Zoological Society; also from articles appearing in the Bulletin of the Antivenin Institute of America.

The Illustrations: The author and the publisher extend credit and their keen appreciation for photographs received from various sources, as follows: The greater number from the extensive photographic files of the New York Zoological Society. Also for series of photographs and separate illustrations from Dr. Afranio do Amaral, Chief of the Instituto Soro Therapico, at São Paulo, Brazil; the Antivenin Institute of America; John S. C. Boswell; Frederick Colville; William Fox (for the frontispiece of the king cobra); Andrew Halbren; Dr. Howard A. Kelly; L. M. Klauber (for the series of western rattlesnakes); Robert Lewis; Douglas D. H. March; Otto Martin Locke; Lewis Photographic Service of Panama City; R. Marlan Perkins; Raymond Stadelman; Anton Vestby (Honduran reptiles) and Dr. A. H. Wright.

CONTENTS

SNAKES OF THE WORLD

CHAPTER I

THE SERPENT'S WORLD

A LITHE black form is stretched upon the top of an old stone wall. The long and slender body lies in slightly suggested undulations. It appears tense and yet again soft and pliant as its outline follows the slightly uneven surface of the stones. Its hue is really blue-black and it glows with the luster of a new gun-barrel. The effect upon the average observer is three-fold. The thing is startling, it is decorative, and it is wholly incongruous—this vivid form so bold in contrast to its surroundings. The head quivers slightly. If the observer's eyes are keen this is seen to be caused by the rapid darting of a forked tongue. Then the black object appears to flow over the opposite side of the wall. There is a rustling murmur among dried leaves—a hissing-scrape—the sound so characteristic of a rapidly moving snake, and the thing is gone.

Thus we meet the blacksnake, an inoffensive type and a useful one, but startling, nevertheless, unless one has some knowledge of serpent life.

The supposition may be that such creatures are aimless wanderers, to be thus encountered now and then; that they crawl into some hole to pass the winter and emerge the coming year to prowl again and bob up in unexpected places.

Summing up the life history of the average blacksnake produces an interesting picture. It gives an idea of snakes generally. The serpent is lifted from the thought of a mere gliding thing in the grass and assumes individuality among the legions of animal life.

To begin with, the blacksnake is hatched from an egg. Some snakes are viviparous and produce living young and others are oviparous; that is, they lay eggs. The egg-laying kinds exceed the others in number, but not by a great majority. But to return to the origin of the blacksnake.

A female blacksnake has been steadily searching for a suitable hollow under a large flat stone. She is seeking a stone thick enough to absorb the sun's rays and retain considerable of this heat during the night. The stone must also be thick enough not to pass too great an amount of heat directly through it to the ground. The hollow beneath must be in ground or debris soft enough to be readily shoved about with her body in forming a nest for her eggs. The ground must be moderately damp. The rock should be on a hillside. While moderate dampness is sought the ground should be well drained. A part of the necessary moisture needed to develop the eggs will come from condensation beneath the rock during the night. With these requirements to be met the search for a suitable place will take a number of days. The time is invariably during the very early summer.

Finding the proper place the female serpent crawls beneath the rock and from the center shoves the earth outward with folds of her body. A circular or ovoid area is hollowed, with protective, sharply sloping sides and within this the eggs are laid to the number of one to two dozen. They are creamy white with a pliable, but tough covering. In form and size they are not unlike the eggs of the smaller birds. They are a bit more cylindrical perhaps, but this does not hold good with all snake eggs. Their chief difference is the pliable shell, like very thin leather.

The female blacksnake takes no further interest in her eggs, and has no further thought of her future young. She goes her way.

The eggs actually grow. They absorb moisture and from threadlike embryos the infant serpents within them increase in size until they are tightly packed within the eggs which have increased a third in diameter and may become lumpy and irregular in outline. A sharp point upon each infant's snout has developed—the "egg tooth"—this used to slit the shell and escape. The period of incubation has covered about eight weeks.

Emerging from the eggs the little serpents stay close by their nest for a day or so. They are quite unlike the parent, being gray, with large brown blotches. Within a week they are eating insect larvae, possibly young grasshoppers. This is very different food from that which they will seek when they have grown a few inches, but that is the way with all very young snakes, the early feeding habits of many of which remain a mystery.

Growth is rapid. They increase to twice their size by Autumn, but

remain quite unlike the parent in retaining their gray coat, although the brownish blotches are becoming darker. With the tang of chilling nights the inclination is to seek a deep fissure among the rocks and once it is found not to wander far away from it during the day. This is to be the winter shelter. The young serpent has already explored it—gone deeply into it. Whether or not that force called instinct prompts the reptile to realize that the fissure is deep enough to shelter it from penetration from frost, is a question. Certain it is that its investigation leads it to shelter safe from that curious point on the thermometer we call "thirty-two" if the scale be Fahrenheit, or "zero" at Centigrade. That is a fateful point in the decrease of temperature for most snakes. They can endure, while benumbed and motionless in hibernation, a temperature of close to freezing, but at or below that point where water freezes they are likely to be killed.

Well before the first slight frosts the little serpents of the brood are safely stowed away. Possibly a few have found the same crevice. They are sleek and fat and as during the winter sleep animation is practically suspended, they will emerge in much the same condition with the spring. Their next year's hibernation will be under quite different conditions. Not far from where they are lies the parent's den and they will find it. A few of them may have already found it.

From this point we will select the story of an individual. Possibly the story of the snake noted on the stone wall. Spring has warmed the ledgy bank and a young serpent issues from the hibernating crevice. It lurks near the sheltering fissure during the fickle weather of late April and early May then starts afield possibly reconnoitering along the borders of a marsh—for last year's frogs, developing during the summer from tadpoles, form ideal food for a snake of this size. There is a brief rest, hiding in a pile of loose stones as the serpent's lidless eyes are becoming dim with the thickening of the old skin. The eyes become white, like bubbles filled with smoke. Then they clear as an oily secretion forms under the old epidermis loosening it over the entire body.

The snake pushes the loose skin back over the upper jaw and lower jaw by rubbing among the rocks, then crawling forth catches the moist, tissue-like garment in the stubble and slowly crawls out of it, turning it wrongside out the entire length of the body clear to the tip of the tail. Right at the point where the skin is being turned backward there is a slight writhing of the scaly sides of the body—a con-

tracting to the rear, where the old epidermis is still encased and a muscular expanding forward of this. The skin slips backward and delicate as it is there is not a tear. It is an exquisite job, skillfully and slowly performed. It may take a full half hour. But there is a snake-skin in the grass! The whole garment is inverted. The integument that has covered the jaws gapes open and on the head-parts are the coverings of the lidless eyes like miniature, strongly concave lenses.

This early summer shedding is an event. The slim young creature glistens like new satin. It is a darker gray. The spots are fainter and will be gone after the next shedding. Wild mice are to be hunted in the nests, very young examples that are easily swallowed. With the assimilation of such prey growth is speeded. By late summer the young reptile is over two feet long and close to matching the lustrous blue-black of the parent. Only the abdominal parts are lighter—a pale, slaty gray.

A chill is again descending upon the woods at night. This is particularly apparent when the nights are still—when no breeze is stirring. On such nights there is a very heavy dew bringing into sharp evidence the webs of spiders which spin in the grass. At the very beginning of this period the blacksnake has turned its nose "homeward". But what is home? This means the parent's den. And here the snake is guided by an influence as remarkable and inexorably systematic as the autumnal migration of birds.

It may be two miles from the den when the seasons start to turn. Separating it from its goal may be marshes, undulating brooks, labyrinths of stone and tangles of vegetation. The force which appears to guide it is sense of direction. What else could there be? The topography of the ground produces hills and canyons. The vegetation is the equivalent to sightless jungle. The rocks present mazes of passages, but the serpent steadily works toward the den where its parents have hibernated for years, where their ancestors have hibernated, and their ancestors back for hundreds, and possibly much longer periods of years. The den of the adults is a specific spot—a ledge on a wild hillside, usually facing south. The whole side of the hill or mountain may be ledgy, but in that expanse of rock there is some spot where a fissure, or series of fissures lead a great distance inward and downward. The snakes found it ages ago. I have wandered over a whole mountainside and seldom found more than one den. The serpents that prowl the area for a mile or more know that spot and re-

turn to it each fall for shelter from *cold*. That word signifies the turning point in a snake's existence. Activity is influenced by the temperature of environmental air. The serpent's normal blood temperature is usually one degree lower than that of the air. A temperature of seventy to ninety is best conducive to its vivacity. Below seventy it slows down. At fifty it is nearly helpless. At forty it shows bare signs of life. Above ninety it seeks cooler shelter, undergrowth or damp ground where evaporation produces a lower temperature at the immediate surface. Even the serpents of the tropics avoid open places in the full glare of sun and desert types are averse to venturing abroad during the day unless scattered patches of vegetation offer close-lying oases of shelter from the heat.

So guided from the plight of exposure to cold the serpent starts for the den with the Autumn. It may linger at times through areas which I call "transient rocks".

These are large masses of stone retaining considerable heat from the sun as the night comes on. In such places, which are usually good feeding grounds, the snake may hesitate during a period of "Indian Summer", but moves on again after a shock or two from cool nights, warning it of frosts not far away.

A typical den is on the southerly slope of a hill or mountain of ledgy character. There may be a precipitous face of rock and at the bottom a jumbled mass of great fragments weighing tons. The spot denotes cataclysmic forces in action in dim ages past. Such forces have shattered the face of the cliff and among these shattered portions is a crevice at the bottom, or there may be several adjacent crevices. These form the den. The area is secluded and tangled. Wild grape writhes its way among the rocks. Numerous struggling trees have sought root wherever they could. "The crevice", however, is usually adjacent to a platform of broken stones or open patch, or patches, where in the spring the serpents emerge and in clusters lie intoxicated with the return of the life-giving sun with its temperature so necessary for their activity.

The blacksnake finds the hibernating lair of its parents and ancestors, ascending the slope past the first hibernating crevice of its early youth, where now with its stouter body it could barely squeeze in. It glides through the tangle of grape and woodbine to find other members of its kind, and still others of the serpent clan very different from itself. There are copperheads and rattlers on the shelf of the ledge, coiled tightly in precise circular fashion as is the way of these fanged

species, each with a symmetrical, and lateral loop of the neck laid flat upon its coils ready for a lunge of the head. The blacksnake may glide directly over some of these forms, but there is never a move on the part of the poisonous members, seldom as much as a tongue flash. The serpent clan is particularly tolerant or passive about the changing of position, arrival or departure of other members unless such are of the attacking or cannibal types and in the northerly areas of the blacksnake's range there are no such disturbing enemies. The blacksnake is alleged to attack the rattler, but he does nothing of the kind. He may eat an occasional young garter or ribbon snake, but he never battles with the rattler. He has no means of fighting such a powerful snake. Despite the scientific name constrictor, the blacksnake is not a constrictor. The title was applied to him years past by Linnaeus, in times when the respective habits of serpents were but vaguely noted.

So the rattlers, copperheads, and blacksnakes go into the den together in fine fraternity. I have seen bevies of heads of the three kinds peering from the crevices in spring when they had been lured by the warming ground to peek out, but were not inclined to venture forth as yet.

Such is the typical mountain den. Other kinds of serpents are not so keen about the higher ledges. The big mountain blacksnake, a slower and much heavier serpent than the racer occasionally takes advantage of such dens, but prefers sheltering deep in some disintegrating hollow of a big tree where the rotting debris is safe from freezing temperature. The striped snake and water snake prefer crevices in shaly banks close to streams.

During May the ledge-dens are populous with the emerged members—on certain days. These are times when the air is still and shade temperature along the ledge is close to seventy. As the ledge usually faces south and is in a great sheltered pocket of the mountain—for we have noted how particular the serpents are in selecting this spot—the ledge area is warmer than the outside open country.

May is the breeding season. It is the only breeding period throughout the warm months. During this time of the year occasional blacksnakes, of either sex may deliberately attack a human intruder upon the ledge. I have had them follow me twenty-five feet or more and make long sweeping strikes as high as my knees. Possibly one in twenty individuals will do this. The others skim over the rocks in flight with a grace and speed that invariably causes me to ponder just how they do

it. I have never noted a rattler or copperhead indicate any hint of actually attacking a human, as does the harmless member of the ledge clan.

There is no thought of eating among any of the serpents on the ledge until the mating period is over. By the end of May the exodus into surrounding woods and meadows where food is numerous is well under way. There is an outward stop at the transient rocks, then the clan radiates out in all directions. A favorite path of exploration is, oddly enough, provided by their greatest enemy—man. This is the old stone wall with its sheltering labyrinth of passageways and offering good hunting for the smaller rodents.

By mid-June, if the season is normally warm the average den is deserted. Selected as it is to get every benefit of the Spring sun the rocks are too hot for the snakes. On mountains running to a flat top and with numerous shelving rocks sun-sheltered by brush, some of the rattlers may remain not far from the den if hunting is good and water is available. Around the greater number of dens, however, one may look for days during the summer and see not the sign of a snake. The clan is scouting far afield and some may be as much as two miles away.

In a way, such habits apply to all serpents. They are not aimless wanderers. They live in little worlds of their own. Even in the mild winters of southern Florida, where hibernation is short and there may be practically no frost, I have noted that the great diamond rattler, found singly, here and there the greater part of the year, has its favorite spots to congregate in moderate numbers during the cool season. There are no extensive dens, but every rattler has its homing spot and six or eight may gather here each fall. The favorite sheltering place is under the roots of a great pine, which, standing well out of the soil at the base of the tree, offer cave-like shelters beneath, these extensively hollowed out by some burrowing mammal, or possibly a big gopher tortoise. The tropical serpents have similar places. And with them the shelter may be utilized in avoiding undue heat instead of the be-numbing touch of lowering temperature avoided by their northern allies. The roots of sage brush or fissured rocks form dens for the desert kinds. But all of them have specific places to which they regularly return, which places are the mating grounds. Summer wanderings are directly guided by two necessities—food and water.

CHAPTER II

THE SCOPE OF THE CLAN

THERE are slightly over two thousand different kinds of snakes. A large majority of this number is composed of non-venomous kinds, in great variety of form and size. The extent of this majority is far greater than ordinarily surmised.

There is but an approximate one-eighth of the known species of serpents with highly-developed poison conducting fangs and of this fraction not more than sixty per cent are really deadly to man.

Owing to radiating phases of development the scope of the serpent clan has produced a rather complicated classification. There are over a dozen distinct families and three hundred genera. Snakes range in size from thirty foot pythons weighing in excess of three hundred pounds to midgets less than six inches long which could glide through an orifice an eighth of an inch in diameter. In relationship the serpents are immediately allied with the lizards, in fact are assigned to the same scientific order—that of the scaled reptiles. Snakes differ from lizards in the body skeleton, being composed simply of a backbone and ribs. With a few there are vestiges of pelvic bones and rudimentary (internal) hind limbs. In considering the relationship, it should be understood that there are forms of legless lizards, of serpentine outlines but they lack the loosely-connected, expansible jaw structure for engulfing the prey entire, characteristic of snakes.

But why, comes the natural question, can the snakes—limbless creatures so similar from a general point of view—form so many families? Classification is based on the following points:

On the structure of the skull, which is of major importance in the separation of families. The skull may be of a type not to enable the serpent to swallow comparatively large food; that is the lower jaws may not be provided with the lever-like connections to extensively move forward to grasp and swallow by subsequent pulling of recurved teeth. There is a fair-sized family distributed through the Old and New World tropics of such species. All are small and mostly live in ant-hills and feed upon ant larvae. There is the family of boas and

8

pythons of the New and Old Worlds respectively. They have elasti-cally attached jaw mechanism enabling them to swallow very large food. They have rudimentary, internal hind limbs, which project as a pair of spurs from the body. The teeth of serpents, both in number, size and development greatly vary. The scalation covering their bodies, both in the number of rows, shape of the scales and their ar-rangement forms the basis for separation. With the poisonous ser-pents there is a sharp line of distinction from the other kinds owing to the presence of grooved or hollow fangs to inject poison. With one family the fangs are short and straight, and rigidly set. With two others they are of such length, they are necessarily attached to movable bones and fold back against the roof of the mouth when the jaws are closed. One family is composed of members which live in the sea and have a vertically compressed tail like an oar. Such are the differences which separate snakes into families.

The family of Colubrine serpents dominates all others by its size in numbers and far flung distribution of its members. It is made up largely of the typical harmless serpents of the world but there is an extensive series of species which have short fangs at the rear of the upper jaw and a comparatively mild poison to benumb their prey. The Colubrine serpents occur in every country where snakes are found. The family is so extensive that it is divided into several subfamilies. Its members differ from boas and pythons in having no vestiges of rudimentary hind limbs. This family contains approximately half the genera of all the known species of serpents. Some of these genera are so extensive that the family greatly dominates in the classified lists of serpents. While some of its members attain a length of ten feet, these larger kinds are slender and whip-like and are nowhere near the bulk of a boa or python of that length. Diminutive species are abun-dant, some of them scant of an eighth of an inch in diameter. Among species of moderate size, form varies from stout to extremely slender. While the greater number are moderately slender some have wide heads, thick bodies and resemble poisonous snakes of the viper type. Thus it is incorrect to figure that harmless serpents may be readily distin-guished by slender outline. The blacksnake, "milk" snake, striped snake, water snake, tropical rat snakes and the European grass snake are among the Colubrine kinds without rear fangs—in fact, typical harmless snakes. The family contains many species of great value to man as rodent destroyers.

Closely allied to the Colubrine snakes is a family which warrants recognition as such, only by possession in the upper jaw of a pair of short, rigidly set poison fangs. The members are ninety per cent slender, looking quite like the typical harmless serpents, yet among them are some of the world's most deadly reptiles. Here again is an illustration to shatter the common idea that poisonous serpents may be distinguished by form alone. Indiscriminately mixed with harmless serpents of ordinarily narrow head and moderately slender body, no one but an expert could distinguish members of this dangerously deceptive family. They are known as the Elapine snakes, the cobras of Africa and Asia, the Indian kraits, the African mambas, the Australian black and tiger snakes, and the brightly colored, slender coral snakes of the New World.

In the development of serpent life a number of the Elapine types appear to have taken to the sea and become highly specialized in the development of a vertically compressed, oar-like tail. These actual sea serpents form a recognized family, although they might be regarded as marine kraits or cobras. There are over fifty species, which range in size from three to twelve feet. They abound in the Indian ocean and western tropical Pacific.

Two families are composed of members which have reached the zenith of perfection in fang development. The long, poison-conducting teeth are like hypodermic needles. With their excessive development has come the perfection of a mechanism enabling them to be folded against the roof of the mouth when the jaws are closed. These are the vipers. The typical vipers are found only in the Old World and form a family in which is the European viper or adder, the Indian tic-polonga or Russell's viper ("The Speckled Band" of Conan Doyle's tales), the puff adder, rhinoceros viper and Gaboon viper, of Africa.

The other family of vipers is both New and Old World, although more elaborately represented in the former. Its numbers are distinguished by a deep pit between the eye and the nostril. Owing to this marked and curious development they are known as pit vipers. Among them are the rattlesnakes, copperhead and water moccasin of North America, the fer-de-lance and bushmaster of the American tropics and species rather similar to the copperhead and moccasin occurring in Asia, besides a number of medium-sized terrestrial and arboreal Asiatic species.

CHAPTER III

THE DISTRIBUTION OF SNAKES

WHEN serpents are collectively considered their distribution offers some interesting details. These might receive but cursory attention if injected here and there along extended descriptions.

While allied to lizards, the serpents present a rather different condition in world occurrence. Both lizards and snakes are far more abundant in species or kinds in the tropical latitudes, but lizards rapidly decrease in species in the temperate latitudes north and south of the equator, while serpent life is represented by a generous number of species well through the temperate zones and some of these, particularly in the northern temperate latitudes are abundantly represented in numbers well beyond the areas where lizards cease to occur. An example of this might be given in the New England states, where the lizards have dwindled to a single small species and that but sparingly seen. In that same area there are over a dozen species of snakes, the greater number rather generally common. Hence the serpent among all reptiles has become adapted to lower temperature conditions and through its care in selecting favorable hibernating quarters, as indicated by specific snake "dens", has most extensively pioneered in extending its numbers from the headquarters of the reptiles—the zones of heat and humidity.

With the exception of several inconsistencies in island distribution snakes occur in practically every part of the world where reptile life is possible. In the northerly hemisphere they dwindle to scant numbers in Canada slightly beyond the 50th parallel of latitude, while the grass snake and the European viper extend into Siberia. Serpents are usually more abundant, however, in the representation of their respective kinds in the temperate zones, than in the warmer climes. In all of the areas through which I have traveled and hunted I have never noted a greater abundance of serpent life than in some of the easterly counties of New York, or adjacent counties of New Jersey

and Pennsylvania. The same condition may be observed in Europe
with the widespread and common occurrence of the grass snake and
the viper, and similar conditions exist in the temperate latitudes of
eastern Asia.

In number of species the United States is rich in serpent life.
Here are over a hundred kinds of non-venomous snakes and close to
twenty poisonous species. Many of the species are extremely abundant. Europe, to the contrary, has rather a scant number of species,
there being not much over a dozen non-venomous and half a dozen
venomous kinds, although several of the species are extremely common.

Serpents have also spread through various types of terrain and
many have become highly specialized to markedly different environment.

Thus even the deserts have their respective types, while strictly
arboreal forms inhabit the jungle forests, swift, gliding kinds the
open places, semi-aquatic species the margins of ponds and streams
and forms with a vertically compressed, oar-like tail live in the tropical seas. The more highly specialized, poisonous species are particularly interesting in their distribution. Rattlesnakes occur only in the
New World and their headquarters are in the southwestern United
States where over a dozen kinds occur. Thence their distribution
radiates northward with but a single species in the northerly Pacific
region and plains states and two in the northeasterly portion of North
America.

There are two other species in the southeastern states. Several of
the essentially southwestern species extend easterly into Texas and
southerly into Mexico. Curiously enough, the extension of rattlesnake
distribution ranges all the way to the Argentine, but is represented by
only a single species throughout the tropical area. There is no doubt
but that in time some particularly keen scientist specializing in tropical
life will gather a series of Central and South American rattlers and
by their markings indicate the advisability of defining separate species,
but even in that event there can be no doubt as to the fact that the
tropical rattler is a distinct type, varying only a bit in pattern and lacking among its wide-spread races the variety in size, pattern and form
of the rattlers in their headquarters, which is the United States.

Practically every portion of the United States is inhabited by
poisonous snakes except northern Maine, although a full two thirds

of this area is inhabited only by rattlers. The copperhead is confined to the easterly states, the water moccasin to the southeast and the coral snake to the southerly areas.

Southern Mexico, Central America and South America, have a quite different race of poisonous serpents. The lance-head vipers, of which the fer-de-lance is a common type, are the dominating poisonous snakes of the New World tropics. There is also the great bushmaster and numerous coral snakes.

Consider then, the continents of North and South America, with their connection of Mexico and Central America. That far-flung area is practically everywhere inhabited by poisonous serpents. Where the continents join, the Gulf of Mexico and Caribbean indent the shores to form a great crescentic nest within which rest the luxuriant, tropical islands of Cuba, Jamaica, Hayti and Porto Rico, which harbor extensive series of reptilian species. Yet no poisonous serpent occurs upon these large islands. Nor does any poisonous snake occur anywhere in the West Indies except far southward in the chain, in Martinique and St. Lucia. Other great islands have no poisonous snakes, though close to infested mainlands and one of these is Madagascar.

The viper has never been found in Ireland although common in England and Scotland. Hawaii has no serpents. In marked contrast to this lack of island distribution is the case of a particularly deadly lance-head viper found on a very small island off the coast of southern Brazil about forty miles southwest of the Bay of Santos. This island is of steep and rocky slopes with separated patches of tropical vegetation. It has barely three quarters of a square mile of surface. Yet it teems with this tree viper which attains a length of between three and four feet and has developed a powerful poison to instantly subdue its prey, which consists of small birds which live upon the island. It has been found only on what is little more than a large sea rock washed on all sides by the open ocean.

Asia and the Malayan regions in the aggregate, despite their vast tropical areas have no greater variety of poisonous snakes than the New World. A considerable number may be listed from the entire area, but the species are actually not so bunched in their occurrence as in the New World. Several pit vipers, rather similar to the moccasin and copperhead are common in eastern Asia as are a number of

terrestrial and arboreal species of rather small size, but similar to the New World lance-head group, while the tic-polonga, or Russell's viper occurs through India, Malaysia and in the Dutch East Indies, upon the Island of Flores and even abounds upon such diminutive islands as Komodo. This true viper, without pits, is the tropical Orient's only good-sized representation of the typical vipers which have their headquarters in Africa. The vipers have done better in extending their range into Europe where half a dozen species occur. Several species of large Elapine poisonous snakes abound in the Oriental region. These are the kraits and the common cobra. There is also the rarer king cobra, the Old World's largest poisonous serpent. These cobras again are northerly allies from the great headquarters in Africa. There they occur to the number of a dozen kinds, with additional, immediately related forms. The cobras range from the sterile north coast and the margins of the great deserts, and south of the desert areas to the southerly part of the continent.

With Africa the center of cobra distribution, it is also the focal point of occurrence of the typical vipers—those species without pits. No pit vipers occur in Africa. The African vipers exist in lesser number of species than the pit vipers of tropical America, but they occur in every part of the continent except the lifeless wastes of the desert areas. They range well into the margins of the deserts, however, in the shape of forms highly specialized to traverse the sands by throwing lateral loops of their sand-colored bodies. The tropical and southerly portions of Africa are practically everywhere inhabited by big vipers with bodies that are proportionately so enormously stout and provided with such tremendous heads and excessive length of fangs that they are the most grotesque and hideous of all serpents as well as being frightfully poisonous. Then again there are slender and strictly arboreal vipers in Africa and others which look not unlike the harmless serpents, as they have plated heads. There is a genus of African vipers which have narrow heads and are burrowers.

Of all countries, Australia is the most remarkable in the character of its serpents. There are no viperine snakes—and there are comparatively few non-venomous serpents. Included among these are some species of moderate-sized pythons. But Australia has an extensive snake fauna. This consists of Elapine snakes, allies of the kraits and cobras and the coral snakes of the New World. With the

exception of a single species, the death "adder" which improperly carries the name owing to its stout body, they are of moderate thickness or slender build, with narrow, indistinct head, and look like the harmless snakes of other countries. Some of the most innocent in appearance are the most dangerous.

CHAPTER IV

GENERAL HABITS

THERE has been much conjecture about the methods of locomotion of serpents. The speed, strength and agility of many
species appears astonishing. The most spectacular illustrations are presented by the larger, slender-bodied types which can glide
with the speed of a running man. Here is true specialization, presenting a group of creatures which have lost their limbs yet acquired
remarkable dexterity with apparently little effort, through no visible
means.

Some of the slower gaits of snakes may be readily understood. The
lateral "looping" of the Old World desert vipers and the precisely
similar gait of the "sidewinder" rattlesnake of the deserts of the southwestern United States is no more nor less than a mechanically well
regulated necessity to keep from sinking in the sand. It exists only
among desert serpents and may be readily understood. The slow, forward progress of a rattlesnake or viper is actually not a glide, but
closely watched will be seen to consist of a movement of the ribs beneath
the skin which might be compared to a centipede clad in the skin of a
serpent and using its limbs in walking fashion. Such a gait, of the
slower moving species, when not frightened, is also assisted by hitching
forward, and drawing back, of the cross shields beneath the body, which
have their sharp and overlapping edges directed backward. Boas and
pythons also move along the ground in this fashion. Tree climbing
appears to be a combination of this method and of a following and
recently elucidated action which explains the possible and apparently
effortless speed of the racers and a number of other slender-bodied
kinds.

Doctor Walter Mosauer, of the University of Michigan has for
some time been conducting experiments with the gaits of serpents and
has come to the following conclusion: That the forward speed of the
quick moving species depends upon one or more declivities or projec-
tions upon the ground. They may be slight, in fact barely discernible.

All that is necessary is some form of resistance from the rear enabling the serpent to push forward. The action is indicated by the forward progress of quickly moving serpents being in undulations, never in a straight line. The undulations may be slight, but there is always some part of the body indicating a lateral bending to one side or the other.

The rear of the lateral loop, or there may be several loops, indicates a spot or several areas offering resistance for the elongated body to be pushed forward and utilized in rapidly thrusting or "feeding" it ahead. Doctor Mosauer made a number of photographs of serpent tracks on soft, uneven ground in studying these gaits and also made many experiments with specimens on smooth surfaces in which pegs were imbedded at frequent intervals. He found that snakes could maintain a high speed among the pegs, but on reaching a smooth surface where nothing existed for anchorage and pushing of the lateral body folds the serpent floundered, literally tried to "swim" over the area.

Some of the strictly arboreal serpents of the slower moving kinds, such as the tree boas and tree vipers have a dextrously prehensile tail which coils like a spring around a bough to make their lofty perch, on what may be slender branches, the more secure. Nearly all serpents swim gracefully and fast and some, like the freshwater snakes, are expert in quickly diving to the bottom to hide or pursue prey. The poisonous marine serpents are particularly expert swimmers, provided as they are with a vertically compressed, paddle-like tail and they are often seen a thousand miles or more from shore. Most of the smaller, burrowing snakes have either a conical head, or sharp, wedge-shaped snout to quickly bore into soft ground.

Methods of killing the prey have naturally developed along particularly unique lines. Many snakes feed upon animals capable of formidable defence from teeth and claws. As the serpent is limbless subjugation must be quick and particularly efficient or the elongate body, clad only in thin, soft scales, would be subject to grave injury.

Constriction or squeezing is employed by a large number of the non-venomous kinds. Their attacks are necessarily sure and quick and the enveloping coils are flung about the victim before it has an opportunity to bite. Such serpents may stealthily stalk a mammal or bird with the neck drawn into a lateral S-shaped, striking loop or may lurk in undergrowth and strike the animal as it goes by. The serpent strikes with widely distended jaws, the object being to so close upon the prey that the recurved teeth will be firmly engaged. The

animal is drawn toward the snake, the body of which is literally flung around it.   These movements are nearly simultaneous in most instances.   The whole operation of seizing the prey with the jaws, coiling about it and the beginning of constriction may be completed within a couple of seconds' time.   The prey is too confused by the rapid development of attack to defend itself and the seizure by the serpent is usually so manoeuvered that the animal is not in a position to use its teeth, while its feet are hopelessly bound.

Constriction is not so powerful as has been alleged by some writers. It is intended only to render it impossible for the animal to breathe.   It is a quick method of killing, quicker and more positive than is indicated among the habits of carnivorous mammals.

Even with the constriction of the boas and pythons the bones of an animal are not broken.   Such force is unnecessary and is not employed nor is the serpent capable of it.   Not every attack is successful in evading injury.   The animal may leap and turn at the instant of being struck which throws the serpent's calculation in advancing its coils, out of kilter.   The animal's head may thus not be in a position to be drawn through the loops of quickly thrown coils and in the general tangle it may be in a position to bite the reptile, but the snake pluckily holds on and squeezes the tighter with the object of rendering the defence of the prey as short as possible.   I have seen many snakes with large scars, particularly pythons which had been bitten by wild swine.

Some of the smaller Colubrine snakes quickly swallow their prey alive, this being typical of the toad and frog eaters.   They are provided, however, with special teeth to assist them in the operation.

Toads and frogs usually puff up prodigiously when seized by such snakes and would be extremely difficult objects to engulf entire unless the greatly inflated body could be punctured to release the air.   This is accomplished by greatly enlarged teeth in the posterior portion of the serpent's mouth.

A similar provision, though employed in quite a different way exists among the so-called rear-fanged serpents.   A large number of such species inhabit the warmer latitudes.   Most of them are but mildly poisonous to humans, in fact seldom bite and accidents from such kinds are rare.   They feed largely upon lizards, which would form awkward, struggling prey unless quickly subdued.   The serpent's grooved fangs carry a benumbing poison.   The prey is seized and with several quick forward motions of the maxillary bones the

upper jaws are so advanced that the rear fangs are brought into play. They serve a double purpose—as hooks to hold the prey and to inject their paralyzing poison.   The victim is soon limp and inert and swallowed without more ado.

The deadly Elapine snakes, such as the kraits, cobras, mambas, the prevailing species of Australia and the New World coral snakes seize and hold their prey in similar fashion.   Many of them feed upon larger prey than the rear fanged serpents, but their poison is far more powerful and more shocking in its action; a cobra has no hesitation in attacking, holding, and will quickly subdue a savage rat.

One of the most dramatic manifestations in Nature is illustrated in the method of the vipers in killing the prey.   With these creatures, the fang development has attained its greatest perfection.   The fangs are elongated hypodermic needles and the venom can thus be deeply injected into small animals.   The use of the term "vipers" indicates the feeding habits existing among the New and Old World pit vipers and the typical vipers without pits—the prey, for instance, being similarly subdued by rattlesnakes and the thick-bodied vipers of Africa.

But few of the vipers retain their hold of the prey after striking it. Their usual action is to strike from a lateral S-shaped loop of the neck, either while gliding or from a coiled position.   The whole action, from the launching of the head forward until the return to the original position, with closed jaws, appears like nothing more than a flash of movement.   The human eye is unable to diagnose the operation, yet the same is complex in several perfectly completed actions.

As the jaws start forward in the strike they are widely opened. The long, recurved fangs on their movable bones swing forward until they point almost directly at the object to be struck.   Reaching the target they are imbedded partially by the thrust and by a biting movement simultaneously started.   At the instant of the biting movement, in fact creating that movement, the masseter muscles in the upper jaw contract and in so doing press against and squeeze the poison glands. The bite is accompanied by an instantaneous jet of venom from the hollow fangs, which leaves the orifice at the tips now deeply imbedded. The flash of withdrawal of the fangs is almost as quick as penetration and the serpent resumes the original position.   The whole process of striking, injecting the poison and return to the lateral loop of the neck is accomplished as quickly as the fall of an object like an orange from one's hand to the ground.

Injected into the vital parts of a small animal the effect of the poison is almost instantaneous. Death may occur within a few seconds. Often the bitten animal drops with scarcely a quiver. At all events consciousness is very short and the serpent calmly awaits the result, confident that its prey cannot escape.

It appears to be generally believed that quickly administered wounds through fleshy parts are comparatively painless and if this is truly the case that flash of the viper's fangs and deep injection of a quickly overwhelming toxin form the cleanest method of killing in obtaining food that exists among the vertebrate animals.

The food of snakes exists in variety from ants' eggs to tapirs. The diminutive and lowly burrowing forms are largely insectivorous and the young of some of the moderate-sized active species feed largely upon insects while extremely immature. Rodents are eaten by many kinds of snakes all over the world and the rodent eaters vary their diet with birds. Frogs, toads, lizards and fish form the diet of many kinds. A considerable number feed only upon warm-blooded prey (mammals and birds) while others of similar size take only cold-blooded prey (frogs, toads, salamanders and the like). Both types would starve if these foods were reversed and offered them. The rat snakes and the larger species of rattlesnakes are examples that will take only warm-blooded prey. The water snakes and striped snakes persistently refuse such food. Some of the larger species are omnivorous. The common blacksnake will as readily eat rodents and small birds, as frogs and the young of other snakes. It will not eat toads, however, while the fine and big black gopher snake of the southeastern United States will readily take any of the ordinary types of snake diet, including toads. Some of the rodent and bird-eating types will also swallow eggs, engulfing these entire and breaking them with the muscles of the throat or swallowing them all the way to the stomach where the shells are dissolved by the gastric juices. An African species lives altogether upon eggs and has bony ridges in the throat for cutting the shells. The giant constrictors—the boas and pythons—feed largely upon warm-blooded prey although occasionally varying the diet with a big lizard, such as an iguana or a monitor.

A fair number of snakes are largely cannibalistic and some entirely so. The king snake of the southern United States frequently eats other snakes and sometimes the poisonous ones, being immune to their bites, and the tropical American mussurana appears to feed altogether

upon snakes and more frequently the poisonous kinds.   Like the king snake it is immune to bites of the pit vipers.   The venomous coral snakes confine their diet to small snakes and lizards, while another poisonous species, the great Malayan king cobra is a notorious cannibal, preferring snakes to other food although it appears to confine its depredations among the harmless species and to be afraid of the vipers. Cannibalistic serpents, in fact all the species which feed upon cold-blooded prey, appear to digest their food quicker and feed at more frequent intervals than those subsisting upon warm-blooded prey. They may require food at intervals of five days to a week apart. Snakes taking proportionately larger and heavier food will retain normal weight at feeding intervals of from ten to twelve days.   The bones and even the teeth of mammals are dissolved by the gastric juices, but the hair or fur is not affected by digestion, even retaining its color and luster.   Likewise, the hoofs of wild swine, small antelope and deer swallowed by pythons and boas are not digested, there being an affinity of these horny substances to hair material in a compressed or solidified form.

Owing to rodents forming a large part of serpents' food a number of the snakes are of important economic value to agriculturists in many parts of the world.   The particular prevalence of a number of species of snakes, including some of the very dangerous kinds is often brought about by multiplication of rodents occurring about outlying human settlements.   The fer-de-lance is seen rather infrequently in the jungle areas yet it may be common in the areas adjacent to plantations where slovenly human practices resulting in the accumulation of trash heaps about ramshackle buildings are conducive to the breeding of rats.   It is a case of automatic balance so frequently indicated among wild creatures.   Thus the prevalence of venomous snakes in a number of areas is not altogether an evil.   There is no doubt about the effectiveness of the prairie rattlesnake in the United States as a check upon the multiplication of extremely destructive ground gophers in the wheat belts. Even the timber rattler of the Eastern states plays an important part as a rodent destroyer during man's persistence in exterminating hawks and owls.   As rodent eaters snakes are particularly efficacious.   They are fitted to prowl into the nests and burrows of the smaller and more injurious types and to devour not only the adults but the litters of young.

The Serpent's Tongue: All snakes, non-venomous and venomous,

from the most diminutive species to the largest pythons have a forked tongue, which is in frequent use as an investigating organ when the reptile is in motion or particularly alert. This quivering member, swept through a vertical plane, with tips expanded, imparts a sinister effect to the snake in the eyes of the misinformed. Thus the tongue is sometimes thought to be a stinging organ. It is in no way connected with the venom apparatus of poisonous species. When at rest the tongue is drawn into a tubular sheath in the lower portion of the mouth.

This highly specialized tongue appears to be an organ of various functions—to detect vibrations and to instantaneously "taste" various odors either in the air or on the ground. The sense of scent through the nostrils seems to have given way to this keen pick-up by the indispensable tongue. With some snakes the tongue is also used to intimidate. The owner slowly waves it with widely spread tips, or thrusts it forward and thus holds the tongue motionless like an elongated "sting." With such antics so common it is no wonder that snakes often are thought to have actual stings. With the greater number the tongue is blue black, but with some it is vermilion at the base and black at the fork, or more startling, among the kinds particularly prone to threaten, the organ may be yellow or pale green, or of some other "poisonous" hue.

CHAPTER V

GENERAL CLASSIFICATION

THUS far the author has refrained from the use of scientific terms, but the detailed story of the serpent clan brings us to the specific separation of families and the points to be considered in the identification of individual kinds or species. In the brief review headed the "Scope of the Clan" the first step has been taken. It is now in order to sum up the technical points.

The *Class* of Reptiles is divided into *Orders,* of which there are four. They stand as follows: 1. The *Rhynchocephalia,* represented by a single species, the Tuatera of New Zealand, which is the sole remnant of an order long extinct. 2. The *Loricata,* composed of the crocodiles, caimans and alligators. 3. The *Chelonia,* or turtles, terrapins and tortoises and 4. The *Squamata,* the lizards and snakes.

An order is in turn divided into families, the latter made up of genera (the plural for genus). The respective genera contain the species.[1] Some genera of reptiles are large, containing from two to five dozen species. A number of genera contain but a single species. The placing of species in one or another genus means that they are markedly different, or indicate *generic distinction.* All species are designated by at least two scientific names. We will take the technical name of the water moccasin as an example. This stands in the scientific lists as *Agkistrodon piscivorus. Agkistrodon* is the generic name and all the species of that genus have the first half of the name thus applied. *Piscivorus* is the name indicating the species—in fact is known as the *specific name.* There are but three New World members of the genus *Agkistrodon* and they stand thus:

> *Agkistrodon mokasen* — The Copperhead Snake
> "   *piscivorus* — The Water Moccasin
> "   *bilineatus* — The Tropical Moccasin

There is yet further analysis of the scientific name, and we will again consider that of the water moccasin. In the strictly scientific

[1] The designation "species" is alike in both singular and plural.

lists it would appear in the following manner: *Agkistrodon piscivorus* (Lacépède).　What is the meaning of the name within the parenthesis?

It signifies the name of the scientist who first described the water moccasin as a new species.　There is also significance in the parenthesis. Its presence shows that since Lacépède named the water moccasin that classification has been rearranged from the results of later, detailed studies, species have been regrouped and a later generic arrangement produced.　Hence Lacépède's original full name for the species has been changed.　His original specific name still stands, but his first and full designation has been altered.　The parenthesis enclosing the name of the authority or sponsor of the species always indicates this.　If there is no parenthesis to enclose the name of the authority, such as *Crotalus cerastes* [2] Hallowell, no change of the generic assignment of the species or any other change as to the standing of the species has been made since it was described as new to science.

These scientific names are based on Latin or Greek, which in science are considered universal languages.　Hence that name of the water moccasin, *Agkistrodon piscivorus* may be translated as follows: From the Greek *"Agkistron"* meaning a hook and "odon", a tooth, this relating to the curved fangs of the species.　The specific name is from the Latin *piscivorus* (fish-eating).　Thus these Greek or Latinized terms form "code" titles in the universal language of the lists of science. "Popular" names would be of scant value in designating groups of species among scientists of various languages.　So called popular names are, in fact, but local in significance.　The term "blacksnake", placed before a Brazilian scientist reading only Portuguese and in a country where there are many kinds of blackish serpents, would be as useless to him as the local term of "cruzeiro", for a locally well-known Brazilian snake, in lists of a scientific worker in America, England or Germany.　Some reptiles have a dozen or more common or "popular" names according to locality.　The scientific names in universally understood form, the lists always under careful scrutiny and continuously undergoing a world-wide accepted and cooperative process of perfection, thus stand as the language of science among all nations.

There remains another point to round out in the diagnosis of the scientific names of snake, lizard, bird or mammal—for all come under the same technical method of presentation and handling.　This remaining point relates to *trinomial* nomenclature.　It is a modernized

---

[2] The Sidewinder—A small desert rattlesnake.

method of denoting enough definite variation occurring among species to warrant a defining varietal or *subspecific name*. As an example we can take the scientific name of the Pacific rattlesnake, *Crotalus confluentus oreganus* (Holbrook). The third name indicates that here is a variety of *Crotalus confluentus* and the name of that variety is *oreganus*. The name of the authority is enclosed within a parenthesis as Holbrook, back in 1840 naming this type of rattlesnake *Crotalus oreganus,* considered it a distinct species. In latter years, with extensive series of specimens for study and comparison, experts in the analysis of reptile relationship deciding that the Pacific rattlesnake represented no more than a western race or variety of the prairie rattlesnake, *Crotalus confluentus,* hence designated it in trinomial nomenclature, but still gave Holbrook credit for the name *oreganus*. When a trinomial designation, like that relating to the Arizona bull snake, *Pituophis catenifer rutilus* Van Denburgh, occurs, with no parenthesis attending the name of the authority it is understood that Van Denburgh discovered and named *rutilus* as a variety or subspecies of the rather broadly distributed *P. catenifer,* applied his description in modern, trinomial definition and that no changes in his original naming of any kind have occurred within the lists up to the one bearing the name as acceptable and up-to-date.

With the full significance of a species well understood the way is open for a general introduction to the serpent clan along lines of classified arrangement. The snakes are included within the same order as the lizards, as their relationship is clearly shown in comparison to families of lizards of which the members have either vestigial limbs or externally show such slight traces of these members that with their elongate bodies and gliding motions they might readily be mistaken for snakes. They differ in certain skeletal characters, particularly in the skull, which lacks the loosely constructed, alternately movable jaw bones. Moreover these particularly serpentine lizards have movable eye-lids, while the eyes of a serpent are always "open"—being covered with a transparent, immovable covering under which the eye itself moves as with other animals. It appears that the closest relationship between lizards and snakes is approached among the former by the family *Anguidae,* including such forms as the American glass "snake" and the European scheltopusik, and that among the snakes the relationship seems closest with such forms as the small burrowing species with rather simply formed skulls, vestiges of a pelvic girdle and

internal hind limbs; also with the boas and pythons, which have inner vestigial hind limbs, and members of several closely related families. There is, however, a clear enough line of distinction between lizards and snakes to warrant two suborders, the *Sauria* and *Ophidia,* respectively.

Conveniently, though not scientifically expressed, the snakes may be said to shape into three series, which the author will designate as A, B, and C and in building up a list for a comprehensive view of the whole group, will use this designation:

Series A is composed of what may be termed the more primitive types of snakes, these being the small burrowing species with vestiges of pelvic bones and internal rear limbs. Also the pythons and boas which have internal rear limb bones. Three other small families, of rather small burrowing members fall into this group and while their members lack rudimentary limbs they otherwise indicate close relationship to the boas and pythons. The members of this series show clearest relationship to lizards among all the snakes.

Series B is by far the most extensive in this simple grouping of the serpents. Its related families and subfamilies illustrate a radiation from a vast non-venomous aggregation to fanged species. There is a series of rear-fanged, mildly poisonous members associated in a family of fangless species. Immediately following is a full family provided with front fangs and a highly virulent neurotoxic venom. There are phases of specialization along lines of adaption to arboreal life, strictly aquatic life in fresh water or remarkable suitability to a marine existence. Such are the Colubrine serpents and immediately allied families. Externally, with the exception of the strictly aquatic species, the members all over the world bear a certain likeness, which renders them distinguishable. The character of their teeth primarily forms a basis for separating them into subfamilies and families: (1) All of the teeth may be solid. (2) There may be simple grooved fangs in the *rear* of the upper or (3) deeply grooved, almost canaliculated fangs in the *front* of the upper jaw. Other differences will be brought out in the detailed list.

Series C has already been mentioned as composed of the most highly specialized or "recent" serpents. These are the long-fanged viperine types of which there are two families, the poison-conducting teeth of such excessive length they must be "folded" against the roof of the mouth when the jaws are closed. The listing follows, in detail:

SERIES A

Family *Typhlopidae*: Small, worm-like burrowing species inhabiting the warmer latitudes of the New and the Old World. There are two genera and slightly over a hundred species, few of which attain a length of over fourteen inches. The scales are smooth, rounded and polished and of much the same size above and beneath. The eyes are buried under the head shields and may be seen only as faint spots. The jaws are practically toothless, the prey being restricted to insect larvae and white "ants" or termites, in the nests of which these small snakes are frequently found. The prevailing coloration is brown and there is usually no trace of pattern. Despite their degenerate form these worm-like snakes have vestiges of pelvic bones and rear limbs hidden beneath the skin. They are thought to represent remnants of ancient serpent life which have undergone degeneration in taking to burrowing habits. Their ancestral stock appears to have been widely distributed as is evidenced by their present cosmopolitan distribution even on isolated ocean islands, which may be vestiges of former continents, but where during the present, no other species of serpents exist. They occur on Christmas Island, which stands comparatively alone and remote from the scattered South Sea group. The inclination of all members of this family is to immediately bore their way back into the soil if exhumed from their hiding places. *Typhlops* is the largest genus with close to a hundred species, inhabiting southern Europe, Asia, Malaysia, Africa, tropical America and the West Indies.

Family *Leptotyphlopidae*: Small and cylindrical, glossy, worm-like burrowing snakes resembling the members of the preceding family. While the members of the *Typhlopidae* have a scant indication of minute teeth on the transverse edges of the maxillary bones, the members of the present family have teeth only on the lower jaw bones. The bones of the pelvic girdle are even more pronounced than with the former family. There are two genera and about thirty species, the greater number being contained within the genus *Leptotyphlops,* with species in the southern United States, tropical America, the West Indies, Asia and Africa.

Family *Boidae*—(Subfamily *Pythoninae*): The first section of the big constrictors is a small subfamily of but seven genera and slightly over twenty species. Five of the genera contain only one or two species respectively. *Liasis* of Timor, New Guinea and North Australia con-

tains six species. The genus *Python* contains nine species and but four of these are the only huge snakes of the Old World. The distribution of the seven genera includes Asia, Malaysia, Africa and Australia. There is one exception. *Loxocemus,* with a single species occurs in southern Mexico. The members of this subfamily differ from the closely related *Boinae* in a skull characteristic—the provision of a pair of supra-orbital bones and also in the tendency of a small bone on the forward portion of the skull, this known as the premaxilla, to carry a few small teeth. Externally viewed there is practically no difference between pythons and boas.

Subfamily *Boinae:* This is a larger subfamily than the closely allied *Pythoninae.* There are thirteen genera and approximately forty species—there being about twice the number of boas as there are pythons, moreover the subfamily is strongly represented in both the New and the Old Worlds. There is, however, but one really huge member—that is to compare in size with the great pythons of India, Malaysia and Africa. All of the really large members are New World, several species of *Constrictor* (formerly *Boa*) attaining a length of eight to ten feet and one growing to be fifteen feet. Distribution is remarkable, as a typical boa of the *Constrictor* type so common in the American tropics occurs in Madagasar, while that island also forms the habitat of a fine tree boa, with characteristic prehensile tail, of which there are four species in the American tropics. There are burrowing species among both the pythons and boas, but this tendency is more developed among the boas. Small species of this kind occur in the southwestern United States, southern Asia and northern Africa. The distribution of the *Boinae* includes the extreme western and southwestern United States, the entire area of tropical America, a considerable portion of the West Indies, the Moluccas, New Guinea, southern Asia and northern Africa. Two genera, each with a single species are characteristic to Round Island, near Mauritius in the Indian Ocean.

Family *Anilidae:* There are three genera and a half dozen species. Vestiges of the pelvic bones and internal hind-limbs are much reduced although there is a pair of claw-like spurs at the vent. These are cylindrical, burrowing snakes about a yard long. The colors of several are very striking. *Anilius scytale* of tropical America is of a brilliant coral red, with black rings. The species of this family inhabit South America, Ceylon, Indo-China and Malaysia.

Family *Uropeltidae:* There are no vestiges of hind limbs or pelvic

bones, but otherwise the members show close relationship to the former. They are small, the body rather rigid, cylindrical and quite stout with tail abruptly terminating in a flat shield thought to be used in burrowing. The eyes are extremely small. The scales are smooth and glossy, of much the same size above as beneath. Most of the species are of beautiful coloration. There are seven genera and about forty-five species confined to India and Ceylon.

Family *Xenopeltidae:* Contains but a single genus, with one burrowing species of southeastern Asia.

SERIES B

Family *Colubridae:* This is by far the largest family of snakes. Provisionally, it is best as yet to indicate divisible sections as subfamilies. In later studies coming with comparison of accumulating series of specimens some of these subfamilies may either be accorded full rank, or the trend may be the other way. Carefully traced relationship sometimes causes groups to lose their individuality. It is equally possible that *additional* subfamilies may be selected from the present grouping. Considering the present series of subfamilies the *Colubridae* shows a grand total of close to two hundred and fifty genera and well over a thousand species, as follows:

Subfamily *Acrochordinae:* These characteristic non-venomous snakes are limited to five genera, each containing a single species. The teeth are solid. The body is covered with small granular scales, which, with most of the species, are the same beneath as on the back. The strictly aquatic species largely inhabit tidal areas of rivers and occasionally swim into the sea. Distribution includes the low-lying coastal areas of southeastern Asia and New Guinea. One is found in the Khasia Hills of northeastern India. This is essentially an Old World group, although the single species of *Nothopsis* inhabits Central America.

Subfamily *Colubrinae:* These are the typical harmless snakes of the world. There are over one hundred and fifty genera and well over seven hundred species. Among the varied genera the teeth may vary in length, they may be of uniform size, enlarged anteriorly or greatly enlarged posteriorly, or may even show traces of grooves, but there are no poison-secreting glands. The species range through great variety in size and form. Many are less than a foot in length while some of

the rat snakes attain a length of at least ten feet.   Form ranges from comparatively stout to whiplike outlines or excessively slender with arboreal types.   A number of races are indicated among these serpents and some of these with further study may warrant distinction as sub-families.   Examples of such differentiation are the constricting king snakes, and the constricting rat snakes of the genus *Elaphe*.   The par-ticularly active and non-constricting racers of the genera *Coluber, Mas-ticophis, Alsophis* and closely allied genera indicate a group, and again there are the so-called *Natracine* species which are largely semi-aquatic, feed almost altogether upon cold-blooded prey and are represented by the species of *Thamnophis* (the largely semi-aquatic New World garter snakes), and *Natrix,* an extensive genus of New and Old World water snakes.   Such species occur in practically all parts of the world where snakes are found.

Subfamily *Dasypeltinae:* A single species, *Dasypeltis scabra,* of tropical and southern Africa warrants separation in having ridged processes of the vertebrae in the neck so developed that they pierce the throat and are used as cutting edges to break the eggs of birds upon which this creature largely feeds.   This might be regarded as a "satel-lite" subfamily of the extensive one preceding it, a condition to be further referred to in connection with a large subfamily later follow-ing.

Subfamily *Amblycephalinae:* The exact status of this group, pro-visionally listed as a subfamily has for a long time been in doubt.   The New World members bear close marks of relationship to the *Colubrinae* and the whole series of species more or less warrants close contact in listing with that subfamily.   Certain modifications of the jaw bones, and other head details, including arrangement of the shields, point to a group of Colubrine-like serpents of largely arboreal habits.   While all of the species are harmless they have very wide, lumpy heads on slender necks.   The eyes are large, with elliptical pupils.   In form they are rather characteristic in the compressed, comparatively slender body. One strong point of identification lies in the absence of a central groove under the chin, a very general characteristic among snakes.   The head thus has but slight power of distension and they are unable to swallow large prey.

Subfamily *Homalopsinae:* This is the first of the fanged divisions of the Colubrine snakes.   The fangs are grooved teeth in the *rear* of the upper jaw.   They are connected with rather small poison glands

and the venom secreted—utilized to benumb the prey while gripped by the serpent—is not nearly so powerful as that of the more highly specialized poisonous snakes later recognized under full family designation. This is a small subfamily of "river snakes", with nine genera and but approximately two dozen species. They are confined to southern Asia, Malaysia, New Guinea and northern Australia. In habits, fine scalation and narrow ventral plates, there is a repetition with these aquatic *rear-fanged* Colubrines in association with the major group to follow, as has been noted with the *Acrochordinae* and the *Colubrinae*. Such parallelism becomes all the more remarkable farther along in the list when we note that the immediately following, dominating division of the rear-fanged Colubrines is followed by a rear-fanged counterpart of the *Dasypeltinae*. Thus the grand divisions of the *Colubridae*, for the sake of convenience in memorizing its scope, may be said to be composed of the typical non-fanged members, the *Colubrinae*, with three associated or satellite subfamilies, and the typical rear-fanged members, the *Boiginae*, in association with two similarly small subfamilies of parallel characteristics.

Subfamily *Boiginae:* There are over seventy genera and nearly three hundred species. These rear-fanged Colubrines hold an analogous position to the non-poisonous *Colubrinae*, and there is largely a repetition of the latter's varied forms, there being constrictors, racers, slender whip snakes and water snakes. There is also a grouping of species matching the lumpy-headed members of the *Amblycephalinae*. Distribution covers both the New and Old World, but these snakes are largely confined to the warmer latitudes. A considerable number of the species have elliptical pupils.

Subfamily *Elachistodontinae:* A single genus and species. This is a rear-fanged counterpart of *Dasypeltis scabra,* having sharp ridges of the vertebrae protruding into the throat for cutting egg shells. It inhabits Bengal.

Family *Elapidae:* Externally the members of this family look quite like the typical Colubrine serpents, for the greater part like the racers *(Coluber)* and the gopher snakes *(Drymarchon)* of the New World. Some are cylindrical and burrowers. A few are whiplike. They are among the most deadly of all serpents. The cobras, kraits and mambas; and the blacksnake, tiger snake and death "adder" of Australia, belong to this family. There are approximately thirty Old World genera and one hundred and fifty species. A single genus, *Micrurus*

(Elaps)—the coral snakes—occurs in the New World with two species in the southern United States and about two dozen in tropical America. Members of the *Elapidae* are characterized by two short and rigidly set fangs in the forward portion of the upper jaw. The poison glands are large and secrete an extremely powerful fluid of neurotoxic reaction.

Family *Hydrophidae:* These are highly specialized marine serpents with fangs similar to the *Elapidae*. But few of the species have broad ventral plates, which predominate among serpents. The members of the family are unique in having a vertically compressed, paddle-like tail. Most of them have a considerably compressed body to assist in swimming. These serpents are very poisonous. They are frequently seen in numbers a thousand miles from shore. They abound in the Indian Ocean and western tropical Pacific. But one occurs in the waters of the New World—off the west coast of Southern Mexico, Central America and northern South America. There are ten genera and over fifty species, which range from two to eight feet in length.

SERIES C

Family *Viperidae:* The typical vipers. An exclusively Old World family with a fair number of small species in Europe, several in Asia and Malaysia, but the greater number and the larger kinds occurring in Africa. Ten genera and about four dozen species form the family. The poison fangs are of much greater proportionate length than with the highly dangerous *Elapidae* and are attached to movable bones enabling them to be folded against the roof of the mouth when the jaws are closed. The European viper or adder, the tic-polonga or Russell's viper of India, the horned viper or Cerastes of desert Africa, the African puff-adder, Gaboon viper and rhinoceros viper are members of this family. Most of the vipers or adders have a thick body—some excessively so—and a flat, distinct head. A few arboreal species have a slender body with particularly wide and distinct head. The pupil is mostly elliptical.

Family *Crotalidae:* The pit vipers, which receive the name from a deep and very distinct pit on each side of the head between the eye and the nostril. While there is a lesser number of genera—six in all—than with the typical vipers, there is more than double the number of species —over eighty. Differing from the typical vipers, the pit vipers occur

in both the Old and New Worlds, attaining their greater variety of form in the latter.   There are approximately fifty New World and thirty Old World species.   The Old World species occur along the borders of the Caspian Sea and in Asia, and Malaysia.   No pit vipers inhabit Africa.   The most unique among the pit vipers are the rattlesnakes, found only in the New World.   The largest species of all long-fanged or Viperine snakes, the tropical American bushmaster, attaining a length of twelve feet, is a member of this family.   Some of the pit vipers are small, slender and arboreal.   The fer-de-lance is a member of this family.   The fangs of all the members are of the same excessive length and movable attachment as with the typical vipers.

An arrangement of the serpents in series based on the structure of the teeth, figures prominently in scientific writings.   As the student may encounter the terms so utilized, it is well to clarify them, as follows:

Aglypha: Non-venomous snakes.   All the teeth solid.   Some may be fang-like in size, but not grooved or canalicular.

Opisthoglypha: Mildly poisonous snakes with a pair or pairs of fangs in the *rear* of the upper jaw, these teeth provided with a simple groove for the introduction of poison.

Proteroglypha: Cobras, mambas, coral snakes and their allies—the *Elapidae;* also the marine serpents—the *Hydrophidae,* with a pair of permanently erect *grooved* fangs in the *forward* portion of the upper jaw.   These poison-conducting teeth are more highly developed than with the rear-fanged snakes.   They are deeply grooved, but have practically folded about the groove to form a canal beneath the anterior surface.   The enfolded groove opens at the tip for the discharge of poison.

Solenoglypha: Viperine snakes.   The fangs of proportionate great length, attached to movable bones and folding against the roof of the mouth when the jaws are closed.   The poison channel is a nearly central internal canal.   The term Viperine snakes applies to both the typical vipers and the pit vipers, the *Viperidae* and the *Crotalidae.*

CHAPTER VI

THE GIANT SERPENTS

WHAT is the greatest size attained by serpents? That is a frequent question.

In over thirty years endeavor to obtain a really huge serpent for the Zoological Park's collection, my largest specimen was just twenty-four feet long. This was a Reticulated or Regal Python, *Python reticulatus,* from Malaya, which I am convinced is the largest existing species of snake. In all of these years, in an endeavor to obtain record measurements from authoritative sources the figures stand at thirty-three feet and another a few inches over thirty feet. Both of these measurements relate to *Python reticulatus.* This is a species of Burma, Indo-China, the Malay Peninsula, thence through Malaysia to the Philippines, whence have come records of several twenty-five footers and some stretched skins that have been discounted.

Python patterns are difficult to describe. *Reticulatus* (Plate 4), has an interweaving of rich yellow, brown and black and an iridescent glow in the high-lights of its folds. Its head markings distinguish it from another great python of India, appearing to be the Old World's second largest snake. The head of *reticulatus* is uniform brown with a narrow black line in the center from the snout to the neck.

The Black-tailed Python or Rock Python, *P. molurus* (Plate 3), has a quite different head marking. There is a dark blotch covering the greater part of the top of the head and shaped like a spear-head pointing forward. *Molurus* attains a length of twenty-two to twenty-five feet, but the largest specimen I have personally examined was a few inches under twenty. This snake is common in India and also found on the Malay Peninsula, but its range into the islands seems to be confined to Sumatra and Java. There are two distinct phases of coloration, one of dark olive and blackish markings, the other of pale gray and dark tan. The latter has a pinkish head and comes from western India. It does not grow to be so large as the dark variety, not appearing to exceed fifteen or sixteen feet.

These phases differ as much in disposition as in hues. The darker specimens are usually irritable and tamed with difficulty. The lighter ones may be quickly tamed and are the favorites of the snake "charmers" of the circuses. In consequence there is a heavy traffic in specimens of the pale color phase among the animal dealers and prices run from thirty dollars for a six footer to fifty dollars at eight feet, thence rapidly mount with additional footage, which means bulk, until a sixteen foot specimen of this handsome snake commands a price of several hundred dollars.

In an article appearing in "Zoologische Garten", Werner very clearly defines the two races of *molurus* as follows:

Var. *ocellata*, color light. The large spots on the sides of the body for the greater part with a light middle area. Only three rows of large spots, a dorsal and on either side a lateral. The triangular spot on the head only distinct on the posterior two thirds. Found in western and southern India from Kurrachee to Madras.

Var. *intermedia*, colors darker. The spots more distinctly set off from the ground color. Spots on the sides of the body without light central area; between the dorsal and lateral rows of spots on either side another longitudinal row of elongated smaller spots. Triangular blotch on upper side of the head distinct to a point lying on the snout. Attains a larger size than the preceding and found in the northeast of India peninsula, Calcutta, Burma and Indo-Malaya. Reminds one of *Python sebae* in body hues.[1]

The Old World's third largest snake inhabits Africa. This is *Python sebae* also called the Rock Python. It appears doubtful if this snake attains a length of much over twenty feet and the average run of adult examples is sixteen to seventeen feet. It inhabits central and southern Africa. *P. amethystinus,* of northern Australia closely crowds the African species for honors and is said to grow to at least twenty feet.

The New World tropics has but one species of giant serpent closely matching the largest pythons in size and this is the Anaconda, *Eunectes murinus,* of tropical South America. There have been many grossly exaggerated stories about its size. The largest specimen ever obtained for the Zoological Park was nineteen feet in length, 36 inches in circumference at the thickest part of the body and weighed 236 pounds. This snake gave birth to seventy-two young which were 38 inches long. The next longest specimen was 17 feet long and also gave birth to

[1] Translated from German.

young.　There were thirty-four in the litter and the infant anacondas were 27 inches long and 1 inch in diameter.

A misleading thing about the anaconda is its proportionately great bulk.　The seventeen foot specimen was as heavy in body as a twenty-four foot reticulated python.

During a trip in South America the author had an opportunity of gathering first hand information from authoritative sources as to records of anacondas and checked a unanimous opinion that twenty-five feet was the maximum length of the species.

It is well to have these details clearly established as too many stories have appeared from sources of alleged adventure into the "interior" and have even crept into books from dignified sources.　These have cited observations of serpents forty and fifty feet long.　Returning explorers have so persistently told me about fifty foot anacondas and the measuring of great skins they might have obtained, but failed to, that I made known an offer of a thousand dollars for an anaconda's skin in excess of forty feet.　Such a skin has never materialized.　The search for records, however, resulted in a huge skin being submitted by C. B. Marshall, of the Radio Corporation of America.　Mr. Marshall purchased the skin during a business trip in Brazil.　The anaconda had been killed in the province of Minas Geraes.　This skin was twenty-one feet and four inches in length and was the largest record of a South American serpent I ever obtained from personal measurement.　Quite recently, however, my friend Dr. Afranio do Amaral, Director of the Institute of Serum Therapy at Sao Paulo, Brazil, told me about the measurement of an anaconda a few inches in excess of twenty-five feet.

As Dr. Amaral is a scientist of international reputation his data are altogether convincing, and appear to stand as the *record measurements* of a New World serpent.

Thus the world's four largest snakes stand thus in point of size: The Regal Python, *Python reticulatus,* of easterly India and Malaysia —attaining a proven length of thirty-three feet; the South American Anaconda, *Eunectes murinus,* attaining a *proven* length of twenty-five feet, but "larger" than the preceding in its greater bulk; the Indian Rock Python, *P. molurus,* twenty-five feet; and fourth in size, the African Rock Python, *P. sebae,* which appears to grow to slightly over twenty feet.

As all of these measurements are considerably in excess of the average run, it is well to note that ordinarily big examples of the re-

spective species would be twenty-two feet for *Python reticulatus,* about eighteen feet for *P. molurus,* seventeen feet for the anaconda and a similar length for an African python. Larger examples are rare enough to attract great attention.

There are other big members of the *Pythoninae* and the *Boinae* but among them twelve to fifteen feet represent maximum length. Recent records indicate that the Diamond Python, *P. spilotes* (Plate 3), of Australia and New Guinea grows to be fourteen feet in length, although the average length is seldom as much as eight. *Python regius,* (Plate 2), is a very handsome and stout species of West Africa. Its average length is about five feet. It is often called the Ball Python owing to a habit, when frightened of tightly coiling into a perfect sphere. The head and neck are so tucked into spaces between the folds that the compact creature, squeezed into the size of a large bowling ball may be rolled ten to twelve feet with a fair push of the hand. The body color is a rich chocolate brown with rosettes of large and medium size and varying shapes, each vividly margined with yellow. This is a particularly attractive and gentle creature and it is almost impossible to induce it to bite. It makes a pretty and pleasing pet.

A few of the pythons are diminutive and some are burrowers. As an example of unaccountable distribution there is a small member of the *Pythoninae* in southern Mexico, on just about the opposite side of the world from the other members of its subfamily. The lone species is scientifically known as *Loxocemus bicolor* (Plate 1).

This little python is extremely rare even in museum collections and after some thirty years of endeavor to obtain and examine a living specimen the author received two examples through the courtesy of W. A. King, of Brownsville, Texas. Mr. King is an alert collector who has in the past obtained such interesting specimens as the big Mexican beaded lizard, the golden diamond rattler of the southerly arid areas of Mexico, rare varieties of the king snake along the Boundary and similar kinds valuable for study and comparison. He collected the two dwarf pythons near Colima. They were beautiful creatures, perfectly gentle and inclined to coil in a ball in one's hand and hide the head among the folds. They were about two and a half feet long and quite stout, of lustrous deep brown over which glowed a purple iridescence in the high lights of the folds. Sparsely and irregularly scattered along the body were cream-colored spots. The head is not distinct from the neck and has a pointed snout, laterally wedge-shaped

which hints of burrowing habits. In a way this snake resembles the Old World species of *Eryx* (though they are true boas), though the body is more shapely and the tail, while short, tapers to a point. The eyes, moreover, are keen, prominent and of fair size. On the under surface these attractive miniatures of pythons have a particularly symmetrical scale arrangement, the scales of the lower sides being quite large and bordering a narrow row of prominent abdominal plates. The immediate character of identification is in the double row of plates beneath the tail. The pygmy boas of southwestern North America have a single row.

The larger species of the python subfamily are egg layers, while those of the *Boinae* are viviparous. Numerous observations have been published about the habit of female pythons coiling about their masses of eggs to incubate them. At such times the temperature of the snake rises from some mysterious cause immediately after she covers the eggs with her coils. Her temperature remains "high" (for a snake) for several weeks, or until the eggs have hatched, or she leaves them. Early studies made at Paris and later at London have showed as much difference as twelve degrees Fahrenheit between the temperature of the incubating snake's coils and that of a male python in the same cage. In tables, in which various figures are given, there is marked variance of results with records made in New York in applying cage temperatures against those of snakes not incubating. I am inclined to think the temperature of both male and female snakes in Europe was influenced by nearby heating pipes not taken into consideration.

The normal temperature of snakes is very close to that of environmental air. It may be a degree lower, owing to cooling from evaporation of skin moisture, or, during the peak of digestion, may be two or even three degrees higher than the surrounding air. A degree or so higher than environmental air has also been noted if a snake is excited. What type of "excitement" or stimulation is attendant to a python incubating her eggs is problematical, but there is no doubt that the serpent's temperature rises and remains quite steadily abnormal until she leaves the eggs.

Snake eggs generally do not receive prolonged attention from the parent. Female snakes are sometimes to be found coiled around their eggs, but this disposition has usually appeared to me to be for the purpose of keeping the mass of eggs from drying, as they require moisture. The smaller egg-laying species do not always long remain with their

eggs. The author has hatched the eggs of such species in trays of damp moss at a room temperature averaging seventy-five degrees Fahrenheit, or approximately twenty-four degrees Centigrade. The period for development of such eggs is from four to six weeks. Snakes' eggs are usually to be found under flat stones, buried in wood pulp, dead leaves or similar debris. Stones absorb heat from the sun and retain some of it over night, while decaying vegetable matter generates a moderate amount of warmth. Such conditions indicate that reptile eggs may require a certain amount of heat over that of average environmental air. It also may be that pythons, owing to the considerable displacement of their several dozen large eggs, find difficulty in locating places conducive to a moderate rise in temperature—so have developed the habit of utilizing the body as an incubating medium.

Dr. Francis G. Benedict, of the Carnegie Institution of Washington, who has for several years been conducting extensive experiments on metabolism, recently made some extremely careful observations of an incubating python in the Reptile House of the National Zoological Park. The instruments used in this instance were particularly delicate and exact, and again, the temperature of the snake's cage was most carefully determined. In a communication to the author, Doctor Benedict says:

"With regard to the Washington python: You might state that this snake, which laid eggs on April 5, was inspected on May 10, and at that time there was a temperature difference between that of the snake and of the environmental air of not far from 3 degrees to 4 degrees Centigrade, thus proving, in my judgment, a definite development of sensible heat."

Subsequent observations with the same snake, with less delicate instruments, indicated a maintenance of an unusually high temperature. The actions of this python were studied by Dr. W. M. Mann, Director of the National Zoological Park, who kindly gave me the following memoranda:

"The python left her eggs definitely June 3, after coiling around them since April 5, when they were laid. There were about twenty eggs. She coiled around them at once. Doctor Benedict sent a couple of men down from Boston and they made very detailed studies of the temperature over a period of one day. We found by cruder measurement, that there was an increase in heat in the coils during incubation, but Doctor Benedict has some very accurate data on this.

"This snake is the African *sebae* that we brought home with us four years ago.   At that time she was about twelve feet long, but has grown three feet since.   She stayed about the eggs most of the time, but got off nearly every evening to drink from the pool in the cage, and one evening when Doctor Lutz was here we went over to visit the Reptile House about ten o'clock and saw her crawl to the other side of the cage, shed her skin, which took about twelve minutes, then go back to the eggs.

"Before sending the mass of eggs to the Museum, we opened up a couple of them and found them simply full of paste in the inside and no evidence at all of an embryo, so we saw at once they were not fertile."

Several members of the largely New World *Boinae* warrant detailed description.   Reference to the Anaconda, *Eunectes murinus* (Plate 4), a true boa, in former paragraphs relating to the python subfamily was brought about by a comparison of size of Old and New World serpents.   The Anaconda, owing to its ranking size is naturally the most spectacular non-venomous serpent in the New World tropics.   Its range stretches through the far-flung strictly tropical South American swampy river valleys.   It is as commonly called the Water Boa or, in Brazilian vernacular, *"Sucuri"*,[2] and leads a semi-aquatic life, spending as much time in the water as out of it, but it is not a particularly good swimmer, nor does it pursue its prey through the water.   It lies in wait in murky waters, the neck reared and supported by the head really floating on the surface, nothing but the top and eyes protruding.   Or it may glide through shallow water among reeds watching for prey, ranging in size from agoutis, to capybaras or a young tapir, as the size of the hunting serpent may designate.   It is also fond of water fowl and may craftily stalk beneath them and seize them from below.   It is able to submerge for ten minutes or so, but not for any extraordinary periods as it is a typical air-breathing reptile.   Its trails may be seen in the mud of the lowlands as it prowls from one lagoon to another and owing to a tendency of "hitching" the great body over soft soil may widen the imprint to hint of a far larger creature than it really is.   This may give rise to startling supposition when humans discover its track.

The murky tropical waters form the anaconda's safest retreat and the largest specimens will glide from the shore and into the sheltering medium upon human approach.   The retreat continues to a safe dis-

[2] This term should not be confused with *"Surucucu,"* which relates to the poisonous bushmaster.

tance upon the muddy bottom and return to the surface is led by nothing more than a careful protrusion of the top of the head to the level of the eyes. The coloration of the anaconda is olive or greenish brown, with large rounded blackish spots scattered along the body. A related species, *Eunectes notaeus,* the Yellow Anaconda (Plate 5), is smaller and of more mottled pattern.

The term "Boa Constrictor" has long been a misleading one. It originated when early naturalists applied it as a scientific title to one of the big serpents of tropical America, but to a species smaller than the anaconda. Later through lack of understanding of the actual condition, but prompted by a vague idea that it applied to big snakes and that such big serpents were constrictors, the title became a "popular" one indiscriminately applied to not only the big serpents of tropical America, but the pythons of Asia and Africa.

The early generic title of *Boa* was for years applied to several fine big serpents of the New World tropics and the lower West Indies. The finest and largest of these species inhabits southern Mexico, the Central American countries and tropical South America. The genus has now been changed to *Constrictor* and *Boa* applied to a genus of strictly arboreal boas (formerly *Corallus*).

Constrictor constrictor (formerly *Boa constrictor*) is the second largest New World serpent (Plate 6). It is commonly and properly known as the "Boa Constrictor", if such a combination of simple and scientific terms can be considered a "popular" definition. It is a handsome serpent, particularly in South America where the markings are a combination of pale tan and dark brown or black, the paler marks arranged in a series of boldly defined, elongated saddles on the back. The dark markings give way to a rich reddish toward the posterior quarter of the body where brick red or crimson may be marbled with darker and paler hues. Central American specimens are usually much darker, with smaller and more obscurely defined saddles. One variation, defined as a subspecies, is olive brown with black markings. In trinomial nomenclature the northerly races are defined as *Constrictor constrictor mexicana* and *Constrictor constrictor imperator,* the latter occurring in Central America. A dark bar from eye to eye and a central band on the head form a cross-like marking. A fine snake of this genus curiously enough occurs in Madagascar.

From an extensive series of records it appears that the Boa in South America seldom attains a length in excess of twelve feet, but in Central

America, while not so attractive in marking it grows to be fully fifteen feet. I have had many specimens from both areas and usually noted one marked difference in habits. This relates to temperament. The greater number of South American examples can be quickly tamed. Some are inclined to strike, but with no great show of ostentation. Central American specimens not only strike repeatedly with a great show of bravado, but inflate the lungs, partially open the mouth and emit long sharp hisses, which are as loud as a moderate steam leak. At the instant of striking the hiss is amplified to startling proportions.

These serpents are the hosts of ticks and I have seen boas in Honduras which were half covered with them, the parasites ranging in size from smaller than an eighth of an inch to several hundred as large as one's finger nail. Occasional ticks are noted on the South American specimens, but I have never seen such infestations as among the Honduran specimens. We remarked at the time that the condition might account for their extremely bad temper, but occasional specimens, found on higher ground and comparatively free of ticks were equally vociferous in their hissing. Most of the specimens noted were in low jungle, inclined to be swampy and a big specimen was found on a tiny islet in a lagoon. The place was a mass of tangled vegetation resembling cat brier and every member of our party was literally showered with ticks in making the reconnoiter.

A series of fine boas of moderate to quite large size inhabit the northerly islands of the West Indies. They belong to the genus *Epicrates*.

The Cuban Boa, *Epicrates angulifer* (Plate 8), is the largest. It is stout and powerful, and attains a length of twelve feet, although these big specimens are now rare. The species is being exterminated over considerable portions of Cuba owing to clearing of land for plantations. In the wilder areas this boa continues to hold its own although gradually becoming decimated in numbers from its habit of prowling into the cane areas to hunt for rats among ramshackle buildings. This tendency has never been reconciled with anything useful by human residents of the island who kill the snakes with the ever evident machete. This is the only really large snake of Cuba, an island with a fair snake fauna but no poisonous species.

The Bahaman Boa, *E. striatus* is characteristic of the Bahamas and San Domingo, fairly common and highly useful as a rodent destroyer. Its maximum length is from six to eight feet and its coloration a mar-

bling of gray and black. Several smaller species of *Epicrates* are characteristic to other portions of the West Indies.

The most attractive member of the genus is a mainland species found from northern Peru and Brazil to Costa Rica. This is the Rainbow Boa, or Ringed Boa, *E. cenchris* (Plate 8), seldom over four feet long, of ruddy brown with irregular rows of large dark rings. This slow-moving and usually gentle reptile gleams with an iridescence like the surface of pearl and a specimen that has recently shed its skin is a really beautiful and remarkable object in the sunshine. The condition is more or less evident among all the species of *Epicrates* and produced by the epidermis or translucent outer skin bearing microscopic and close-set parallel ridges which catch the light. The larger boas and pythons occasionally display a similar condition as the light catches portions of their coils, but none approaches the gorgeous show of a full grown Rainbow Boa, which closely matches the beauty of the flashing morpho butterflies occurring in the same areas, their brilliance produced by the same physical effect.

Tree Boas form an interesting and characteristic group. There are half a dozen assigned to the genus *Boa* (formerly *Corallus*). With one exception they attain a length of about six feet, but the body is slender and vertically compressed, with a long and prehensile tail. The head is large and lumpy, much swollen at the rear and particularly prominent owing to the slender neck. Such outlines give these strictly arboreal boas a very "poisonous" appearance. The eyes are large and the prominent vertical pupil adds to the forbidding aspect. Several of these snakes, particularly Cooke's Tree Boa, of northern South America and the Windward Islands are as savage as they look, doubling the anterior body in a big striking S and lunging at an intruder nearly half their length. Although they are non-venomous, the anterior teeth in both upper and lower jaws are greatly enlarged, fang-like in proportions and may inflict wounds to the depth of three-eighths of an inch. This provision of enlarged frontal teeth is of great value as they feed mostly upon birds and the hook-like teeth instantly penetrate the feathered body of the prey, enabling the reptile to positively retain its hold as it throws its constricting coils about the victim. *Boa enydris cookii* is of almost a uniform golden brown. *Boa enydris,* the typical form, also of northern South America is strongly blotched and marbled with darker tints. (Plate 9).

Tree boas have a characteristic method of securely attaching them-

selves to their high arboreal roosts. The body is seldom coiled around a bough. The serpent draws its body together in a tight circular coil on top of the branch which may be a bare two inches in diameter. The manoeuver is readily accomplished as the coils are balanced by drooping on one side and the other. As the coils are brought tighter, in symmetrical, circular fashion, they are likewise folded farther downward until the snake assumes the position of a ball, the compressed form of the body greatly aiding in this spherical disposition of the coils. Coiled in this way and partially concealed by the foliage they are extremely difficult to see.

The most spectacular of the genus is the beautiful Green Tree Boa, *Boa canina* (Plate 9), of Brazil and the Guianas. It seldom exceeds a length of four feet, but is stouter than the others with proportionately huge head. In color it is emerald green above and lemon yellow beneath. It indicates what might be termed natural camouflage as the markings are of a character to utterly deceive the eye. If it were of unbroken green, its perfectly spherical coil with head tucked in to preserve the outline, might be detected as a green ball, but its outlines are broken by a series of broad and widely separated enamel-white markings along the back and a touch of this same white along the ridge of the back. Above the observer's head, or looking horizontally through the foliage the green of the serpent is difficult enough to detect, but the white markings so effectively mix with vari-sized patches of light or small openings in foliage showing sky reflection that the coiled reptile blends with its surroundings. As if realizing that mimicry was a better defence than pretending to be dangerous this is the most quiet and gentle of the tree boas. It may be handled without show of temper and my captive specimens when gliding away from examination would seek varied places to assume their unique coils, even coming to roost on the back of a chair, then folding into spherical bundles.

As among their larger tropical American allies the tree boas have a distant relative in Madagascar. This is *Boa (Sanzinia) madagascariensis* of similar form and habits, growing to be seven feet long, of brownish hue with a double row of large, darker markings.

The *Boinae* contains a greater number of small, burrowing species than the closely allied subfamily of pythons. These smaller members may be appropriately called Sand Boas. Several occur in the southwestern United States. One of these, the California Boa, *Lichanura roseafusca,* is an attractive little creature, a miniature of its tropical

allies. Its color is yellowish, sometimes silvery, with dark brown or reddish brown bands extending lengthwise. The undersurface is suffused with pink. The length is about two feet. Of the sand boas this is the least inclined to burrow. Its range includes southern California and the peninsula of Lower California. In California it is not uncommon in San Diego County from the coast to the desert areas and it is usually to be noted in the chaparral or among boulders.

The Rubber Boa, *Charina bottae* is a pygmy and ranges farther into the temperate zone than any other member of the *Boinae*. It inhabits the Pacific Coast region all the way from Lower California to the State of Washington and records of its occurrence extend inward to Montana and Utah. This stubby little boa with blunt head and equally blunt tail is cylindrical and clad in small, polished scales. It is also called the "Two-headed" Snake, owing to the bluntness of the tail and the silver Boa, from its grayish coloration. There is no pattern. It is very gentle and when frightened gathers the body into knob-like twists, assuming so spherical an outline it may be rolled about. It spends much of its time burrowing.

In India and Africa there are several sand or burrowing boas. The Rough-scaled Sand Boa, *Gongylophis conicus,* of India is about a yard long, with excessively stout body, but small head and abruptly tapering tail. On the anterior portion the scales are small and feebly keeled. Toward the latter part of the body they become much enlarged and very rough, and a struggling specimen is unpleasant to handle. There is a bold combination of irregular blotches on a paler ground hue.

The Brown Sand Boa, *Eryx johnii* (Plate 11), also of India and about two and a half feet long is specifically developed for rapid burrowing with a wedge-shaped snout. It is of a uniform brownish, with very small eyes, cylindrical body and minute shining scales. The tail is so blunt that it looks like an amputated stump. Owing to this stubby tail the species is also called the "Two-headed" Snake and when coiled in a mass, with the head hidden and the tail protruding as is a common position, the tail might readily be mistaken for the anterior end. Specimens cannot endure captivity unless given sand or absolutely dry earth in which to burrow and hide, hence are of little interest except to exhume for study. Also, they require a high temperature and this should be constant, at about seventy degrees Fahrenheit. If damp or chilled they quickly sicken and die. They are creatures of sterile, desert-like areas. *Eryx jaculus,* the Spotted Sand Boa, oc-

curs in southeastern Europe, northeastern Africa and western Asia. It is smaller and of mottled pattern. There are two others, one of which is *Eryx thebaicus,* of northern Africa from upper Egypt to Tanganyika. It is to be found well into the desert.

In closing a resumé of the subfamilies of pythons and boas several points come to the author's mind. These should be cleared up as they are frequently queried.

We have already noted the speed in seizing the prey among constricting snakes, but there is a query as to just how *hard* the big members are able to strike in reaching for their prey or in defence. There is a reference in one of Kipling's works about a large python striking with great force—and that reference is misleading. I have frequently been asked if a large python or boa can strike an animal hard enough to disable it, and why there is no provision against the great snakes in the Park's reptile house breaking the plate glass panels of their commodious cages.

The answer to all this is that the stroke of a big serpent is not in the nature of a blow. It is quick but actuated with intent to grasp and hence is so regulated that it is at the diminishing point as the extended jaws reach the target. Moreover, the head of a snake is of comparatively light and soft structure, the jawbones loosely connected, the skull thin and light. There are strong muscles to operate the jaws, but the head of a serpent is anything but an object to ram or "butt" an adversary or stun the prey. It might be compared to a hand reaching forward with widely opened fingers to quickly grasp an object. Such a hand might shatter a pane of ordinary window glass, but would be stopped by heavy plate. The big pythons in the reptile house occasionally strike at visitors, but in over thirty years no panel of glass has ever been cracked. Such striking is confined to newcomers. The reptiles soon learn that the glass is an obstacle.

Another point that comes up relates to how big a python or boa should be to be able to overcome a man.

It is not so much a matter of size, as the part of the human that may be enveloped. One phase of the discussion should be understood at the beginning, and that is, that while attacks of such a nature are only *remotely* possible, they have occasionally occurred. Usually the snake seeks to escape, but temperament of individuals varies. An occasional specimen if roughly handled in an attempt to capture it, or get it into a bag or transfer it from one cage to another may throw its coils around

a man and constrict with all its strength. A ten to twelve foot specimen can be dangerous under such conditions if part of its coils entangle a man's arms and others are around his neck.

As a snake in such a position may possibly grasp the victim's clothing with its teeth, it is difficult to disengage its coils by reaching for its head and thus unwinding its body. The tail serves as the proper medium for thus untangling the coils. It is not only harmless, but the power of the constricting muscles is more easily overcome by pulling the coils open from this direction. That is my answer to danger from the big constrictors. A ten to twelve foot specimen can be dangerous if a man is alone and one over this size ranging around fifteen feet or over could immediately render a man helpless and stop his breathing, by constriction. I have cautioned a number of people about the manipulation of big snakes if there is no help within call and my staff of keepers is uniformly cautious in feeding the big twenty-footers, which is done at night. Under the stimulus of keen appetite these giants might make a sweeping stroke, entangle a man in their massive coils and quickly kill him. I doubt if even a twenty-foot python could swallow the average adult human, owing to the breadth of the shoulders, but it is conceivably possible and we take no chances.

As to the occasional, though rare attempts of an angry constricting snake to squeeze a human to do damage I recall the experience of my friend Charles Higby, widely known artist, who kept a few pet snakes in his studio. Higby had several boas which could be trusted, as each had a proven mild and even temperament. He one day received, however, an exceptionally large example of the Florida pine snake. This species does not belong to the family of boas, but like many of the rodent-eating Colubrine snakes, is a powerful constrictor. The specimen was a full eight feet in length, but more slender than a boa, being little more than two inches in diameter at the thickest part. It had struck repeatedly at Higby and hissed in its long-drawn out, characteristic way, but my friend thought he could tame it and looked forward to the interest in doing this very thing.

Alone one evening in the studio he slid the big pine snake from its cage on to a soft rug. The snake struck at him. He slowly crouched, slid his upturned palms under the snake and lifted it from the floor. The action was so slow and gentle that the reptile appeared to be pacified. Higby raised the reptile high over his head, then bringing it gently downward, draped it over his neck. He walked to a mirror to

note the effect.   The jogging of his body as he took several steps threw the snake into its former agitation.   Either to keep from falling, or with intent to use its coils it threw its body around Higby's neck.   My friend didn't like the procedure and started to pull it away.   With the first touch of the man's hands all thought of harmful intent on the snake's part was immediately settled in the affirmative.   The coils were drawn together and vigorously contracted and Higby, first in astonishment, then consternation, decided the snake was trying to choke him. In a few seconds more he found that the reptile was succeeding.   In great discomfort, now mingling with fear, he strode around the studio pulling at the coils but could not locate the snake's head nor tail.   In a moment bordering on desperation he thought of the mirror and returning to it discovered the tail squeezed into the coils behind his ear.   Seizing this he unwound the snake.

What is the largest prey a python or anaconda can swallow?   That is also a frequent question.   I have given this subject close study over a period of years—and have been frequently horrified at tremendously exaggerated accounts that have appeared in books which were accurate on everything but matters pertaining to snakes.

I once fed a twenty-foot python with an eighty-pound, freshly killed pig (approaching the dignity of a hog in size) and the snake had all he could do to get away with it.   At one time his jaws were stretched to a point where I thought he could go no further.   The body of such an animal would be about the same circumference as a small antelope. The short horns of such an antelope, while an inconvenience and greatly slowing down the engulfing process would not eliminate the possibility of a python swallowing such a creature.   This indicates the swallowing limits of snakes around twenty feet in length.   A thirty-footer, with its much greater bulk and broader head would probably be able to swallow an one-hundred and fifty pound hog or an animal equivalent to a female fallow or white-tailed deer.   As serpents of that size are of such extreme rarity I have never been able to inspect one and study its capabilities.   As to pythons swinging from trees and grasping and constricting wild cattle as some stories go, all I can say is that writers of the same have surprising imaginations.   The big snakes never wantonly attack the larger jungle life with malicious intent of merely squeezing it to death.   It should also be understood that constriction is not so pronounced that the prey is crushed into an elongated mass and thus rendered easier to swallow.   There is little or no change in

the form of the animal. It is simply killed by being so squeezed that it is unable to breathe.

Pythons and boas seek rather moderate-size prey and lurk in specific locations where they find such quarry. Part of their food consists of the larger jungle fowl, or the young of the larger mammals. A big anaconda would be satisfied in capturing a fifty-pound capybara. It would probably be afraid of a full grown tapir and retreat from it, but make a stroke for a young one, possible a third-grown individual and be able to engulf it.

Pythons grow slower than boas and looking over a series of records it is indicated that they may require from ten to fifteen years to attain maturity—and even to slowly grow after attaining maturity of breeding size. A boa may attain breeding maturity in from five to eight years, then slowly grow up to fifteen years. The longest record for a python to live in captivity is thirty years. There can be little doubt that the life of the larger species of the *Boidae* is considerably over this period.

CHAPTER VII

THE NEW WORLD HARMLESS SNAKES

IF the reader will turn back to that chapter presenting a *resumé* of the families of snakes, observe the position of the Family *Colubridae,* thence note the description of its largest subfamily—the *Colubrinae*—by far the most extensive grouping among serpents—the status of the species to follow will be clearly understood. The heading of the present chapter, however, should not be misconstrued as indicating venomous characters among the primitive burrowing snakes, the *Boidae* or families in the chapter preceding. They are also non-venomous. The present grouping serves as a review of the broadly distributed, abundant and typical harmless snakes of the world.

Among the harmless serpents of the New World the water snakes and their allies form quite a large series. They are members of a cosmopolitan genus, with even a greater number occurring in Europe, Africa and Asia; the Indo-Malayan region having the greatest number.

The water snakes and close allies have been called the Natracine serpents. Some scientific students have suggested they are distinct enough to form a subfamily. They are mostly of moderate size, inclined to be rather stout, have strongly keeled scales, rather a distinct head and live near the water in which they take refuge when frightened. They are frog and fish eaters, or if of the smaller kinds, feed upon earth-worms, small salamanders or the like. Characteristically they prefer cold-blooded prey. They lack the power of constriction.

In the United States the larger members are often called "moccasins". This is a misleading term as it brings to mind a poisonous snake, the water moccasin of the southeastern states, which is a pit viper. The term water snakes is much more appropriate for the species of *Natrix,* of which there are eleven in the United States, and others extending into Mexico and Central America. In the former they range into New England, and north of the boundary into Canada, thence to the easterly Plains area. Owing to the common practice of calling them "moccasins" there is an erroneous supposition that *poison-*

ous water snakes range over a considerable portion of eastern North America, which is not the case.

The greater number of species of the harmless water snakes of the United States occur in the Southeast where the poisonous moccasin is also found, and are frequently mistaken for it. Some of the big species are equally ugly in appearance and grow fully as large. The main point of difference is their lack of the deep pit of the aquatic viper, which unique organ is situated on each side of the head between the eye and nostril. Also, the non-venomous water snakes have round pupils, while the moccasin has elliptical pupils. Another point of difference may be noted in the arrangement of the broad plates under the tail. The harmless species have these in two rows. With the moccasin the greater number are in a single row.

The Common Water Snake, *Natrix sipedon,* has the broadest distribution. Its range is from southerly Canada to Florida and westward to the Mississippi Valley, covering practically the entire range of the combined species of its genus in North America. The body is quite stout with strongly keeled scales. In the South there are several varieties, one of these a uniform light brown, the underside pale brick red, without spots or markings (Plate 13). The common and most widely distributed form, however, is brown, with broad, irregular crossbands of reddish brown, which show more plainly on the sides. The abdomen is yellowish white, usually brightly marked with red spots and blotches. Large or old specimens may appear a uniform dull brown or almost black. The young are quite different from the adult, being gray, with the cross-bands blackish and very distinct. Large adults are four feet long and fully two inches in diameter. The average size is two and one-half to three feet.

While there are allegations about the water snake being harmful in destroying game fish, this is not at all likely. The game fish, as a rule, are too active for the snake to catch them. It pursues the slower-moving fish, as well as frogs and toads. Frequenting the margins of ponds and lakes, large and small streams, old dams or the stone bases of roughly constructed bridges, the water snake may often be seen basking on a rock, stretched on the bank or even on branches overhanging the water, into which it plunges when frightened. As is the case of all the American water snakes it is viviparous, the young being produced alive to as many as three dozen or more in a litter. They are born during late August or early September.

Three of the largest water snakes have a restricted range. The Brown Water Snake, *N. taxispilota,* occurs from Maryland to Florida and westward to the Mississippi. Its color is dull reddish brown with three rows of square, alternating, chocolate brown blotches. This is a particularly forbidding looking snake with heavy body and long head much swollen at the temples. It reaches a length of five feet or slightly over and a weight of six to eight pounds. The Green Water Snake, *N. cyclopium,* attains an equally large size. The Diamond-back Water Snake, *N. rhombifer,* of the Mississippi Valley, and ranging into Texas, has a net-work of rhomb-like markings on the back. These big water snakes strike savagely when cornered, but in the open are extremely shy. They bask on derelict timber, or twine in clusters on stout boughs overhanging the water into which they drop upon the slightest disturbance.

The Striped Snakes or Garter Snakes, genus *Thamnophis* are closely related to the water snakes, in fact the majority of the species *are* water snakes. The genus is extensive. There are a dozen distinct kinds in the United States. The Common Garter Snake, *T. sirtalis* (Plate 13), with a range from Florida to Canada and westward to Minnesota probably extends further northward in easterly Canada than any other serpent. According to Dr. Thomas Barbour it ranges up to the 50th degree of latitude. It is largely terrestrial in the northern states, but quite aquatic in the south, where it is often found along streams, and dives into the water when alarmed. In many areas this is the most commonly seen of the eastern serpents. Distribution is general and it is fairly abundant near reclaimed or improved areas, where other snakes have long since disappeared. It occurs in many of the suburban areas of New Jersey and New York. Large numbers inhabit an old reservoir site in the northerly part of New York City, and even occur on the northerly portion of Manhattan Island. It is found about everywhere in the rural districts where snakes continue to exist.

The general color is dark brown or black, with three yellowish stripes extending lengthwise. The color beneath is greenish yellow. The skin along the sides, when distended, shows numerous white or pale greenish spots, which are often so arranged that a checkerboard or tessellated appearance is produced when the scales are widely separated after eating, or if the reptile is angry and flattens the body. Coloration and pattern are variable. The stripes may be more or less distinct. When the side stripes are present, they are always on

the second and third rows of scales, counting upward from the abdominal plates. With some specimens, the central stripe may be ragged or broken, and with others from the mountainous areas of New England, the stripe may be very faint or absent. With these, the tessellated pattern of the skin invades the scale coloration, producing a checkered effect. The side stripes remain to assist in identification.

The Garter Snake feeds only upon cold-blooded prey, such as frogs, toads, tadpoles, salamanders and earthworms. The length of a large adult female is about a yard, while the males are seldom over two to two and one-half feet in length. It is a viviparous species, there being as many as thirty young in a litter.

This is one of the various kinds of snakes alleged to swallow its young to protect them in times of danger. Persistent stories of such an exploit make it worth while to review the history and origin of the alleged habit.

During thirty years of observation of serpents under all sorts of conditions in which they are found, I have watched them in areas in the temperate zones, on the deserts and in the tropics, and have carried the story in mind. To these observations are added the studies of captive specimens. Thus the author has had every opportunity to verify the occurrence. I have never noted any hint of it.

Hundreds of letters insisting upon this feat have come to my attention. These follow briefly expressed doubt in articles or remarks during lectures. The farmers of the middle west were particularly disturbed about an article intimating doubt of the story. This article appeared in an important magazine of the central western area. There was such an avalanche of protest it was necessary to write a second article, backing my doubt with detailed explanation. This was followed by additional letters with details from observers who said they had actually seen the thing happen. The belief seems to center in the United States and to be an old story starting back in the days of the Colonists. The story is so good, in matching the eccentric make-up of snakes that it is difficult for a scientist to weaken it with calm arguments. It is woven into the serpent-lore of the states. Natives of the tropical American countries appear to know nothing about it. Clearly, the serpents of the United States—various kinds of serpents—are largely credited with such ingenuity in their maternal interest.

Over the period of years I have mentioned I have never seen a wild

serpent or a captive one make any attempt to swallow its young.   I have never seen a wild serpent make any attempt of any kind to protect its young—and adults with young nearby have been noted under numerous conditions.   The young may incidentally linger near the mother after they are born, or hatched, but the only reason for the contact appears to be the favorable nature of the place, providing nearby shelters for both.   It has always been a case of all members of the group seeking individual shelter—and this is the most practical thing to do.

Figure what might happen if the mother behaved true to the alleged actions of the story!   It is necessary to "stage" the scene for satisfactory analysis: There is a slope of low and tangled vegetation with numerous shelving rocks.   These are partially imbedded in the soil, but project at an angle.   They offer sheltering recesses beneath their undersides and some of these extend inward as crevices.   They are ideal summer shelters for adults and young.   Some of the crevices go deep enough for snakes to hibernate.   At any rate, crevices for escape and hiding are numerous, the area is good feeding ground and a fair number of reptiles are scattered about here and there.   Most of them are invisible as they are within the crevices digesting food.   Others are in similar places awaiting the time to shed old skins.   It is always thus with snakes, but a small portion of their number is ever seen except on the proper days at the dens in spring.

It happens that a female snake is stretched near a shelving rock. It also happens that some of her young, about ten in number, are woven through the grass or on the rocks near and around her.   Her presence near the young is incidental—the group having emerged to the open spot to seek the sun as the sky has but recently cleared after a long, cool rain.   A strolling human has discovered the group; has incidentally stepped right up to them—with indicated threat.   This is a condition I have often noted.   With this setting we will enact the alleged drama of the swallowing process—the performance a composite from condensed details I have received by word and letters, as follows: As the human intruder is discovered the mother snake becomes intensely alert.   She raises her head and utters a sharp hiss.   Following this she places her head close to the ground and widely opens her mouth.   At the sound of the hiss the young start toward her.   They quickly enter her open mouth and disappear down her throat, one after another.   The mother then seeks to escape.

I have never seen this happen nor any action to indicate it ever happens.

What I have seen happen—is this:

The adult snake being the most wary is the first to glide to shelter and disappears like a flash under a rock. The young hesitate. They are not so quick in getting a start, but they have instinctive fear of the human. They scatter in all directions. Those near a crevice glide quickly in. Others, taking no chances in losing the split-second's time in turning in a direction other than the head is pointing, glide straight ahead, threading into the longer grass and out of sight. It is a simultaneous disappearance. There is no lost time—no lost motion. Such a manifestation can be completed so quickly that an experienced collector may not have a chance to capture a single member of the group.

From what I know about men and snakes such a reptilian family exodus is thus conducted in the safest way for the snakes. If the mother should indulge in any spectacular action in pausing to hiss, open her mouth and await a parade of snakelets to make their way down her throat the whole family might be wiped out through the human finding opportunity to seize a stick and kill her, as is the average human way; and the snake is well aware of its danger in the presence of man.

Let us consider that one of the supporters of the snake-swallowing story produces the average arguments.

Suppose the snake had been in the open where there were no holes or crevices. How would she have acted then?

The answer to that is that mother snakes and their young are not to be found traveling in open places where there are no holes or shelters. Snakes never travel around with their young trailing after them like a string of ducks.

But there are other arguments to bolster the story. One writer insists that he killed the female snake after the episode and found a number of young within her—that they were alive and he *counted* them.

An answer is that it is possible to kill one of the viviparous snakes and find young that would otherwise have soon appeared in the world and immediately gone their way, needing no parental care. Such harshly disclosed infants might be quite active.

An occasional narrator, in the face of explanation, insists upon the fact of having seen the snake swallow the young serpents. This is also possible to clear. Adult blacksnakes, the gopher snake and the

king snake are semi-cannibalistic, eating the young of other serpents
—some also swallowing the adults of other kinds.   To an observer
with keen eyes who does not thrash about when out of doors it is a
simple matter to spot a snake ten to twelve feet away.   If a hungry
serpent, of cannibalistic tendency comes across a batch of young of
some other species it quickly swallows them, one after another, warily
watching a human who may be standing a fair distance away, but not
close enough to warrant fleeing from the observer.   The characteristic
motions of a snake's jaws in swallowing, which pull the prey into the
mouth by recurved teeth on jaw bones which move forward and back
might readily impart the impression that the young snakes were quickly
crawling between those jaws instead of being mechanically ushered
toward a hungry stomach.

I have never heard a snake hiss as a call or signal to another.   The
hisses of the minority, which make any sound whatever, are used in their
defence attitudes to intimidate an enemy, so that part of the story
which cites the details of the mother thus "calling" her young weakens
it at its beginning.

It is doubtful if a litter of young snakes could be swallowed by an
adult serpent and endure the salivary secretions of the mouth, which
are of a glairy nature and would veneer and close their small nostrils.
It would seem that they would thus be quickly smothered.   Moreover, they would have extreme difficulty in making their way into the
mother's smooth throat—a procession of a dozen or more—and some
of the species said to swallow their young have as many as fifty in a
litter.

Summing it up, the action appears physically improbable.   If
occasional serpents do behave this way it would seem as if they were
resorting to a foolish practice.   If the race generally developed the
habit there would soon be a lesser number of snakes than there are now
as mothers would sacrifice themselves and their families during a display
of impractical bravado.   The story appears to hinge on two confused
observations—the discovery of a cannibalistic snake swallowing the
young of another species or an examination of a slain serpent containing young ready to be born.   The two findings link up and are
convincing enough to absorb embellishments prompted by good faith,
but lack of technical judgment.

In demonstrating the use of a viscous fluid, of evil odor carried in
glands at the base of the tail, the Garter Snake can be particularly of-

fensive if handled. All of the water snakes and allied kinds secrete this fluid, which is thought to create a scent during the breeding season in attracting the sexes. When such snakes are restrained the glands are opened and the strong-smelling fluid very generously smeared upon an enemy. Other kinds of snakes have similar scent glands. The rat snakes when annoyed exude a pasty secretion of fox-like odor, the copperhead an odor that some liken to that of cucumbers, while a rattler if attacked can eject a spray of musky fluid a yard or more. Some of these odors are faintly sweet and not offensive, but the members of the water snake clan, without exception, can be foully disagreeable.

There are several exceptions in form of body among the striped or garter snakes. One of these is the dainty Ribbon Snake, *T. sauritus*. A specimen a yard long is barely half an inch in diameter. This is essentially a water snake, found in swampy meadows or along streams and often seen swimming. The pattern of the Ribbon Snake is more intense than the garter snake. Coloration is dark brown or black, with a bright yellow stripe down the back and a similar stripe on each side, on the third and fourth rows of scales from the plates of the abdomen.

The food consists of small fishes, tadpoles and frogs. The litters are small, there seldom being as many as a dozen young.

The range is southeastern Canada and the eastern United States to the Mississippi Valley; southward to Georgia and Alabama. A similar species, *T. sackenii*, occurs in the southerly portion of the former's range and into Florida. The stripe on the back is barely discernible, although the lateral stripes are present. It is semi-aquatic.

There is a small genus of miniature members of the Natracine snakes in the United States whose members will long survive the extinction of the larger species in intensively cultivated areas. This is *Storeria*, with three species, and the average length of adult specimens is about a foot. They are commonly known as the Brown Snakes. All inhabit eastern North America. Two range from Ontario into southern Mexico and westward to Kansas. The third occurs in Florida. The two common species are known respectively as Storer's Snake, or the Red-bellied Snake, *S. occipitomaculata* and DeKay's Snake, *S. dekayi*. The former is more commonly found in hilly places and is brown or dark gray with a brilliant vermillion undersurface. DeKay's Snake (the Brown Snake) is the more generally abundant. It is brown or brownish gray with a series of minute black dots in pairs arranged in a

longitudinal row along the back.   There is sometimes a broad, though faint vertebral line of paler hue than the body color.   Beneath the color is pinkish white.   The scales are strongly keeled.

Details about this little snake are worth while as the author receives more queries about it, and specimens for identification, than any of the eastern North American reptiles.   This comes from these small reptiles being found in unexpected places where other snakes have never been noted, in places where the supposition has been that snakes have long been exterminated.   It may be found on an estate of smooth lawns, in cellars or around the foundations of houses.   Under such circumstances, the discovery of a snake may be quite disturbing.

As the little Brown Snake finds plenty of shelter in a rock garden, section of an old stone wall or even the hollows under a flagged walk, and as it is not given to much strolling in open places, it has held its own.   Dull coloration, diminutive size, and the readily obtained diet of earthworms assist in rendering it unique in surviving in localities where even the common garter snake has disappeared.

It still occurs in several areas in Central Park in New York City, hemmed in on all sides by the congestion and bustle of the metropolis. There is an old cemetery, less than a city block square, in the Borough of the Bronx, in New York, where these little serpents are fairly abundant.   Towering apartments loom on all sides.

As the former series of Natricine snakes and their allies shape into a series, the King Snakes and related genera form a similarly well defined grouping.   All are *constrictors* and feed upon both warm and cold-blooded prey.   Again, they differ in being *oviparous*—meaning that they lay eggs in the production of their young.   Their form is supple and cylindrical, the body clad in smooth, polished scales.

Some of the most beautiful of the New World snakes are among these species.   The term King Snakes is fairly well applied as they commonly overpower, kill and swallow other snakes.   The larger kinds are immune to the poisonous bites of the pit vipers, but not to the neurotoxin of the coral snakes (*Elapidae*).   The dominating genus is *Lampropeltis*.   There are over a dozen kinds in North America.

The largest is the Common King Snake, or Chain Snake, *L. getulus* (Plate 22).   Its coloration varies according to locality.   The typical form occurs from southern New Jersey to Florida.   In part of its range it is lustrous black with narrow white cross-bands which fork on the sides and connect in chain-like fashion.   This coloration holds good

until close to Florida, where the bands are distinctly yellow.   Mention has been made of the *typical form*.   Considered in all of its subspecies this is a coast to coast species, although largely of the southern tier of states.   There is a brown form, with indistinct and broken bands in Florida (*L. getulus floridana*); a black form (*L. g. nigra*) with bare trace of markings, in Alabama, Tennessee, Kentucky and southern Indiana; a form with a pale green or yellow dot in each scale (*L. g. holbrooki*), occurring in the lower Mississippi Valley; a form appearing dusted with fine yellow spots (*L. g. splendida*) in the Mexican boundary region, and a particularly vivid form with enamel-white or lemon-yellow rings in California (*L. g. boylii*).   All told there are nine distinct subspecies.   The typical and Florida varieties attain the largest size—from five to six feet.

No more ideal reptile for study or a pet than a King Snake can be picked from the whole serpent clan.   In all of its varieties it is attractive and the greater number of examples remarkably gentle—even immediately after capture.   It is particularly hardy as a captive, feeds readily and lives for years.

Among other kinds of serpents, the King Snake cannot be trusted. It will constrict and eat smaller specimens, attack larger ones and squeeze them to death.   There is no indication of cannibalism among a number of king snakes kept together.   I have watched them kill a rattler or moccasin and although savagely bitten by the poisonous reptile continue to squeeze it until it was dead, and afterwards not appear to suffer from the wounds.   This is an ideal serpent for farms and plantations as besides being cannibalistic and likely to kill poisonous reptiles crossing its path, the food consists generously of rodents—mice and rats—which are quickly dispatched by the agile and strong squeezing hunter.   It prowls deeply into the burrows of rodents in search of litters of young.

Other handsome king snakes are *L. californiae,* of southern California, *L. alterna,* of the Davis Mountains in Texas, *L. catalinensis,* of Santa Catalina Island, Gulf of California and the particularly gorgeous though small Scarlet King Snake, *L. multicincta,* of the mountain forests of California.   The latter is rather rare and the reptile collector looks for it as a veritable prize.   *L. polyzonus* (Plate 22), with red markings, is found in Central America.

The "Milk" Snake, *L. triangulum* (Plate 21), with five subspecies is a slender king snake, ranging from moderate to small size.   The

larger and typical form *L. triangulum triangulum* is found from Maine to Iowa and southward to North Carolina. It is brightly marked, a yard or slightly more in length, and the numerous specimens sent to the author for identification indicate that it is often mistaken for the copperhead, from which it may be immediately distinguished by the smooth scales. Although generally distributed, it is not usually common. Coloration is yellowish brown or gray, with a series of irregular, chestnut-brown or reddish blotches, edged with black. On some specimens these blotches are dark olive. On the sides are smaller blotches in alternation with those on the back. It is white beneath, with oblong spots of black.

This is the reptile thought by many farmers to steal milk from cows; a supposition which must be relegated to the many serpent myths. The subspecies of *triangulum* extend into the southerly and westerly states. They also range into Mexico where they are brightly ringed with red and sometimes mistaken for the poisonous coral snakes.

The beautiful little Scarlet Snake, *Cemophora coccinea,* indicates close relationship to the king snake genus. Twenty-four inches in length and a half inch in diameter are its maximum proportions, but its vivid colors in wide scarlet areas, separated by pairs of black half-rings (encircling the upper surface) these enclosing a yellow half-ring about three scales wide, make up for lack of size. The abdomen is white or yellowish. It inhabits the southeastern states.

This is one of the species said to "mimic" the dangerous coral snake of the South, in displaying the same colors arranged in ring-like pattern. Yet there is a difference that will distinguish the dangerous reptile from the innocuous "imitators," as the yellow rings of the poisonous snake always border the black rings, while among the non-venomous snakes there are pairs of black rings bordering a yellow one. This combination is good to carry in mind in the southern United States, but it fails to carry uniformly into the American tropics where there are many kinds of deadly coral snakes and such a variety of non-venomous imitators that no set rule can be given to tell them all apart. Some of the harmless kinds have ringed patterns almost precisely like the coral snakes, which in the warm latitudes have varied ring combinations.

There is a chain of genera leading through the *Colubrinae* with more or less close relationship to what might conveniently be referred to as major genera. In a general work like this a number of these

smaller genera must be omitted and the route leads to the discussion of separated groupings of outstanding kinds.   This brings us to some fine species, the largest non-venomous serpents inhabiting North America.

Elaphe is the most extensive genus, with ten species.   All are constrictors, feed practically altogether upon warm-blooded prey, small mammals and birds, and several of them attain a length in excess of eight feet.   All are oviparous or egg-laying.   The Corn Snake, *E. guttata* (Plate 17), is the handsomest, though not the largest.   A particularly large adult (six feet long) may be considered to be the most handsome of all North American snakes.   The ground hue is gray, tan or reddish.   On the back is a series of large crimson saddles, bordered with black.   There is a series of similar, smaller blotches on the sides.   The abdomen is white, with large black squares.   As with all species of *Elaphe* the scales are faintly keeled.

The Corn Snake is found from the southerly pine barrens of New Jersey to Florida and westward to the Mississippi.   It receives its name from frequenting fields of ripening grain, where rodents may be plentiful.   It is hence, like its allies, of value in agricultural areas.

The Chicken Snake, *E. quadrivittata* is another handsome reptile of much the same area, but not extending northward of North Carolina. It is pale tan or brown with four dark stripes extending the length of the body.   Its young are gray with square blotches.   These fade and give way to the stripes the second or third year.

This reptile acquires its name from a habit of prowling around poultry houses, primarily for rodents, but taking a toll of hens' eggs if it happens to find them, then unwisely coiling on some overhead shelf to digest the meal.   A five-foot example will swallow three or four eggs at a visit.   The snake seldom makes an effort to break the shells, which within forty-eight hours are dissolved by the powerful gastric juices. A specimen that has recently fed is so clearly a robber of a chicken house that there is no mistaking the circumstances.   Despite these digressions the Chicken Snake should be rated as of economic value as a rat destroyer.   Like the corn snake it is inclined to hunt rodents about ramshackle buildings and the greater number of the author's specimens have been found in the rafters of old and deserted structures where the snakes were hunting for rats and mice or were quietly coiled digesting such prey.   A specimen in Georgia came into my possession under

humorous circumstances.   Just as we were passing a cabin about which a populous family of colored children were playing, a scream came from the buxom mother inside and a large aluminum cooking pot flew through a window and, incidentally, in our direction.   As it struck the ground a big, coiled chicken snake rolled out of it.   Going inside to ascertain the reason for a fine specimen being landed at our feet, the excited negress told me that she had peeled potatoes for the family and reached on a shelf for a pot in which to cook them.   The pot felt heavy and poking inside she discovered the snake neatly coiled within it.   Such inclination of the chicken snake to prowl into deserted houses—and inhabited ones—has resulted in another and not inappropriate name for it—the Yellow House Snake.

Largest of the members of *Elaphe* and attractive from its lithe and powerful body clad in ebony-black scales is the Black Chicken Snake, Pilot Blacksnake or Mountain Blacksnake, *E. obsoleta*.   It has the widest range of the genus, extending from Florida to central Massachusetts and westward into Texas.   The largest example I have measured was eight feet and five inches long.   It was captured in the mountains of Sullivan County, New York.   I believe that this species attains a length of a full nine feet.   It is one of the four largest snakes inhabiting the United States, the others being the Bull Snake, *Pituophis sayi*, of the Plains Region, the Gopher Snake, *Drymarchon corais couperi*, of the Southeast, and the Diamond-back Rattlesnake, *Crotalus adamanteus*, also of the southeastern states.

The term of Black Chicken Snake is applied to *E. obsoleta* only in the southern states, where it is of general occurrence and has the same habit of entering buildings and occasionally stealing eggs as described with four-banded species preceding.   I had two specimens of this snake that had swallowed china eggs and after patiently awaiting digestion, disgorged them.   In both instances the snake had evidently found a nest prepared to induce a hen to lay and with an appetite stimulated by the poultry odor of the place was lured into swallowing the only egg it could find.

I have observed this snake in the extreme South, in Virginia, New Jersey, Pennsylvania and New York and am convinced that the largest examples are found in the northerly and extreme westerly portion of its range.   It is rare to find a specimen much over five feet long in South Carolina, Georgia or Florida while in the North examples over seven feet are not unusual.

One reason for this snake being considered rare over the greater part of the northerly range comes from specimens being in the trees, where they are not observed.   There is an inclination, after feeding, to ascend sloping trees and rest among foliage on horizontal branches. Feathered prey can also be stalked from such places.   I remember a huge old live oak in South Carolina that was veritably a serpent den. A dozen shed skins could be seen along its stout branches.   It was inhabited by large and small specimens of the locally called "black chicken snakes."   There was a similar tree in the mountains near Port Jervis, New York.   This was a very old oak with several large cavities in the trunk and in one of these was a nest of wild bees.   We seldom passed this tree without seeing one or two mountain blacksnakes stretched on a thick, horizontal bough.   When we teased them by shoving up a long pole they would glide into a hole in the trunk and disappear. There was a shattered ledge near the base of the tree and as we had seen rattlers in the vicinity decided that this was a "den" in which the poisonous snakes hibernated and where they were joined in the Autumn by the mountain blacksnakes—descending from their summer quarters in the tree.   It is also possible that they hibernated in deep crevices of the tree itself, as was actually noted in some Spring collecting in another area.   In the Spring I have seen the mountain blacksnake on ledges in the southerly Berkshires basking in close proximity to crevices from which rattlesnakes were emerging.   There is a ledge near the Connecticut shore where the largest aggregation of mountain blacksnakes I have ever seen together assemble each Fall to hibernate.   The term mountain blacksnake in this instance is rather a misnomer as the country is rather rolling with swampy woods.   The ledge, however, is on the southerly side of a wooded hill, half a mile long and of barely 200 feet elevation.   Several dozen of these snakes may be seen every Spring when they first emerge to bask, and scattered among them are as many copperhead snakes, which come from the same crevices.   It is difficult to find a mountain blacksnake in this area during the Summer, the explanation for this seeming scarcity reverting to the note about their fondness for going into the trees.

This species is often mistaken for the common blacksnake, but is larger and proportionately heavier, with a rather wide head, while the black racer is whip-like in build and quicker in movements.   On close examination *E. obsoleta* may be distinguished by the polished though faintly keeled scales (smooth and satiny with the racer) and the

tendency of the scales to show narrow white edges; also by a considerable portion of the abdomen being white.

There are two fine species of *Elaphe* in the Central States. Both are similarly marked, grayish or brownish with a series of dark saddles along the back. These are Emory's Snake, *E. laeta,* found from Kansas southward into Mexico, and the Fox Snake, *E. vulpina,* occurring in Indiana, Iowa, Illinois, Michigan and westward to Minnesota. Thus the latter's range is the most northerly of the North American members of *Elaphe.* Its name comes from an odor exuded from glands at the vent when it is annoyed. However, all of these related snakes can exude a similar odor.

Pituophis is another genus of powerful constrictors. The body scales are distinctly keeled; the head is quite pointed. The four species carry the range from coast to coast in North America. This genus contains one of the four largest serpents of the continent. This is the Bull Snake, *P. sayi* (Plate 18).

The Bull Snake attains a length of close to nine feet. Here is a reptile of much economic importance, occurring over the rodent-infested area of the wheat belt—where it is much needed. The range is approximately between the Mississippi River and the Rocky Mountains and from Minnesota southward into Mexico. This is an area inhabited by various ground gophers (ground squirrels) and other rodents destructive to grain. It is strange that no general campaign of education toward the conservation of the economic types has been undertaken through the wheat states, where the killing of rodent eating snakes with the gradual thinning of their numbers goes steadily on.

The Bull Snake may be defined as straw color, or pale brown, sometimes orange yellow, with a row of large square blotches of reddish brown (or black) on the back and similar smaller blotches on the sides.

While the majority of snakes are silent, there are a few which hiss in characteristic ways, some which vibrate their tails to produce a buzzing sound by rasping against vegetation, and again there is the specifically provided rattlesnake. These sounds are for the purpose of frightening enemies. Some of the harmless snakes hiss sharply, both with inhalation and exhalation of the breath. The small poisonous vipers of Europe do this and rather quickly as if in great anger. This same type of hissing is particularly loud with the tic-polonga or Russell's viper of India. The ungainly and par-

ticularly deadly vipers of Africa hiss slowly and loudly with intake and exhalation of breath.   The cobra utters a sharp, almost sneezing hiss when feinting to strike.   Such hissing types are not provided, however, with any particular development to amplify the sound.   With the several species of *Pituophis* there is a thoracic development to produce a particularly loud hiss.   Thus they seek to intimidate.   They also utilize another method to be noted among several New World genera, particularly the rodent-eaters.   This is rapid vibration of the tail, which, it is not rash to say, simulates the warning of the poisonous rattlesnakes.

The king snakes, *Lampropeltis,* vibrate the tail as do the members of *Elaphe.*   The habit is also common among the racers, *Coluber,* and the closely related whip-snakes, *Masticophis.*   Some of the deadly lance-head snakes, *Bothrops,* of the American tropics thus vibrate their tails.   Even the big and formidable bushmaster, *Lachesis,* utilizes this warning as does the southern water moccasin and the eastern copperhead snake.

In order to produce its loud and warning *hiss* the harmless Bull Snake and other members of its genus utilize a voluntarily erectile filament attached to the air passage opening into the lower jaw.   All snakes are provided with a tube-like arrangement called the glottis, which is actually the windpipe and extends forward into the mouth beyond what might be termed the throat opening.   It is this tube-like arrangement, voluntarily contractile, that is utilized by some snakes to eject and draw in air with sharp hissing sounds.   Contracting the end of the glottis they thus intensify the sound.   With the Bull Snake, there is an erectile ridge immediately in front of the glottis.   The snake hisses only with exhalation of air, but utilizes the ridge to produce the same effect as if one took a card and held it in front of the lips, blowing forcibly upon it.   The sound may be heard for fifty feet or more, and as the snake follows this demonstration by a sweeping strike, the effect is startling.

The members of *Pituophis* are fond of birds, although their toll among feathered prey is but a part of the natural plan in producing a balance of life and is amply compensated for by the good they do as rodent eaters.   They also eat eggs and here again all the species illustrate another point of specialization.

Many egg-eating snakes swallow the egg entire, as described with *Elaphe* and await the action of the gastric juices to dissolve the shell.

Not so with the Bull Snake and its allies. When the egg has passed about a foot down the throat the reptile presses its body firmly against the ground, contracts the muscles in advance and posteriorly to the egg and breaks it.

The action is quite deliberate and consumes a full ten seconds. The egg collapses with an externally discernible crunch and the fragments of shell are swallowed. To my mind the action is just as neat and quickly accomplished as that of the particularly specialized *Dasypeltis* of Africa, which feeds almost altogether upon eggs and has sharp cutting edges attached to the vertebrae, which extend into the throat for the precise purpose of cutting an egg shell into sections. *Dasypeltis* regurgitates the shell fragments.

There is an easterly and a westerly ally of the Bull Snake. The Western Bull Snake, *P. catenifer,* is found from British Columbia into Lower California and easterly into Nevada and Utah. It is smaller than the plains species and the blotches of the back more crowded and numerous.

The Pine Snake, *P. melanoleucus* (Plate 18), occurs from the pine barrens of southern New Jersey to Florida and into the Gulf States. The pattern is striking, the body being dull white on the back and intensely white on the sides. Down the back is a series of large black blotches, close together and not sharply defined on the forward portion, but posteriorly wider apart and in strong contrast. The greater part of the abdomen is marble white. The head resembles that of a turtle, being small with the sharply pointed snout protruding over the lower jaw. A length of six feet is not rare. With Florida specimens the darker markings are inclined to be more brownish, the pattern less vivid and more suffused. Dr. Thomas Barbour considers this a distinct species—*P. mugitus.*

A grouping fits in here which shows relationship to the two previous genera, but the habits are at variance. Among the members of this new group are the Racers, divided among *Coluber (Zamenis), Masticophis* and *Alsophis (Dromicus).* These are whip-like, swift in motion, have no power of constriction, feed upon comparatively small prey, both cold and warm-blooded, have smooth scales and are oviparous —egg-laying. *Drymarchon (Spilotes)* is another genus, with stouter body but similar habits. There are other allied genera.

The familiar Blacksnake, or Black Racer, *Coluber constrictor* (Plate 14), is probably the most generally observed member of this

grouping.   Owing to it being frequently confused with the powerful and constricting mountain blacksnake, ideas about it, coupled with considerable imagination, are sadly mixed.   I have always been inclined to think that Linnaeus had the two species confused in applying the name *constrictor* to the racer, as this specific term is most inappropriately used.

The Black Racer is a smooth and satiny, not shiny snake, uniform black above and beneath, the only break in its monotone being a white patch on the chin and the lower lip plates.   A six-foot specimen may be considered *large* and allegations of longer examples come from confusion with the mountain blacksnake (the black chicken snake).

If disturbed during the breeding season, which is May, *occasional* blacksnakes will actually attack.   They will glide toward an intruder on the ledgy hibernating quarters, striking madly at one's feet or legs. If among dried leaves the tail is vibrated, producing a buzzing sound. These same hibernating quarters may be utilized by numerous rattlers. The two associate in perfect harmony, gliding in and out of the same crevices.   The alleged enmity between them is a myth.   Having no power of constriction the blacksnake lacks means to fight the rattler. It occurs over the whole eastern area of the United States.

It feeds largely upon small rodents and is of economic value.   The distribution is far more general than with the mountain blacksnake, as the Black Racer occurs among the mountains, the low-lying meadows and the farmlands, in fact generally where sufficient shelter remains to retain its hold.   It rapidly disappears from areas of intensive cultivation and ruthless killing has exterminated it from many places where the more secretive and smaller snakes still remain.   The vivid blacksnake as it travels in comparatively open country is too good a target for the shotgun to exist in populated rural areas.   Then again the farmer's son considers it fine sport, if a den is located in the spring, to climb among the rocks and from a good vantage point shoot blacksnakes right and left.   I have often gone over ledges immediately after such a visitation and counted over a dozen or more slaughtered serpents. Coupled with this type of sport, the killing of hawks and owls is producing the most favorable condition possible for the multiplication of the injurious rodents.

The blacksnake cannot endure captivity if a series of other serpents, particularly the tropical species, are in immediate proximity.   It is attacked by small parasites (mites) which the other reptiles harbor

with little annoyance, but against which it appears to have no resistance. For this reason I have long since stopped collecting specimens for exhibition in the Zoological Park. Kept alone or adjacent to local specimens, it does well if its quarters are absolutely dry and the temperature remains even. At best, however, it is a delicate captive requiring sympathetic care, and much at variance with the hardy and phlegmatic mountain blacksnake which lives for years under artificial conditions.

The blacksnake is alleged to resort to the "power" of charming its prey. Allegation of this habit has been applied to various kinds of snakes. As the assertion largely relates to the charming of birds it is not difficult to reach an explanation of its origin.

Many birds have a habit of luring enemies from their nests. They may drag their way along the ground, trailing a wing as if it were broken, but ready to quickly dart forward, or fly, if the interested enemy seeks to grasp them.

A snake in a tree, possibly wandering without definite intent, approaches a nest containing young birds. The mother bird is terrified and seeks to turn the enemy from her brood. Hopping from branch to branch toward the snake she flutters her wings to attract its attention. The snake may not be hungry—and again it may see the nest with tempting food. The parent bird is desperate. She comes closer to the snake. Her wings droop and she appears to sag. The snake considers one thing even though it may not be particularly hungry. If a meal is as easily obtained as this it is well to take advantage of it. It starts for the bird, anticipating an immediate catch.

The anticipated prey painfully retreats a few inches. The snake follows. The retreat continues, but the reptile's appetite has become stimulated. Its mind has now become set upon the capture of that bird, which lures the reptile to the end of a branch and over another interlacing with an adjacent tree. With the serpent well out of the way the bird flies off, the job well done.

Having noted this going on and in some instances being attracted to it by other birds watching the performance and scolding vigorously from near-by trees I have thought how an observer might form the surmise that the bird so strangely fluttering near the snake was "charmed" and attracted toward the reptile.

Occasional birds get into trouble during this luring process. They fail to accurately account for a lateral, striking S the snake may be

craftily forming of its anterior part. There is no doubt about the bird taking note of this, but that loop is deceiving. Carried as a well-opened S it looks particularly menacing and is readily gauged, but the snake has a method of greatly enlarging the loop by drawing it together and at the same time feeding its body into the rearward portion. Any closer approach of the bird may bring it into the striking zone. It is a case of being checkmated at its own game.

Assertions of snakes charming humans are utter nonsense. A nervous human may be rooted to the spot with fear on seeing a snake, but such an occasion is in no way associated with power of charming. A good illustration of the belief is brought out by Oliver Wendell Holmes in that most curious of his books "Elsie Venner." Holmes employed the theme to produce a strong work in fiction, but there are occasional writers who openly cite experiences.

In the central and southwestern states the blacksnake takes on a greenish-blue hue above and yellowish beneath. This variety is known as the Blue Racer, *C. constrictor flaviventris*—the subspecific name pertaining to the yellow undersurface. Another variety occurs in British Columbia and southward through California. Thus the species has a coast to coast distribution.

The Coachwhip Snake, *Masticophis flagellum* (Plate 14), is the high speed member of the racers. It is longer than the blacksnake, the head and neck blackish, fusing into brown on the body. Its extreme agility always coupled with perfect grace in action form a bewildering combination. It occurs from Virginia to Florida and westward to the Rockies, although a pinkish subspecies, *piceus,* occurs in Arizona. Similar extremely active and slender species inhabit the Southwest and are known as the Striped Racers. I have met them on the deserts and moving so fast we could barely overtake them by running.

Alsophis and *Dromicus* are large genera of smaller racers of tropical America and the West Indies. Some are of monotone in brown or gray, some are speckled and others have light or dark bands extending the length of the body. *Alsophis* was rather recently split from *Dromicus.* *A. angulifer* (Plate 24), a very common snake on the plains and savannas of Cuba, is three to four feet long when adult, pale gray with a crescentic black mark on each side of the head. Its anterior ribs are elongated and when angry it rears slightly and flattens the neck in hood-like fashion like a cobra. A related species of Hayti is even more spectacular in this action, rearing quite high and waving the

dilated neck from side to side. It is greatly feared by the natives, but there are no poisonous snakes on that island or on any of the large islands of the West Indies, although seventeen species of *Alsophis* and eighteen of *Dromicus* are listed from the area.

A very handsome and powerful purplish-black, highly polished serpent inhabiting the southeastern United States represents a small tropical American genus. The one ranging into North America is commonly called the Gopher Snake or Indigo Snake, *Drymarchon corais couperi.* It inhabits the southeasterly states. This is one of the four rated as the largest of North American serpents.

The Indigo Snake frequents areas where the gopher tortoise digs its deep burrows, and gliding into these when frightened it has thus acquired its equally common name of Gopher Snake. It is a striking sight to note one of these big creatures trailing its glittering black length among the low scrub oaks and scant vegetation of the sand barrens. Some of the negroes recognize its value as a rodent killer and it is occasionally seen in the neighborhood of cabins, where it is unmolested and hunts for rats. In fact the nearer to the tropics one wanders the more tolerance for harmless snakes is to be noted, owing to their vermin destroying habits. This is by no means pronounced, but there is less of a ruthless and uniform slaughter than upon the farms of North America—the tendency of the greater number of persons to grasp a stick and kill a snake. I remember my surprise in looking out of the window of a train in Costa Rica at a commotion in a ditch some workmen were digging. They were laughing and throwing handfuls of sand at a snake a full six feet long that was scrambling by them and which managed to make its way up the side and glide away. There was no attempt to kill it. I asked them if they were afraid of it and an answer in Spanish amounted to: "It is of a good kind, Senor."

The big indigo snake of the Southeast has extended northward from the tropical area. In the easterly corner of North America it is blue-black, slowly giving way to extremely dark olive in southeastern Texas and Mexico. In Central America it is light olive to pale brown and in South America becomes black again on the forward portion and golden yellow on the latter half, a remarkable and striking coloration. This is the typical form, commonly called the Cribo or Rat Snake (in Portuguese). The blue-black form in the United States is recognized as the subspecies *couperi* and the Mexican and Central American form as *melanurus,* owing to it being more or less suffused with black, al-

though the name is not reconcilable to some specimens that approach greenish hues or tan.   The habits of the North American subspecies, in fact all the subspecies, are similar to those of the blacksnake.   It does not constrict, feeds upon frogs, toads, birds and rodents, and is occasionally cannibalistic in swallowing other harmless serpents.   It may be told from the blacksnake by its highly polished scales and reddish hue beneath the chin instead of a white patch, and also by its proportionately stouter body.

It has been noted that big serpents of this type are commonly called rat snakes in tropical America.   The longest of them all, although of very slender build is the Black and Yellow Rat Snake, *Spilotes pullatus* (Plate 16), found throughout Central America and tropical South America.   For a Colubrine serpent it grows to the surprising length of close to twelve feet although a coiled specimen of that length would not appear as large as an eight-foot indigo or gopher snake.   The coloration is particularly striking.   It consists of bold and irregular patches of ebony black and bright lemon yellow.   The scales are excessively large, there being but few rows about the body.   The back is ridged, dispelling the cylindrical aspect of most snakes.   When this snake is angry it vertically flattens the neck and by thus separating the scales intensifies its bold pattern.   It is the most showy harmless reptile of the American tropics.

In selecting additional representative New World harmless snakes there is a curious genus (*Heterodon*) of North America which should not be passed by.   There are four stubby species, their maximum length about a yard.   The snout is turned up like a wedge.   They are called the Hog-nosed Snakes, but the respective species have been generously provided with sinister appellations owing to the airs they put on in pretending to be dangerous.

Their anterior ribs are elongated and may be laterally spread in a manner to make the neck as proportionately wide as that of a cobra although the area of flattening is more elongate and not gracefully rounded like a "hood."   Moreover, the hog-nosed snakes also flatten and widen the head until it assumes a most formidable, triangular outline.   During such antics the reptile rears the neck on a sloping plane. These actions are accompanied by long and sharp hisses.

To one unacquainted with the ways of snakes, such actions are alarming.   The flattening of the neck distends the scale rows, causing the mottled pattern to be particularly vivid.   If the intruder ventures

fairly close the snake makes a feint at striking; as if warning one to keep out of harm's way.

These actions are impelled by pure bravado, and this is of short duration. If the snake is further annoyed it appears to be attacked with convulsions. The head is twisted to one side, the body kinks, the mouth gapes helplessly open and the tongue lolls from it. There is further kinking and twisting and the reptile rolls upon its back. It is a fine piece of acting, in simulating death agonies, then complete demise. Everything is perfect but the snake's insistence on remaining upon its back. If rolled over on its crawling surface with a stick it will dextrously turn upon its back again.

The hog-nosed snakes feed almost altogether upon toads—occasionally upon frogs—and have enlarged fang-like teeth in the rear of the upper jaw to hold the prey, and to puncture the body of a victim which resists swallowing by prodigiously swelling with air. The long teeth are in no way poisonous. These snakes live in dry, usually sandy areas. *Heterodon browni* is found only in southern Florida, *H. simus* has a fair range over the southeastern states while *H. nasicus* occurs from southwestern Iowa, Kansas and Nebraska to Montana and southward into Mexico, being particularly common along the Mexican boundary from Texas to Arizona. It has the most pronounced snout of its genus. *H. contortrix* is the common eastern species found from Massachusetts to Florida and westward to Minnesota and Texas. It is known as the Flat-headed "Adder," Hissing "Adder," and other names in keeping with its antics. The common belief points to its being very poisonous. Its airs are not in keeping with the average venomous snake which seeks to quickly administer a poisonous bite with its fangs when attacked, or thinks it is to be attacked, and thus throws the enemy into confusion, when it escapes. The show put on by the hog-nosed snake is an ostentatious display characteristic of *harmless* reptiles, but so pronounced by the present little group that the members have acquired, and sadly to their detriment, a very evil reputation.

Quite recently the name of the eastern species was changed to that by which the copperhead was known—*contortrix*. Its name was formerly *Heterodon platyrhinus,* but Dr. Thomas Barbour, after a careful examination of the later editions of Linnaeus, found that owing to an error in early nomenclature, confusing two species, the hog-nosed snake was renamed, *contortrix,* in the 12th edition, thus rendering that specific

name untenable for the copperhead, the specific name of which is now to be noted in the systematic lists as *mokasen*.

The eastern hog-nosed snake is most abundant in sandy areas, and is found in considerable numbers in some portions of Long Island, immediately back of the sea beach. It is also common in sandy areas in New Jersey. It is by no means confined to sandy regions, however, as it is also found in the mountains, although sparingly. The scales are keeled. A large specimen is three feet long, but the greater number are two to two and one-half feet long. Coloration and markings are extremely variable, but the usual hue is yellowish or brown, with dark brown or black irregular cross-bands. Some specimens have bright shades of yellow or red, the latter being particularly evident anteriorly. Occasional examples are entirely black. These are usually observed in elevated areas.

Two very dainty uniform leaf-green serpents occur in the easterly and central portions of North America. These are commonly known as the Green Snakes, and represent two genera—*Liopeltis* and *Opheodrys*. With one the scales are smooth and satiny. The other has rough, keeled scales.

The Smooth Green Snake, *L. vernalis* (Plate 21), is most frequently seen in damp meadows. It is green above and whitish beneath, is slender and seldom as long as twenty-four inches. It is one of the few serpents ranging northward into southern Canada. Its distribution extends southward to Florida and westward to New Mexico. The Rough-scaled Green Snake, *O. aestivus* is green above and yellow beneath, extremely slender and sometimes attains a length of a yard. Its range is much more southerly than the smooth-scaled species. Central New Jersey appears to be its northerly limit, thence it occurs southward and westward over areas of distribution of the other green snake. Both are unique in feeding largely upon insect prey, searching for grasshoppers, crickets and smooth-bodied moth and butterfly larvae. Their young are fond of small spiders.

Diadophis is made up of pretty little snakes of North America, which have a peculiar color pattern among the four members. They are known as the Ring-necked Snakes. Many persons finding these serpents—which are no thicker than the end of a pen-holder when fully grown—think they have discovered something of great rarity and interest. This results from the curious and attractive coloration. The scales of the body are lustrous gray or blue-black without markings of

any kind. Around the neck, and in bright contrast, is a ring of yellow or pinkish. This may vary from pale lemon yellow to the hue of a tangerine orange, or, with western specimens may be coral pink. The underside matches the hue of the ring and usually has a central row of dark spots.

The general make-up of these little snakes is so dainty that observers with no knowledge of reptiles seem by inference to consider them harmless and the author has received many specimens in containers sent by mail, packed with grass in which a tiny snake is finally discovered. The query is usually along the same lines, as to what the *rare* specimen really is; that the observer has never seen or heard of anything of the kind before.

Actually the ring-necked snakes are not at all rare, but very secretive. They hide under flat stones or the loose bark of fallen trees. They prefer cool and damp places. The eastern Ring-necked Snake, *Diadophis punctatus,* is seldom thicker than a quarter of an inch and is from ten to fifteen inches long. It prefers damp woods, feeding upon earthworms and small salamanders. Numerous specimens may often be found under the top stones of an old, broken dam, which no longer acts as a spillway. One or two specimens may be found under favorable flat stones in such a situation—stones a foot or so in diameter that are concave beneath—and then again a group of them may select a particularly good hiding place. The author has turned over a stone and found as many as a dozen at a time. There is not an instant to lose in such a situation as every member immediately scurries for shelter.

D. punctatus is found from southern Canada to Florida and westward to Illinois. *D. arnyi* occurs in the Central States. *D. regalis* ranges through Texas, New Mexico and Arizona, well into Mexico, *D. amabilis* is confined to the Pacific Coast region, from Oregon into Lower California.

There are two large serpents in eastern North America which in looks and action stand quite by themselves. These are the Mud Snakes. Each represents a genus of a single species. The genera are *Abastor* and *Farancia.*

The mud snakes grow up to six feet, have a cylindrical body with small, bluntly rounded head barely distinguishable from the neck, and smooth scales as polished as glass. The eyes are placed toward the top of the head, with thick, protective eye-plates and are quite perceptibly directed upward. The whole make-up is that of a burrowing type,

although of impressive size.   Both are of exceptionally brilliant coloration, which is intensified by the glistening scales.   They are also the subjects of erroneous stories.

Both species are inclined to lie in a half coiled position in grassy hollows or ditches near shallow water.   The big loop of body may nearly approximate a circle in form—and the mouth and tail may incidentally be close together.   I have sometimes mistaken these snakes for a bicycle tire thrown into a watery ditch.   Here appears to be the reason for the origin of the hoop snake story.   The supposition seems to have become established that, if a snake rests in this position, it can take its tail in its mouth, elevate the body to a vertical position, and rapidly roll like a hoop.   The story is topped off with a sensational thrill.   This relates to the "hoop" snake's power to sting with its tail. There is an allegation that the "sting" is fine and sharp, like the point of a needle and retractile within the tip of the tail.

There is usually some basis for such suppositions.   The story has probably originated from the actual presence of a needle-like spine on the tail of both of the mud snakes.   It is harmless, however, being nothing more than a particularly fine and sharp terminal scale, similar to, but considerably sharper than the pointed scale on the tail of many snakes.   But what is particularly interesting in this instance is the fact that the snake uses it, and deliberately, in a very apparent effort to frighten anyone endeavoring to handle it.   The end of the tail is directed against one's hand or arm and the sharp point thrust against the skin.   It pricks like a needle, may penetrate the skin and even draw a droplet of blood.   The action is startling enough to cause the investigator to drop the reptile, and it appears that the snake is fully aware of this and seeks such action in endeavoring to escape.   Thus may be summed up the basis for the "hoop" snake and "stinging" snake stories.   The two reptiles responsible for these tales may be outlined as follows:

The Rainbow Mud Snake, "Stinging" Snake, "Hoop" Snake, *Abastor erythrogrammus,* occurs from southerly Virginia southward to Florida and westward to Alabama.   The length is from four to six feet and the diameter up to two inches.   The body hue is a lustrous dark purple with narrow vermilion stripes.   The sides are longitudinally banded with orange, the scales red tipped.   These brilliant colors are repeated on the abdomen, but reversed in arrangement, the greater area being red with rows of purple spots.

The related Horn Snake, Red-bellied Snake, "Stinging" Snake,

or "Hoop" Snake, *Farancia abacura,* is found over the same easterly area as *Abastor* but extends farther westward—into Louisiana and in the Mississippi Valley northward to Indiana.   Its pattern is quite different, but no less brilliant.   It is iridescent ebony-black with vermilion bars extending upward on the lower sides from the abdomen which is of intense vermilion or brick red.   Six-foot specimens are not rare and these may be slightly over two inches in diameter.   Unfortunately, these beautifully colored reptiles cannot long endure captivity if kept in quarters where they may be seen.   They constantly seek to hide.   Their wanderings on the surface in a wild state are apparently of but brief duration and for short distances.   The pupils of the eyes, which are mere pin points, clearly indicate adaptation for an underground life.   It is difficult to induce the captive to feed even though provided with damp soil in which to burrow.   The successful experiments we have made were with large troughs containing about two inches of water.   These were generously provided with tadpoles and the mud snakes would half swim, half glide through the water with sweeping of the head from side to side in capturing the food.   We never succeeded in inducing them to take anything else and barely half of our specimens could be coaxed in this manner.

CHAPTER VIII

THE OLD WORLD HARMLESS SNAKES

COMPARED with the United States, Europe has a rather scant serpent fauna although some of the individual species are abundant. There are two kinds of harmless serpents in England, the Grass Snake and the Smooth Snake. The former is alleged to have been observed in Ireland, but it is certainly rare on that island if now existing at all. No authentic records have come to the writer's attention in the past twenty-five years. There are species of *Natrix* (Water Snakes) in continental Europe and several of *Elaphe,* similar to the Chicken or Rat Snakes of North America. There are also a few species of *Coluber,* similar to the North American Racers and some small, near allies of the New World King Snakes. Some scientific authorities in the past placed these Old and New World species within the same genus—*Coronella.* Generic distinction is indicated as the Old World species are viviparous, while the American King Snakes lay eggs. The Smooth Snake is included within the genus *Coronella.* In the general run the European serpents are considerably smaller than those of the United States.

There appear to be two focal points in abundance and variety of the harmless Colubrine snakes. These are in the southerly portion of North America and the Indo-Malayan Region. The typical *Colubrinae* has not extensively invaded South America, nor Europe or Africa. Its members are well represented in all the great land areas mentioned, but there is a concentration of species in the specific New and Old World regions mentioned.

The Water Snakes, *Natrix,* are far more elaborately represented in the Old World than in the New. With approximately a dozen species in the Western Hemisphere there are more than fifty in the Old World. They attain their greatest concentration of species in the Indo-Malayan area.

A broadly known kind is the Common Grass Snake, Water Snake

or Ringelnatter, *Natrix natrix,* which in its wide distribution and general abundance holds the familiar place of the "common snake" of Europe as does the garter snake in the United States. Like most water snakes its scales are keeled. Its usual coloration is olive, or greenish-gray with rows of small black spots. The most common phase has a broad yellow or whitish collar behind the head. In southerly Europe there are numerous color variations. Some lack the pale collar and one has light stripes extending from head to base of tail. This species lays eggs.

A very pretty species of *Natrix* occurs in Italy, Switzerland, in the Rhine and Moselle Valleys thence throughout southeastern Europe, into Asia and northern Africa. This is the Dice Snake or Tessellated Snake. Its color varies from sulphur yellow to gray or pale green. There are rows of small square spots, everywhere arranged in alternation or in tessellated pattern. It is technically known as *N. tessellatus.* The Viperine Snake, *N. viperinus,* is gray with dark zig-zag markings along the back, which causes it to look like the poisonous European viper or adder. It is confined to southern Europe and northern Africa. These European water snakes are of much the form and size of the North American garter snakes, although the ring snake while averaging two and a half to three feet, occasionally exceeds these dimensions.

A large species of India, *N. macropthalmus,* has elongated anterior ribs and spreads its neck like a cobra. A number of the Malayan water snakes attain large size and proportionately heavy body like the big pilot water snake and the green water snake of the southeastern United States. *N. piscator* is frequently noted in the rice ditches of southern China. *N. tigrina,* the Japanese Water Snake, occurs in Japan, Korea, Manchuria and China. Seven distinct kinds of *Natrix* occur in the Philippine Islands. There are several species in Africa and one of these, the Black-backed Grass Snake, *N. olivacea,* ranges as far southward as Rhodesia. Species of *Natrix* inhabit even the northerly portions of Australia, a country with but few harmless Colubrine snakes, though generously populated with the fanged *Elapidae.*

Coronella is a genus allied to that containing the American king snakes. The scales are smooth and the head is not distinct. The species are constrictors. Two occur in Europe. The Smooth Snake, *C. austriaca (laevis),* is the more generally known. It is one of three species of serpents occurring in England, the others being the common

grass snake, and the poisonous viper or adder.   In England, however, its range is limited to a few southerly counties, these including Hampshire and Dorsetshire.   The other two species are more generally distributed.   In continental Europe it occurs in France, Belgium and Germany, thence southward into Spain, Italy, Sicily and Greece.   It also occurs in southern Sweden and Norway.   The author noted a specimen crawling into a hedgerow high in the mountains above Oslo (Kristiania).   This northerly occurrence (approximating the latitude of the southerly tip of Greenland) may be explained by the warming sea currents affecting the area.   Occurrence probably diminishes rapidly in going inland.

The Smooth Snake is seldom over two feet long.   The color is brown, inclined to be ruddy, with dark spots along the back and sometimes pale stripes on the sides.   The dorsal blotches often cause this snake to be confused with the common and poisonous viper or adder. It may be readily distinguished by its smooth scales—the viper having roughly keeled scales.   It is delicate as a captive, usually refusing to feed.   In a wild state it prefers small lizards.

Bearing in mind the fine species of *Elaphe* inhabiting North America, it is of interest to note the distribution of this important genus in other parts.   There are close to fifty species all told and they are distributed from Europe, through southerly Asia, throughout Malaysia to Japan.   Two occur in the Philippines.   Typical members of this group have not extended into Africa.

The Four-lined Snake, *Elaphe quatuorlineata,* is the largest serpent of Europe.   It grows to be six feet long, inhabits southerly and southeastern Europe and western Asia.   In form, color and pattern it is remarkably similar to the yellow chicken snake of the southeastern United States.   The color is pale brown with four dark bands extending the length of the body.   There is one unmistakable point of definition and that is a dark streak extending from behind the eye to the angle of the mouth.   The American species has a pale head, without markings.

The Leopard Snake, *E. leopardina,* is the prettiest of the European snakes although one of the smallest of its genus.   Its habitat is also southern Europe and western Asia.   The ground color is pale brown with a series of reddish or rich brown saddles along the back, these black edged and alternating with smaller dark blotches on the sides.   The blotches are sometimes fused to form wide bands.   There is a bold black

fork at the rear of the head. The length is seldom much more than a yard.

The leopard snake and the closely allied Aesculapian Snake, *E. aesculapii (longissima)*, while particularly attractive do not take kindly to captivity. It is difficult to induce them to feed. This is contrary to the habits of the greater number of species of *Elaphe*, which among all snakes are the most satisfactory for observation in captivity and live for many years. The Aesculapian snake is of particular interest as it is alleged that these reptiles were introduced into Europe by the Romans to be kept in the temples erected to Aesculapius. This is also indicated by a freak distribution. The normal range appears to be southerly Europe, but there are "spotty" areas of occurrence in Germany and Austria, where these snakes are abundant in restricted, local areas. This is a slender and graceful reptile, its scales shining like glass. It is one of the exceptions in its genus in having smooth scales, although some of the species have such faint keels they are barely distinguishable. The body is brownish and may range to nearly black. There is usually little or no pattern except a dark streak behind the eye.

The Racers are well represented in the Old World particularly in the regions bordering the Mediterranean, thence eastward into India. Many of them are included within the same genus—*Coluber*—as the blacksnake of North America, in fact this genus may be said to have its headquarters in the area outlined. In habits they more closely resemble the North American members of *Masticophis* (whip snakes), which is immediately related, as the greater number inhabit areas where the summer is very dry while some prefer the margins of the deserts. Without exception, they are delicate as captives. They are extremely susceptible to dampness. The author has found that if kept upon sand artificially heated and when sun is deficient they are supplied with brilliant artificial light with a fair emission of ultra-violet they do much better. Then again their food is difficult to supply as most of them are fond of small lizards. Another factor against confinement is their great activity. They are of roaming inclination when wild. The slower moving members of *Elaphe* offer an interesting contrast, as they are content to leisurely prowl over restricted and given grounds and between times coil and doze in secluded nooks. They illustrate differences in habits which render it possible to keep them contented as captives, if generously supplied with readily obtained food.

The Dark Green Snake or European Whip Snake, *Coluber jugu-*

laris, is found farther into Europe than the other species. It occurs in France and Italy thence eastward into Asia Minor. It occasionally, though rarely, reaches a length of six feet and while its name indicates a greenish hue this is extremely variable and may range from olive to brown. There may be a tendency of light and dark body hues to form close-set parallel stripes. Being one of the larger members of *Coluber* its food is more varied than the others, including small rodents and birds. Nevertheless it does not long endure captivity.

The Horse-shoe Snake, *C. hippocrepis,* is smaller, seldom over four feet, found in southeasterly Europe and the dry north coast of Africa. It receives its name from an unusual marking on the head. The body pattern is striking and attractive, pale reddish or ruddy yellow with a row of dark, yellow-edged blotches along the back. There are similar spots on the sides. The blotches are often so closely spread over the ground color as to form a ring-like effect upon the entire body. There is a dark marking on the head in shape like a horse-shoe. This is margined with yellow and so prominent as to suggest the species' name.

C. florulentus, C. algirus, and *C. diadema* inhabit the northern coast of Africa where the summers are long, hot and dry. Their distribution extends into desert conditions. I have noted them in areas where the summer drought had burned the grass as dry as a straw mat and the dust was so thick and fine that a tap of one's foot caused it to "splash" like water from a puddle. Yet they looked as sleek in scale and color as if squeezed from a paint tube. I have often wondered where such creatures obtain fluid nourishment, but was informed in Algeria that a dew or condensation forms at times on leaves that are close to the ground. It is possible they thus obtain hanging drops. They appear to feed largely upon small lizards which scurry here and there.

There are two big racers in India and the westerly portion of the Malayan region. One of these, the Greater Indian Rat Snake, *Ptyas mucosus,* is the longest Colubrine serpent of the Old World. It grows to be ten feet or slightly over in length, is slender and whip-like, olive or pale brown, often with black cross-bands on the posterior portion. The eyes are large and brilliant. It is nervous, swift of gait and fights savagely when cornered. The lesser Indian Rat Snake, *P. korros,* grows to be seven to eight feet, and is of olive-brown hue. There are no dark cross-bands on the posterior portion.

In unpacking snakes from the East the author has always been

wary about boxes of mixed specimens containing alleged rat snakes. These harmless serpents look remarkably like king cobras in hue and form and it takes a keen eye to distinguish younger specimens of the latter from the innocuous kinds. Several unpleasant incidents have prompted this care. There has been a great deal of careless packing and labeling of snakes in the past, a reprehensible practice now being eliminated. The author has been endeavoring to segregate boxing of poisonous serpents, in fact to discontinue the shipping of dangerous specimens except for strictly scientific purposes and under competent escort.

The rat snakes are abundant in India and of economic importance as rodent destroyers. They have ridged backs, producing an emaciated appearance, even while in normally good condition.

A review of the procession of Old World Colubrine genera would seem interminable to any but the most technical students and nowhere does this appear in entirety except in the monumental and strictly scientific series by Dr. George Albert Boulenger, published through the British Museum and which required thirty years of preparation. The modern tendency in scientific writings is for specialists to review blocks of genera in extending their studies to clarify hitherto doubtful relationship. Some keen worker may sometime revise Boulenger's great catalogue, entering the many new species that have been discovered since its completion more than thirty years ago. Even as it stands, no library of the systematic herpetologist is considered in working order without it.

We will close this review of the typical harmless Colubrine serpents with mention of the tropical whip or tree snakes of *Leptophis* (Plate 19), a cosmopolitan genus. These really beautiful creatures are slender, almost vine-like in form with rather distinct head and large, bright eyes. They feed mostly upon lizards and tree frogs. Their colors range from metallic, lustrous green to gray and golden bronze. Simulating the branches and vines they have a habit of waving the head and neck from side to side like a branch gently agitated by a breeze. Their size varies from two to five feet, but owing to their slenderness even the largest specimens appear fragile and harmless. Usually, when disturbed they swiftly glide away through the foliage, but when escape is impossible their only defence is a harmless bluffing, a flattening of the head, with the mouth kept widely open and the head weaving from side to side in an endeavor to appear as dangerous as possible—an un-

convincing gesture from such a dainty creature. The metallic body hues seldom carry much pattern, but most species have a black bar from the eye to the angle of the mouth. These pretty snakes are common in Indo-Malayan regions and much resemble those found in tropical America.

For nearly fifty years a small group of harmless snakes has occupied the dignified standing of full family recognition under the head of the *Amblycephalidae,* or Chunk-headed Snakes. As all are devoid of fangs, they have formed a disrupting wedge in the scientific lists by appearing between the poisonous Elapids and the Vipers. This arrangement stood owing to old deductions that their jaw bones showed certain modifications indicating that they represented ancestral stock whence the Vipers were derived—an alleged "link" between the Colubrine serpents and the Viperine types. But series of specimens for scientific study have extensively accumulated during recent years and specialists have taken groupings of genera for intensive investigation. Recent studies of the so-called *Amblycephalidae* have shattered the status of family recognition. Intergrading characters link them with the *Colubrinae* or typical harmless snakes and have been definitely enough expressed to pick the grouping from where it stood and absorb these reptiles within the *Colubridae.* Provisionally they may be granted entity as a subfamily, the *Amblycephalinae,* their indicated relationship close to the *Colubrinae.*

The chunk-headed snakes have usually a lumpy head with very large eyes and cat-like pupil. The body is moderately, or extremely slender and compressed. The neck of some of the species is of such length and so excessively slender that it appear incongruous. In elongated character, for instance, a specimen three feet long may have a body a half inch in diameter in the central third then taper into a neck not thicker than a wooden match, for ten inches of its length. The tail is equally remarkable in trailing off into a number of inches like string. The slender neck looks quite too small to nourish the body in swallowing food. It would lead one to suppose that these curious snakes cannot swallow anything but very small prey, and such is actually the case. These serpents feed mostly upon slugs, also insects, particularly the larval forms. Their jaws are capable of but slight distention and they may be recognized *by the absence of a groove extending along the center of the chin,* which is strongly evident with the greater number of snakes. They live in bushy places and are graceful climbers, al-

though slow and deliberate.   Their patterns are mostly brown, with coarse, darker blotches.   There are half a dozen genera and about forty species.   About a dozen inhabit southeastern Asia, with *Ambly-cephalus* the largest genus.   The majority are found in tropical America.   In the observation of captives the student has an opportunity of making valuable notes as their habits are little known.   Further systematic investigation may warrant a revised subfamily rating.

In the chapter relating to a review of the families and subfamilies of snakes, the status of the *Colubridae* and its subfamilies has been concisely shown.   The first subfamily was the *Acrochordinae* or strictly aquatic river snakes.   It preceded the great subfamily *Colubrinae* or typical harmless snakes, and that is its correct position in the lists.

The River Snakes or *Acrochordinae* are swung in at this point, however, in the discussion of the Old World harmless serpents.   The reason for this has been to keep the discussion of New and Old World *Colubrinae* in unbroken continuity.   With one exception, *Nothopsis,* with a single species occurring on about the opposite side of the globe from its allies, the river snakes inhabit the Old World.   The exception is found in Panama and Costa Rica, Central America.

No more unprepossessing, dun-colored or stupidly acting members (at least in captivity) exist in all the serpent clan than these river snakes.   It is a small subfamily of five genera, each curiously limited to a single species so far as known.   These range from India to New Guinea.   Length is from four to six feet.   The body is covered with granular scales, which extend beneath in place of the smooth abdominal shields of most serpents.   The form is flabby, lacking the usual serpentine grace.   The only hint of this is when these creatures swim, with a certain deliberation that proclaims their perfect adaptation to a permanently aquatic life.   Some of them wander well into the sea.

The Elephant Trunk Snake or Karung, *Acrochordus javanicus* (Plate 12), is representative of these ugly reptiles.   It occurs from India, through Malaysia to New Guinea and is particularly common in the Malay Peninsula in streams and canals.   Its scales above and beneath are so rough they appear like close-set warts.   The color is mottled brown above, dull yellow beneath.

The natives have long recognized the value of this reptile's skin in being particularly tough and durable and use it for their drum heads. Quite recently the skin came into broader use with the world-wide vogue of reptile leather for shoes and leather novelties.   The mottled skin

known as "water snake" is that of the Karung.   It is bleached to softer
hues, carefully tanned, then pressed between powerful rollers so the
granulation of the scales gives way to a smooth surface.   Just how long
these snakes will last, as the slaughter for skins continues, is problematical.   The author was informed by a member of one of the leather
companies that three hundred thousand skins had been received and
tanned within a single year.   Karung and young python have led the
favorites among reptile leathers, but the water snake has been most in
demand for "dress" shoes owing to the smaller scales and subdued colors.   There is a tendency with python skin for the edges of the scales
to wrinkle and turn up with wear.   Nevertheless, close to two hundred
thousand young pythons were also killed in twelve months' time to
satisfy the demands of the leather dealers.

As a captive the Karung gives little indication of the possible value
of its skin.   Its uncouth body, coarsely wrinkled within the curves of
the irregular loops, lies for the greater part of the time at the bottom
of a deep tank.   At intervals the head rises to the surface and the tip
of the snout is protruded to breathe.   My keepers have told me that
they kept an eye on a specimen while working at nearby cages and noted
that it would remain with its head at the bottom as long as half an hour.
Thus it appears that this snake can absorb a certain amount of oxygen
from the water, aerate the blood by a slow swallowing and ejection as
occurs among turtles; this process being alternated by actual breathing.

A specimen under observation was savage when taken from the
water and handled, not striking, but quickly snapping sideways.   It
had an enormously developed forked tongue, proportionately twice the
size of an ordinary snake, but it was used sparingly, making occasional
single sweeps.   It refused fish and frogs for several months and upon
showing signs of emaciation we decided to force feed it.   This was
done with young carp and was easily performed, the snake being held
by my assistant while I grasped a fish with a pair of polished forceps a
foot long and ran the morsel down the snake's throat about six inches.
My assistant massaged the fish a bit further down while I grasped another.   We gave the snake four three-inch fish, once a week and continued this for a year.   It grew plump and between times was offered
fish to induce it to feed of its own accord.   During one of these attempts
it snapped at a fish and quickly swallowed it, then took several more.
From that time it continued to feed at regular intervals.   I invariably
noted how flaccid it appeared when removed from the water and how

awkward it was in pushing its body forward in labored kinks. It made no attempts to glide. Its actions branded it a strictly aquatic type, and such development crops up in three separated portions of the classification of serpents.

Mention has already been made of "satellite" subfamilies among the Colubrine snakes. The former subfamily of the river snakes is one of these and the *Dasypeltinae,* with a single genus and species of Africa, is another. That species is worthy of a moment's pause as its counterpart, but in another grouping will later come to our attention.

The Egg-eating Snake, *Dasypeltis scabra* of tropical and South Africa, warrants definite distinction. It feeds exclusively upon eggs and its throat is highly specialized for the swallowing of such food. There are few teeth—and they are not needed. The jaw bones are particularly mobile and the throat capable of great distention. When the egg is engulfed to a short distance behind the head it comes into contact with large cutting processes which extend from the vertebrae into the throat in the form of bone-like rasps or knives, which cut through the shell. Longitudinal constriction of the neck muscles then squeezes the shell into a compact mass which is adherent owing to the skin within the egg. The shell-bundle is then regurgitated. The amazing thing about the performance is the size of the snake. It is seldom more than two feet in length and by no means stout. In spite of this it has no difficulty in swallowing eggs three to four times the diameter of its neck. Dr. E. G. Boulenger, Curator in the gardens of the Zoological Society of London, explains that two specimens devoured between them one hundred and twenty-four pigeons' eggs in the course of a year.

This snake is olive or light brown, with three rows of dark spots. It has very roughly keeled scales. No more remarkable phase of specialization exists among the serpents of the world, yet this same development appears as an indication of tendency or parallelism in another "satellite" subfamily in the following chapter.

CHAPTER IX

THE REAR–FANGED SNAKES

THIS chapter relates to poisonous snakes, but it is not so headed as the reptiles under discussion do not warrant such emphatic designation. We have arrived at the consideration of a series of subfamilies of the *Colubridae*. One of these is extensive, with about seventy genera and approximately three hundred species. All the members have developed a simple fang structure in the *rear* of the upper jaw—and a comparatively mild poison. They appear, however, to have little thought of using their short fangs in defence. The fangs are provided with a longitudinal groove, from the base to the tip for the flow of venom. This is an open groove, not so deeply channeled nor with the fang folding around it to form approximately an enclosed canal, as with the *Elapidae*. Some species have a pair of these grooved fangs, others several of them.

These reptiles have never been included among the dangerous serpents. As they do not strike at an intruder with intent to use the fangs, the venom-conducting teeth can only be engaged or imbedded if the snake deliberately advances its jaws in the "chewing" motion of serpents utilized in obtaining a firm hold or in swallowing the prey.

The toxicity of their venoms, which is considerably lower than that of the Elapine or Viperine snakes, is sufficient to benumb the prey. This consists largely of frogs and lizards. Fatalities from such serpent bites are so rare, if any, that reports fail to reach sources of responsible deduction, yet the larger members of the series should be regarded with caution. I know of several large species, of "gentle" disposition when handled, and one of these is the allegedly dove-like Mussurana. But they can paralyze their prey in rapid fashion. These larger members should not be carelessly handled. It is the so-called tame snake that has a chance to deliberately bite. Members of this group make dubious pets, but are of great interest as study specimens.

However, the rear-fanged or *Opisthoglyph* snakes should not be given a bad reputation. Their record is too clean as regards accidents.

They are in a different class from reptiles with lethal poison, which deliberately seek to use it during fright or defence.

The dominating subfamily in the series *Opisthoglypha* is known as the *Boiginae.* Its members run the same variety of habits as the fangless *Colubrinae* and they also radiate in the same variety of form. There is to a certain extent an analogous condition to the mammalian order *Marsupialia* which furnishes forms to "match" the members of other orders, there being a marsupial bear, wolf, cat, marmot, mole, mouse and so on. This is parallelism—without relationship. With the *Opisthoglyph* or rear-fanged snakes there is, of course, near relationship to the fangless Colubrine serpents. Nevertheless it is decidedly interesting to note what again can properly be called parallelism here in the "matching" of genera of subfamilies. And again, the *Boiginae* has two satellite subfamilies as does the *Colubrinae.* Thus, hovering on both sides of the *Boiginae* is the small subfamily of rear-fanged Indo-Malayan river snakes (*Homalopsinae*) and an egg-eater *Elachistodon,* of Bengal, the sole representative of a single genus forming the subfamily *Elachistodontinae,* with ridge-like processes extending into the throat—a fine rear-fanged match for *Dasypeltis,* the fangless egg-eater of Africa.

As to some of the groups of rear-fanged members within the main subfamily, these indicating this parallelism, the following may be mentioned:

The numerous species of African *Psammophis,* which in looks and actions are like the racers of the New World; *Dispholidus,* also African (the Boomslang), which is similar to species of *Coluber;* the numerous species of *Pseudoboa,* of tropical America, which are similar to the North American king snakes, and also are constrictors. *Leptodira* (Plate 26) and *Himantodes,* rear-fanged members of the New World tropics, are particularly interesting. These genera are largely composed of lanky, slim necked species with lumpy head and big eyes with elliptical pupils. They have been called the Dipsades or Chunk Heads, also Night Snakes. With some the body is half an inch thick but the neck is long and wiry. Such grotesque forms indicate a marked phase of parallel development to the fangless members of *Dipsas* and *Leptognathus,* of the *Amblycephalinae.*

The *Opisthoglypha* has produced one phase of eccentric specialization unmatched anywhere else among the families of serpents. This is a genus of Flying Snakes (*Chrysopelea*) occurring in southerly

India, Burma, southern China, the Malay Peninsula, Sumatra, Borneo and Java. They are small—under a yard in length—with rather stout body which may be extensively flattened by extending the ribs and also rendered concave beneath. These snakes are lizard eaters, crawl out on high, horizontal branches and if frightened or quickly deciding to change their location, instantly convert the body into a scaling plane and go soaring for a considerable distance, either alighting on the ground at a converging angle upon brush or the branches of another tree when the body is as quickly rendered cylindrical and the reptile glides away. *C. ornata* ranges throughout the area of the genus, also being found in Ceylon. It is always of decorative markings although difficult to describe as some specimens are bright green, others olive and as many of them are black. There are always, however, spots or blotches of rich yellow or red and the head of the lighter specimens is black, the yellow or reddish markings brightly apparent as spots or transverse bands.

Most of the rear-fanged snakes occur in the warmer latitudes. A few diminutive kinds are found in the southern United States, in the westerly portion, but the species pile up in approaching the tropical zones of both the New and Old Worlds.

Some of the arboreal forms are excessively slender and prettily colored. *Oxybelis* (Plate 29), with four species ranging from Mexico into South America, is composed of whip-like, arboreal forms. The Green Whip Snake, *O. fulgidus,* of Central America reaches a length of four feet, but at its thickest part is barely half an inch in diameter, with a long string-like tail. Its head is long and narrow terminating in a sharp point. Accentuating the elongated appearance of the head, two hues of green are split by a narrow line. This snake is of an exquisite pale leaf green, with a narrow, lemon yellow stripe on each side. If frightened, it thrusts its neck straight forward, then slowly waves the head from side to side, simulating the movement of a stem in the breeze. The author had four of these specimens in a cage containing a green bush and there was frequent amusement in asking friends to count how many there were. Right under one's eyes it was difficult to differentiate their bodies from the stems and foliage and few observers could be induced to say there were more than two. They fed upon small lizards and quickly killed them with their benumbing poison.

Dryophis is a similar genus of eight species inhabiting India, Ceylon, Burma and Siam. Several grow to a length of five feet, but there

is the same excessive slenderness as with the New World tree snakes. The Long-nosed Tree Snake, *D. mycterizans,* has the head so elongated that it terminates like the sharpened lead of a pencil. This is also a leaf-green reptile, but the skin between the scales is black and there is a startling effect when it is angry and the body is distended by breathing, the green scales appearing like jewels studded in a necklace. More astonishing is the reptile's idea of frightening the object of its anger. It spreads the head and widely opens the mouth. The black pigment of the skin extends inward to the throat so the entire mouth appears as if saturated with ink. To one not initiated in the ways of snakes the reptile seems "poisonous" in every sense of the word.

In a country where serpents are numerous, particularly in the tropical countries, certain kinds become prominent from being large, especially dangerous or portraying some characteristic habit. They thus stand out among a legion of others. One of these, throughout tropical America, is the Mussurana, *Pseudoboa cloelia* (Plate 28), belonging to a genus of about a dozen rear-fanged members which employ constriction in addition to paralyzing venom in subduing the prey. The Mussurana looks and acts like a king snake, although its body is of a glistening blue-black. It reaches the dignified length of eight feet, ranges from Guatemala well through Brazil and seems to be the sworn enemy of the deadly fer-de-lance and its near relatives. It seeks the poisonous serpent as its prey, fearlessly attacks it, squeezes it to death, is frequently bitten but scorns the wounds from the fangs and swallows members of the pit viper family that may be but a few inches shorter than itself. It not only is immune to the powerful haemolytic poison, but is tough enough to endure the wounds of fangs half an inch in length.

I have placed the two combatants in a sanded arena of my motion picture laboratory, watched the action from every point and photographed it. It cannot be called a fight, as the fer-de-lance is mastered from the beginning. The poisonous snake never has a chance to escape with its life. One episode in particular, carefully noted, will show what happens:

The fer-de-lance was from Honduras and slightly over four feet long. It was a vigorous, savage specimen which struck at us repeatedly. The mussurana was possibly a foot and a half longer. With the pit viper in a defensive position the mussurana was liberated. It glided about the enclosure for a moment then made straight for the poisonous reptile. The fer-de-lance turned and glared at the new-

comer, but made no attempt to bite. It was alert but did not seem to sense danger, although it nervously vibrated its tail until the tip faded into a blur.

The mussurana "nosed" its adversary with quick flashing motions of the head as if studying where to seize it, then like a flash grasped it at about the anterior quarter. The seizure was accompanied by a commotion of both bodies. The mussurana drew the viper toward the constricting coils of its body and started a twisting motion which literally ravelled the long bodies, and gave it its first encircling folds. This was simultaneously countered by the fer-de-lance turning and burying its fangs in the body of its adversary. It was a bite, which if upon a human finger or a hand, would have spelled grave disaster. Two small drops of blood appeared on the lustrous black surface of the mussurana, but the wound only stimulated it to further action. With a dexterity difficult to define in words or understand, its preliminary, subduing tangle changed to a series of wraps like the coils of a spring. The constricting folds thus became symmetrical to cover a full foot of the body of the fer-de-lance, which in a last desperate effort to breathe lost all definite intent to bite, gasped several times and during the wobbling of its head was freshly seized by the mussurana immediately behind that member. Thus the pit-viper was rendered helpless. The mussurana made frequent chewing motions and the masseter muscles bulged over the temporal portion of its head. This very clearly showed its effort to imbed its rear fangs and inject the benumbing poison. But the venom is not quickly effective upon such prey. Possibly the latter is too large—and being poisonous itself has a certain resistance against the other's venom, though of a different kind than its own.

Constriction continued for a full twenty minutes when the victor worked its jaws around to the snout of the vanquished fer-de-lance and started on the slow and laborious task of swallowing it entire. The corkscrew coil was slackened and the prey slowly drawn through it. The body coils were of assistance as there was considerable reflex kinking and writhing up to the time the tip of the tail disappeared down the mussurana's throat. The swallowing operation consumed about fifteen minutes' time.

These snake eaters occasionally vary their diet with rodents which they find in prowling through burrows and into crevices. Their benumbing poison seems to act quicker in subduing a warm-blooded an-

imal, in fact it has always been surprising to me to observe how slowly the venom of the mussurana functions in quieting the specific serpentine prey and even that of the big and deadly king cobra with its powerful fangs. And in using the word "deadly" I refer to the power of its poison upon mammals—upon which it rarely feeds. Both of these notorious cannibals take a long time to subdue their prey with the fangs. The mussurana could get along without them owing to the strength and agility of its constricting folds, but I have seen a king cobra imbed its fangs twenty times or more during a period of a full half hour before its prey was fully subdued. Here it would seem that specialization has gone a bit wrong. All snakes even the harmless species have a certain resistance to snake venom, of all kinds, yet these serpent eaters have not specifically developed a venom to indicate clean dispatch in killing their prey. The rear-fanged, lizard-eating snakes show far better adaptation.

From all of my investigations the mussurana seems to be rare. March told me in Honduras that only two specimens had been brought in to him in a year and this was against several hundred specimens of fer-de-lance that had been collected. Dr. Brazil gave me similar advice. The natives know the habits of this snake and it is seldom killed. They also regard it as very gentle in its habits toward man. Dr. Brazil told me that in years of observation he had never seen one attempt to bite while being handled and in presenting me with a six-foot specimen at São Paulo, draped it around my daughter's neck. I felt assured by the good doctor's explanation, but confess that this was the last time the specimen was so handled. It seems precarious to trust too explicitly a six-foot snake with strong fangs and poison glands.

This species is particularly hardy as a captive. The late Theodore Roosevelt brought me a specimen on his return from the River of Doubt expedition and it lived about ten years. It was a Brazilian example, blue-black with a blackish stomach. Central American specimens are mostly white beneath. Young specimens are coral red.

Of the rear-fanged snakes that look like racers, the Boomslang, *Dispholidus typus,* of South Africa, is particularly savage and its bite is feared. F. W. Fitzsimons, Director of the Port Elizabeth Museum, made a series of experiments in injecting fowls with the poison of this snake. All died within a few minutes' time. Mr. Fitzsimons relates an accident which occurred at his laboratory when one of his assistants, a vigorous young man, was bitten on the forearm by a boomslang.

Within twenty-four hours he sank to a condition of collapse and his life was saved with difficulty. The curious thing about this closely observed case was the hemorrhagic effect of the poison. There was great swelling and discoloration, even a discharge of blood from the mucous surfaces of the mouth. A remarkable manifestation about this case was the appearance of great areas of extravasation on areas remote from the bite—on the face, the opposite arm from the bite and on the thigh. The observations upon this patient's symptoms proved conclusively that the poison of at least some of the rear-fanged snakes is not essentially a neurotoxin, which type is largely active in paralyzing nerve centers, and produces little blood destruction. As the boomslang feeds frequently upon warm-blooded prey a poison of the haemolytic type is highly effective. Such poisons, however, are usually slow in subduing cold-blooded prey. Further investigations of poisons of the rear-fanged snakes may demonstrate that the ratios of the toxic elements of their venoms greatly vary. Owing to the comparatively small amount of venom which such reptiles secrete, the difficulty in extracting it, the small size of many of the species and the failure to include them among the "deadly poisonous" snakes, investigators have not been attracted to investigations of such types. For years they received scant or no recognition as actually poisonous snakes.

The so-called Bush Snakes or Night Snakes are rear-fanged species, a number of which parallel the species of harmless genera. These are slow-moving usually with compressed very slender body, smooth scales and chunky heads. The pupil is elliptical. One of the genera is *Boiga,* with over twenty species found in tropical Africa, southerly Asia, New Guinea and northern Australia. One of the larger is particularly handsome. This is the Mangrove Snake, *B. dendrophilus* (Plate 25), occurring from the Malay Peninsula to the Philippines. It is glistening black, with golden rings spaced rather widely and regularly apart. It is strictly arboreal, but coiled upon a bough looks more like some decorative thing than a living reptile. The high polish and intensely black scales so set off the rings that they look as if freshly painted upon the creature. This snake grows to be six feet long. Its rear fangs are of fair size and very useful in holding feathered prey—and quickly killing them. Like many of the Opisthoglyphs it is gentle toward man, but I have often told the keepers at the park not to trust it.

* * * * *

It was during the preparation of this manuscript that the author received the greatest surprise in the many years he has studied the serpent clan—and it related to a rear-fanged snake. It was in the form of a booklet, printed as an author's extra, and came from Professor J. Graham Kerr, of the University of Glasgow, in Scotland. Its title was "*Bothrodon pridii,* an Extinct Serpent of Gigantic Dimensions." The article contained a photograph of a poison fang as long as the claw of a tiger.

As the poison-conducting teeth of the rear-fanged snakes are short in proportion to the body length, the size of this monster is open to thrilling conjecture. Speaking in gross terms, the fang is approximately nine times larger than that of a six-foot boomslang. Theorizing from such a comparison we have indicated a poisonous snake nearly sixty feet long, or twice the size of the largest pythons existing today. As the specimen was obtained from the silt-like deposit of Pleistocene or later age which covers the region of the Gran Chaco (southerly South America), the general animal life was much as it is today, the area under consideration indicating peccaries and various rodents as food, if such a monster would deign to note the latter. If it was quick and savage like the boomslang, it presents an awesome picture, the first extinct monster that was *poisonous,* coming to scientific attention. Indeed the thought it inspires rather dulls the conjectural image of that dinosaurian star, *Tyranosaurus,* whose races passed away ages before this mammoth Bothrodon prowled the soil.

Professor Kerr remarks about his discovery: "Comparison of the fang of Bothrodon with that of surviving members of the group Ophidia shows the most close resemblance with the fangs of Opisthoglypha, *i.e.* the group of Colubrine snakes which point the way towards the most highly evolved modern poisonous snakes the Cobras, Rattlesnakes and Vipers. This resemblance with the Opisthoglypha comes out especially in the position of the poison groove on the side of the fang rather than on its anterior face, where it is situated in vipers and rattlesnakes. Amongst existing genera of Opisthoglypha certain species of *Philodryas (e.g. P. schotti)* approach particularly close to Bothrodon in the position of the poison groove.

"The peculiar form of the poison fang of Bothrodon enables us, I think to arrive at a definite conclusion as to what was its function. Its strongly curved hook-like form indicates that it was used not for striking, but for the effective retention of the struggling prey while the poison passed into the wound and did its work."

Fossil serpents are rarely found, as the skeletons of such reptiles are fragile and subject to rapid disintegration. However, some pages about such remains have been written in the scientific records. Soon after the discovery of *Bothrodon,* Mr. Barnum Brown, of the American Museum of Natural History told me that one of the museum's expeditions in Patagonia had discovered portions of an extinct serpent ten inches in diameter. The character of this reptile had not been determined. Remains of non-venomous Colubrine and Elapine snakes have been found in the Lower Miocene of Germany. Extinct Crotaline species have been discovered in North America and the Old World. The finding of *Bothrodon* will add new zest to that fascinating adventure of hunting big game in the rocks.

CHAPTER X

THE POISONOUS SNAKES OF NORTH AMERICA

THE poisonous snakes of the New World, comprising some of the most deadly known species, and some of great abundance, have not been considered collectively in terms that may be broadly understood. The North American species are quite different in their make-up from the tropical types. Their venoms are different and require treatment by specific grades of serum to produce the most efficacious results. With the exception of the eastern copperhead, the southeastern water moccasin and two small coral snakes in the southerly latitudes, the greater area of North America contains but one type of poisonous serpent—the rattlesnake. There is, however, a considerable number of species of rattlesnakes. Over a dozen distinct kinds of these characteristic serpents occur in various parts of the United States. There is great variety in size, pattern and coloration. They inhabit a variety of country, some being characteristic in frequenting deserts, others plains, swampy areas or mountains. Thus North America may be said—simply speaking—to have four "types" of venomous serpents, the rattlesnake, copperhead, water moccasin and coral snake —the latter being a small and rather degenerate representative of the Old World cobras, kraits and mambas.

Practically every portion of the United States is inhabited by poisonous serpents—although we might accord to a few states in the northeastern corner of this far-flung area the reputation of being nearly or quite free of them. These are the states of Maine, New Hampshire and Vermont. There are occasional reports of rattlers in the southerly portion of Vermont. The northerly states to the westward are liberally inhabited by rattlesnakes which extend their habitat well into Canada. This condition extends westward to the Pacific Coast. The southeastern states, warmed by their contact with the Gulf Stream, with thick tangles of river swamps and humid coastal areas, harbor large numbers of poisonous serpents. Texas, Arizona and New Mexico are very liberally supplied with rattlers. The Pacific states also have large

numbers of rattlesnakes, while the interior states show "spotty" occurrence, abundant in some areas, moderately so in others.   The writer doubts, however, if there are any portions much more abundantly supplied with venomous snakes than some areas of Massachusetts, Connecticut, New York, New Jersey and Pennsylvania, where the timber rattlesnake and copperhead infest the mountain ledges.

The species of rattlesnakes vary in size from several that are not larger than the average striped snake to the huge and formidable diamond-back, which attains a length of over eight feet and a circumference of about twelve inches.   Throughout the northeastern portion of the United States there is but a single abundant species—the Banded or Timber Rattlesnake, although in western New York a small rattler—the Massasauga—is occasionally found and becomes rather common in the eastern central states.   The timber rattlesnake gives way on the eastern plains to a species of wide distribution—the Prairie Rattlesnake, which, in its variation or races, extends westward throughout the Pacific region, and into the Southwest.   Going south, in the eastern United States, there is another rattler from about the central portion of North Carolina.   This is the diminutive Pygmy Rattlesnake.   Slightly farther south is the range of the big southern Diamond-back, which attains the greatest length of any rattlesnake, and is one of the most formidable vipers of the world.   The Mississippi Valley forms the western boundary of this deadly species, its place being taken in Texas, thence westward to eastern California, by the big diamond-back of the arid regions—a close second in size, attaining a length of seven feet or more, with the same proportionately heavy body.   Going westward into its habitat, we enter the headquarters of the rattlesnakes in the Southwest.

At least six species of rattlesnakes are found in Texas, but the southwestern states have twice that number of distinct kinds.   Most of them are confined to the desert areas.

In this distribution of poisonous serpents in North America, two species of moccasins must be considered—the Water Moccasin and the Copperhead Snake (highland moccasin, pilot snake or chunk-head), which are members of the same family as the rattlers.   The water moccasin is common in the swamps and sluggish waterways of South Carolina, Georgia, Florida, Alabama and Louisiana—also portions of adjoining states.   The distribution of the copperhead is extensive.   It ranges from southern Massachusetts to northern Florida, westward to Oklahoma and Texas in the south, and to Illinois in the northerly

portion. It will thus be understood that over the actual West, the only type of poisonous serpent is the rattlesnake (except for a coral snake in the Mexican boundary region).

The rattlesnakes, copperhead and moccasin are members of the Family *Crotalidae,* called Pit Vipers, owing to the presence on each side of the head, between the eye and the nostril, of a deep pit, appearing more prominent than the nostril itself. Another external characteristic renders them unique from the Colubrine snakes. This relates to the form of the pupil of the eye, which is elliptical. With practically all the North American non-venomous species, the pupil is round. The arrangement of the plates or scales under the tail forms a third differentiation. They occur in a double row, from the vent to the tip of the tail, with the non-venomous species, while with the poisonous snakes, the plates from the vent to the tip of the tail are in a single row, except with the copperhead, where the scales separate into two rows near the tip of the tail.

The Crotaline serpents are provided with a pair of long, hollow teeth in the forward portion of the upper jaw. These are the fangs, which have an orifice at the tip, like a hypodermic needle, for the injection of poison when they are driven into an offending object by a combination strike and bite, or by a deliberate bite alone. A tubular connection from the base or top of each fang extends backward to a poison gland on each side of the head.

At the instant of biting, the muscle over each temporal poison gland is contracted, forcing venom forward and out of the hollow fangs. The dual wounds produced are no more nor less than hypodermic injections. The strike and bite are so simultaneous that the reptile appears to instantly return to the former defensive position after the out-thrust of the head from a lateral S-shaped loop of the neck.

The fangs are on movable bones and fold back against the roof of the mouth when the jaws are closed. They are covered with a sheath of delicate flesh which is forced back when the fangs are imbedded in an object.

These North American pit vipers do not spring or jump at an intruder. They strike from one-third to one-half their length. They can as readily strike when crawling, as the neck is usually kept laterally looped if they are angry, for out-thrust in defense. They can also quickly turn and deliberately bite without recourse to darting the

head from a loop. Their disposition is not to attack, but to defend themselves when closely approached. All are viviparous, giving birth to living young to the number of about a dozen.

In the preceding details, we have a clearly indicated significance of the broad distribution, variety of species and attending hazard of the North American pit vipers.

The status of the *Elapidae* occurring in North America is quite different. The Old World is the headquarters of many deadly species developing from Colubrine sources, which is the Elapine origin. There the cobras, kraits, mambas and dangerous Australian species represent the *Elapidae* in a variety of form and size ranging up to the great king cobra, probably the world's most dangerous wild creature. The Elapine serpents have short, rigid and permanently erect fangs in the forward portion of the upper jaw. The greater number of them look like the typically harmless Colubrine snakes, from which there is practically no difference except in possession of fangs and extremely dangerous poison of largely neurotoxic action. It is only in recent years that scientific workers have accorded them full family recognition owing to their fangs. They were formerly considered as a subfamily of the *Colubridae*.

The New World, including North and South America, has but a single Elapine genus, *Micrurus* (formerly *Elaps*). In the southeastern United States, thence along the region of the Mexican boundary, there are two of these small, poisonous serpents, which are commonly known as Coral Snakes. They are different in form, coloration and habits from all of the other North American poisonous snakes. They are slender, with smooth and glossy scales. These North American species are usually well under three feet in length. The head is not distinct from the neck. Coloration is brilliant and in the form of rings of red, yellow and black. These reptiles are of burrowing habits, although occasionally found prowling.

The bites of coral snakes are very dangerous. The venom attacks the nerve centers and is thus quite different from that of the rattlesnakes and moccasins, which destroys the red blood cells and breaks down the walls of the carrying vessels.

The southeasterly species, known as the Coral Snake, Harlequin Snake, or Bead Snake, *Micrurus fulvius* (Plate 32), lives much of the time in the ground, though it is sometimes seen in the fields during spring plowing. There are wide rings of crimson and black, the latter

narrowly bordered with yellow. Several small harmless serpents "imitate" the coloration to a remarkable degree. Close inspection, however, will show that with the non-venomous species, there are pairs of black rings bordering a yellow one, the reverse of the poisonous type.

The coral snake feeds largely upon the young of other serpents and upon lizards. It does not strike. If stepped on or actually touched, it will turn and deliberately bite, retaining its hold. Accidents are infrequent, but fatal cases from its bite have been reported. Its range is from South Carolina and Mississippi to Florida, the Gulf States, thence southward into Mexico and Central America.

The Sonoran Coral Snake, *Micrurus euryxanthus,* is similar to the eastern species, but the black rings are proportionately narrower and the yellow marginal rings much wider. Its range is southern New Mexico, Arizona and northern Mexico.

Following the orderly arrangement of classification a review of the species of North American poisonous snakes next brings us to descriptive details of the Pit Vipers, the first genus being *Agkistrodon,* that of the moccasins, with two kinds to consider. The most extensive in distribution and the most commonly encountered is the Copperhead Snake, *A. mokasen* (Plate 52), also called Pilot, Rattlesnake Pilot, Chunk-head and Highland Moccasin. Its range is from central Massachusetts to northern Florida (not including the peninsula), westward to Illinois, thence southwest through Missouri and into Oklahoma and Texas.

Coloration is vivid and rather characteristic, owing to the separation and fair symmetry of the blotches. The body hue is pale brown, pinkish, or light reddish brown, with a series of large blotches on the sides, somewhat like inverted Y's. These blotches are usually of a rich, chestnut brown. When examined from above, a number of the markings will be seen to unite across the back, producing a continuous pattern across the body, the central portion being narrow and broadening on each side, giving the outline of an hour-glass. The top of the head is without marking, and often slightly paler than the body hue. The undersurface is usually pale, pinkish brown, with a row of dark spots on each side. There is some pattern variation in intensity of the blotches, which may be paler in the central area and outwardly margined (very narrowly) with quite a pale tint, which accentuates their intensity.

Large specimens are about three feet long, but occasional four-

foot specimens are noted.   Curiously enough, the largest specimens which ever came to the writer's attention were captured in the immediate vicinity of White Plains, Westchester County, New York, where an example measuring four feet and five inches, and approximately two inches in diameter, appears to form a record for the species.

The water snake and hog-nosed snake are sometimes mistaken for the Copperhead, owing to their proportionately thick bodies, and gross similarity of markings.   The poisonous species, however, carries its points of marked differentiation in having elliptical pupils, prominent cavity or pit between the eye and nostril, and greater number of plates under the tail in a single row.   The milk snake is also confused with the copperhead, but is more slender, while the blotches are irregularly rounded and narrowing as they approach the sides, instead of spreading widely, as with the copperhead.

While the bite of the copperhead is very dangerous, and there are records—although not common—of fatalities from such injuries, it is not so poisonous as the timber rattlesnake found over much the same area.   The copperhead's fangs are proportionately shorter, its venom not so virulent, and the amount of poison injected into a bite of lesser quantity, owing to the serpent's smaller size.   In habits, it is very quiet, preferring to lie perfectly still when an intruder enters its lair, and escape detection owing to its pattern and colors closely resembling the fallen leaves around it.   Seldom will it make any attempt to strike, unless very definitely annoyed or attacked, or if it is stepped on.   Most of the cases of copperhead bites which have come to my attention have resulted from the latter condition, and have related to persons wearing low shoes—many of the bites being on or near the ankles.   If a copperhead fears it is about to be attacked, it will impart a rapid, vibrating movement to the tail, and if among dried leaves, produces a distinct, buzzing sound, readily heard for about fifteen feet.   It will coil and fight bravely if cornered, but at the first opportunity, quickly turn and glide to safety in some crevice.

Distribution remains extensive owing to protective coloration and secretive habits.   Copperheads are still found along the top and at the base of the Palisades of the Hudson, while the Rattlesnake appears to have been exterminated from that area for close to fifty years. Throughout Pennsylvania and New Jersey, the Copperhead is generally distributed, except in regions of intensive cultivation.   There are various areas of New York where the species has not been re-

corded. It is common from the latitude of northern Westchester County, well up the Hudson and past the easterly border of the Catskill area, also in counties to the west. While showing a decided preference for mountain areas, as illustrated by its abundance in elevated regions of New Jersey, Pennsylvania and Connecticut, it does not occur in the Catskill Mountains proper, and in but few portions of the Berkshires; nor in the general area of the Shawangunk Mountains, in Sullivan County, except on the easterly side of the Neversink River, although it is abundant along the Delaware River. It is common in Connecticut both along the shore and in elevated regions, also in the coastal area of Rhode Island. The species does not extend northward of central Massachusetts, hence may be eliminated from consideration in the states of Vermont, New Hampshire and Maine.

Ledgy, wooded hills, with a base of wild, damp meadows, form the favorite prowling grounds of this snake, as it searches for small rodents, birds and frogs. During the summer it is often seen along old stone walls, which offer shelter and a congregating place for rodents. With the Autumn, it returns to specific crevices among the rocks, to hibernate, and it is close to such locations that the young are born during August or early September. From six to nine young are produced in a litter, and the tails of the infant snakes are bright, sulphur yellow. Many specimens from Texas have very wide, consequently fewer bands, most of these encircling the back and not narrowed at the top as with eastern specimens. These wide-banded specimens usually retain the yellow tail as they mature.

The Water Moccasin or Cotton-mouth Snake, *A. piscivorus* (Plates 53 and 54), receives one of its names from its commonly aquatic habits. Over most of its distribution it lives along streams, lakes or in swamps and is particularly abundant along abandoned rice ditches of the southeasterly and Gulf States. The term "cotton-mouth" comes from the habit of opening the mouth in threatening fashion, the mouth parts being whitish. It is a much larger and more dangerous reptile than the copperhead, also considerably more pugnacious. It attains a length of six feet, but the average is three to four feet. The colors are dull brown or olive, crossed with darker, usually obscure bands. The young are brightly marked with transverse blotches on a reddish ground. Its distribution is from Virginia, throughout the state of Florida and westerly along the Gulf States into eastern Texas. Inland there is a northerly extension up the Mississippi Valley to south-

ern Illinois, Missouri and western Kentucky. The great valley has, in fact, formed an avenue of northerly extension of several of the southern reptiles to about the latitude whence they extend upward along the Atlantic Coast, the latter northerly trend being accounted for by the warm influence of the Gulf Stream close outside. Extension up the valley with its swamps and canebrakes and converging streams is probably the result of conditions combining comparatively low land and good shelter. In the central area between the two extensions distribution is confined to a point several hundred miles farther south. If a shaded map were prepared of this distribution it would show a blunt wedge extending up the Mississippi Valley and a half wedge along the coast, the latter shading coming to a point near Norfolk in Virginia. The coral snake has a similar distribution, and is said to extend even farther northward than the water moccasin in the Mississippi region.

In company with Marlin Perkins, Curator of Reptiles of the Zoological Gardens of St. Louis, the author found the moccasin abundant in swampy canyons in Illinois, near Murphysboro, which is close to seventy-five miles north of the convergence of the Ohio with the Mississippi and situated in the Ozark Mountains. Extending upward from the canyons are great, shattered ledges of limestone and among these are extensive rattlesnake dens. Water moccasins were commonly observed well up in the hills among the ledges in company with timber rattlesnakes. They hibernate with the rattlers in these rocky places and even in summer are to be found among the rocks apparently ascending to such places for the young to be born, as the latter were found in typical rattlesnake dens. The Ozark Mountain people call this snake the "Trap-Jaw" owing to its habit of lying motionless, with jaws widely extended in threatening fashion when disturbed.

A genus of small rattlesnakes fits as a wedge between the moccasins and the main rattlesnake genus. This is *Sistrurus,* with but two recognized species in North America, one of such miniature proportions that it is like a rattler seen through the wrong end of an opera glass. These snakes appear to be closely related to *Agkistrodon.* The tops of their heads have large symmetrical shields like the moccasins and they frequently feed upon frogs, which is contrary to the habits of the main rattlesnake genus, the members of which, at least when fairly grown, or when mature, seem to feed exclusively upon warm blooded animals —mammals and birds.

The Massasauga, *Sistrurus catenatus* (Plate 71), is a small, brownish or grayish rattler with chestnut-brown blotches on the back, and a similar row on each side. This, and its related species (the pygmy rattlesnake) may be distinguished from members of the rattlesnake genus *Crotalus,* by the symmetrical plates on the top of the head already mentioned, as compared with numerous small scales between the orbital plates of the typical rattlers.

The Massasauga is from two to three feet long. Occurrence is from western New York, through Ohio to Nebraska, northward into Michigan and Ontario, and southward to Texas and northern Mexico. It usually frequents swampy places. Essentially, it is a western species though found in a limited area in western New York and western Pennsylvania.

Mr. Edward T. Whiffen, who has been much interested in the occurrence of this reptile in New York State, has written about it in the New York Zoological Society Bulletin as follows:

"The Massasauga, a species of dwarf rattlesnake, is still to be found in New York State, in and around Cicero Swamp, which, with some interruptions, stretches across the northern parts of Onondaga and Madison Counties, between Oneida and Onondaga Lake. The main swamp is said to be fourteen miles long and seven miles wide in its greatest extent. It consists of the swamp proper, in which are numerous 'islands,' or higher areas of land. Next to the dry land is the 'shore,' a wet, marshy strip, from seventy-five to one hundred yards wide. Beyond the 'shore' is the swampy land proper, fairly dry in summer and covered by a dense growth of trees, bushes, ferns and moss. In some places this moss is knee-deep. Many of the bushes are of the huckleberry variety, and it is among these that the Massasauga is frequently seen in August and September, when berry-pickers go out into the swamp.

"The Massasauga seems to like the neighborhood of swamps, though it shuns the actually wet places. In the harvest season it is usually found either in the hay-fields or out-lots, or it may be seen out on the moss among the bushes, or under the evergreen trees. However, it may occur almost anywhere. A gentleman told me that two years ago he found a large Massasauga in his wood-pile, about six feet from the house. Others reported having found the snakes in their cellars, or under the steps. There is an abundance of frogs and mice in the meadows, and frogs and birds in the swamp; and such con-

ditions account for the presence of the reptiles in those places.   In the hay-fields the Massasaugas seem to select the damper spots, where the growth of vegetation is heaviest.   There they are frequently cut in two by the knives of the mowing-machines.   Newly cleared fields, where there are plenty of stumps and berry bushes, are also favorite lurking places of this reptile, which is sometimes seen sunning itself on a stump, or lying coiled among the bushes.

"Older residents assured me that the snake is much less common than formerly, when its range extended over the entire northern part of the county.   Its disappearance is due probably to ceaseless slaughter and to the draining of the swamps.   That it is still fairly common may be judged from the fact that the killing of a dozen snakes in an area of perhaps a hundred acres was reported within the space of two weeks' time.   One of these snakes had sixteen rattles and two had ten. Six or eight was a common number.   The whole region is abundantly supplied with reptile life, milk snakes, ribbon snakes, garter snakes, water snakes, etc., being of frequent occurrence.   As much of the swamp has little value for tillage purposes and as the timber is small and comparatively worthless, the massasauga, though in diminishing numbers will probably continue to be found in the region for some time."

In the southerly part of its range, in Texas and northern Mexico, it takes on a subspecific name, *edwardsii,* the blotches being proportionately much reduced in size.   A related species, *S. ravus,* is confined to Mexico.

The Pygmy Rattlesnake or "Ground" Rattler, *Sistrurus miliarius,* seldom more than sixteen to twenty inches long, has a rattle so minute it would be unnoticed outside a distance of about eight feet.   It is common from southern North Carolina throughout Florida and westward to Oklahoma and Texas.   The body hue is grayish, with a series of rather widely separated, rounded blotches, and a reddish band along the back, this more vivid on the anterior portion.

The author has found this slate colored and fiery little rattler to prefer dry areas, with low vegetation.   He found them numerous in an area known as "the sand hills" in Hampton County, South Carolina, where the vegetation consisted of scattered scrub oaks.   The sound of the miniature rattle is like that produced by some of the smaller buzzing types of insects that "sing" in long grass.   It may be distinctly heard six to eight feet away, but one is not inclined to pay attention to it,

except for its persistence, and as insects usually stop "singing" as one draws in immediate proximity the slight buzz assumes sinister individuality for this reason. For many years the bite of this small rattler has been scoffed at as incapable of doing little more than producing a swollen hand or the like. The theory has been that the species was too small to do serious damage. Of late, a series of studies of its venom have shown that it is particularly powerful and that drop for drop it is indicated to be of higher toxicity than the poison of the larger species. Like all poisonous snakes, large and small, it warrants the greatest respect in handling during capture or study.

Crotalus is the main rattlesnake genus. Its fifteen well defined North American species range in size from the powerful eight-foot diamond-backs of the southeast and Texas areas to the little Willard's Rattlesnake, which does not appear to grow over fifteen inches long. However, the greater number of the species grow to a length of about six feet. They are highly dangerous, owing to their powerful fangs and the amount of poison expended at a bite.

The western rattlesnakes have recently received detailed studies which have resulted in radical changes of long-standing names. These studies have been rendered possible from large series of specimens accumulating in the scientific institutions, affording extensive opportunities for comparison. The most detailed investigations have been conducted by Dr. Afranio do Amaral and Mr. Lawrence M. Klauber. The former presented a provisional key to the rattlesnakes in a bulletin of the Antivenin Institute of America. Mr. Klauber followed this with a lengthy paper in the Transactions of the Zoological Society of San Diego. The more important findings relate to the relationship of the Pacific Rattlesnake, long considered a valid species, to the Prairie Rattlesnake and the definite races or subspecies of the latter in the Southwest. Also the status of the Tiger Rattlesnake, showing it to be truly an Arizona and north Mexican species.

Thus the rattlers of the Plains, the Pacific Region and the Southwest are now listed as follows:

The Prairie Rattlesnake, *Crotalus confluentus confluentus* (Plate 74), and its races or subspecies, has the widest range of any North American species of its genus. Its extension into Canada indicates that it ranges farther north than any other rattlesnake. The distribution of the typical form covers the Great Plains from the longitude of eastern Nebraska to the Rocky Mountains, extending southward

to central Texas along the easterly range, and to the Mexican border to the westward. Extension northward is into Canada, at least to the fiftieth parallel. This snake appears to be abundant in the vicinity of Medicine Hat.

Usual coloration is yellowish to brown, with a symmetrical row of darker, rounded and separated blotches on the back, these narrowly bordered with yellow or white, and a distinct V-shaped marking of light color on the large shield above each eye.

Despite its poisonous nature, the prairie rattlesnake is undoubtedly of considerable economic importance over a great area, owing to its being one of the natural enemies of destructive rodents.

The Pacific Rattlesnake, *Crotalus confluentus oreganus* (Plate 76), is the common and only rattlesnake of the Pacific region north of southern California, and represents a westerly race of the prairie rattlesnake, from which it differs in tendency toward darker markings, even to suffusion of black, and the edges of the blotches fusing in a rhomb-like chain. In southern California, its range overlaps most of the other California species except *Crotalus atrox* (the large and abundant western diamond rattlesnake ranging from Texas into eastern California) in the area of the Colorado desert. It occurs over varied country, embracing the mountains up to altitudes of eight thousand feet, the seacoast levels, inland plains, and desert areas. It is as much at home on the sterile slopes of desert mountains as in regions of heavy timber. The range is from British Columbia southward through Washington, Oregon and California, and into Lower California. It also occurs on Santa Catalina and Los Coronados Islands. Eastward the habitat extends into Idaho, Nevada, Utah and Arizona, overlapping the typical form.

While occasionally attaining a length of five feet, the average size is between three and four feet. There is a variation in pattern and hues, ranging from brown to grayish or greenish, with large dorsal blotches edged with a paler hue (the lighter margins in strong contrast), to blackish specimens with no markings but the paler edges indicating the dorsal blotches. Such specimens are sometimes called "diamond-backs."

In the northern portion of the range, this snake congregates in the Fall at specific crevices in rocky ledges, in preparation to hibernate. Large numbers annually return to these places, which are the so-called snake dens. Such habits are similar to those of the prairie rattlesnake,

along eroded river banks, and the timber rattlesnake on mountain ledges in the East.

The following additional subspecies of *confluentus* have been recently named:

The Great Basin Rattlesnake, *Crotalus confluentus lutosus* (Plate 74), occurring in the Plateau Region from the Rockies to the Sierras, including Utah, Nevada, northern California east of the Sierras, southeastern Oregon and southern Idaho.

The Midget Faded Rattlesnake, *Crotalus confluentus concolor,* recorded from Utah and Colorado.

The Grand Canyon Rattlesnake, *Crotalus confluentus abyssus* (Plate 75), is a form observed only in the Grand Canyon of the Colorado, in Arizona. Klauber states, "In the Grand Canyon occurs a peculiar phase of *Crotalus confluentus,* distinguished by its vermilion or salmon coloration and an almost complete absence of markings in the adult."

The Panamint Rattlesnake, *Crotalus confluentus stephensi* (Plate 75), has been thus far recorded from northwestern Esmeralda County, Nevada, and Round Valley, Mono County, California, southeasterly to Clark County, Nevada, and northern San Bernardino County, California. It appears that this snake has formerly been confused with Mitchell's rattlesnake—the white or bleached rattlesnake—(the species following), but the sponsor for its subspecific name describes a difference in the arrangement of the head plates. It has also been confused with the tiger rattlesnake, which appears to be confined to Arizona and northern Mexico. It is a rather pallid, desert form.

Mitchell's Rattlesnake, White Rattlesnake or Bleached Rattlesnake, *Crotalus mitchellii* (Plate 73), illustrates marked adaptation to a desert life. It is a pallid species, with obscure, transverse markings. Its length is from four to five feet. The keels of the body scales are quite high and rough, and there may be an indicated relationship here with the rattlers of Mexico, which would be diverse to the taxonomic arrangement. Some examples are almost white. The usual hues are yellowish, gray, or even pinkish. It frequents desert mountain slopes, among rocks. Scattered cacti and thorny bushes are the usual lurking places. A coiled specimen resembles a big tuft of faded cotton among the rocks.

Distribution is from central Arizona to the base of the foothills on the western slope of the Coast Range in California, from northern

Los Angeles County southward throughout the entire peninsula of Lower California; also on Santa Margarita and other islands in the Gulf of California.

The Tiger Rattlesnake, *Crotalus tigris* (Plate 77), receives its name from the tawny body hue, with darker markings of ring-like pattern. It inhabits the deserts of Arizona and northern Mexico, preferring the higher slopes, among the rocks.

The Lower California Rattlesnake, *Crotalus enyo,* occurs in Lower California. The anterior markings are rhomb-like, becoming narrower, or band-like on the posterior portion. It appears to be confined to the southerly portion of Lower California and coastal islands.

The Horned Rattlesnake or "Sidewinder", *Crotalus cerastes* (Plates 72 and 73), is a strictly desert species of small size and pallid hues occurring in southern California, Nevada, Arizona and portions of southwestern Utah. The large scale above each eye is developed into an upright horn. Living on dry and yielding sand, this snake progresses by throwing lateral loops of the body forward, causing it to move off at an oblique angle to the direction in which the head is pointing, and with such a degree of agility as to appear grotesque and warrant the name "Sidewinder."

The Spotted Rattlesnake, *Crotalus triseriatus,* is a small grayish species, with rows of spots extending lengthwise, but fusing into cross-bands on the tail. It is reported as rare and occurs in the mountains of southern Arizona and northern Mexico.

The Green Rattlesnake, *Crotalus lepidus* (Plate 71), another small species, seldom exceeding twenty-four inches, can readily be distinguished by its greenish or greenish-gray hue, marked by *widely separated and narrow rings of black.* It has always been regarded as of rare occurrence, although the range extends along the region of the Mexican boundary, from Eagle Pass on the Rio Grande, westward through New Mexico and Arizona. Its distribution into Mexico is not definitely known.

Willard's Rattlesnake, *Crotalus willardi* (Plate 77), appears to be the smallest of the rattlers and of rare occurrence. The length seems to be not more than fifteen inches. It is recorded from Arizona and northern Mexico. Two parallel white stripes, one on the lip and the other extending from the snout thence beneath the eye and to the lower and rear portion of the jaw, are characteristic.

In swinging the grouping of the distinctly rhomb-marked rattle-

snakes into the list at this point, we are not following the exact continuity of their listing in strictly technical arrangement, but seeking for convenience to form a zoo-geographical account.   The following seven species are also western.   They have a more or less symmetrical chain of diamond markings along the back, but it should be remembered that the darker, particularly the blackish specimens of the Pacific rattlesnake have the skin so suffused with dark pigment that there are no blotches discernible, in fact no markings but the paler edges indicating what would be the location of the dorsal saddles.   These light markings form a chain of rhomb-like design.   The prairie and Pacific rattlesnakes and their close allies were probably derived from rhomb-marked ancestors in the southerly latitudes.

The Western Diamond-back Rattlesnake, *Crotalus atrox* (Plate 81), may be rated the second most formidable serpent of North America, as to bulk and amount of poison expended at a bite—the first place, in point of deadliness from size going to the great diamond rattler of the southeastern states.   The Western Diamond-back Rattler, however, holds first rank in the number of fatalities in listing snake bites, owing to its abundance over a wide area.   It is extremely common in southerly portions of Texas and northern Mexico.   In vast expanses of ledgy hills, canyons and shattered rocks that repel the human invader of its realm from any parts but the trails, it will probably hold its own indefinitely.   Its areas of *habitat* have extensive rodent life which multiplies at a rate highly conducive to rattlesnake abundance.   The Diamond-backs of Texas and Mexico grow large and fat.   They commonly attain a length of six feet and a weight of fifteen pounds.   Occasional specimens exceed a length of seven feet.

Given to an inclination for considerable prowling into the open places, this serpent is particularly dangerous in its sudden defence when approached.   Its habit is to quickly throw the body into a coil, sound the rattle and deliver a blow.   If suddenly surprised the warning and stroke may be almost simultaneous.

The pattern consists of a chain of symmetrical rhombs on a grayish ground.   Examples from the sterile areas are pallid, with obscure rhombs and vary from gray to yellow or even pinkish.   The tail of this and the several closely allied species of the Southwest and Lower California is vividly marked with black and white rings.

Precisely defined the range may be given as embracing Texas and the southerly fringes of the states immediately north, thence extending

westward through New Mexico, Arizona and into California.   Occurrence also covers a wide area in northern Mexico, with northern Lower California included.   As to its extreme westerly occurrence, Klauber states: "The Colorado Desert in California; likewise northeastern Lower California and Tiburon Island."

While this snake inhabits a belt of latitude where hibernation is not prolonged—in fact is an essentially southerly rattler—a series of remarkable observations have been made by Mr. T. E. B. Pope, Curator of Reptiles of the Milwaukee Public Museum.   It appears that about 1920 several snakes of this species escaped from a circus while it was located near the ridge of limestone hills in the westerly portion of Wisconsin.   The area is seamed with fissures and ideal rattlesnake ground, *Crotalus horridus* being quite common.   The conjecture is that at least one of the escaped serpents was a gravid female.   At any rate, the species has become established, young have been born and have since grown and bred, and spread for many miles along the shattered cliffs, indicating adaptation to endure the long and severe winters of Wisconsin.

The western diamond rattlesnake has several close allies, as follows:

The Mojave Diamond Rattlesnake, *Crotalus scutulatus* (Plate 80), recognized by enlarged scales on the top of the head.   It ranges from the arid Southwest into northern Mexico.

The San Lucan Diamond Rattlesnake, *Crotalus lucasensis,* restricted to southern Lower California.

The Tortuga Island Diamond Rattlesnake, *Crotalus tortugensis,* of Tortuga Island, Lower California.

The Cedros Island Diamond Rattlesnake, *Crotalus exsul,** which is reddish and apparently recorded only from Cedros Island, Lower California.

The Red Diamond Rattlesnake, *Crotalus ruber* (Plate 80), is distinctly reddish (usually of brick-like hue) with rather obscure and narrow rhomb-like markings.   It is a common and rather large species, though of limited distribution.   The average adult is from four to five feet long, but it occasionally attains a length of six feet.   Klauber defines its range as follows: "The narrow belt in California and Lower California west of the desert to the coast, from the north line of Riverside County in California to north central Lower California, but excluding the coastal plains of Los Angeles and Orange Counties.   It occurs also on Cedros and certain Gulf of California islands."

* It is possible that this snake represents nothing more than an island race of *Crotalus ruber.*

This powerful rattlesnake is at times curiously gentle, showing little excitement if disturbed, and no inclination to strike. It is sometimes difficult to induce it to rattle. Again, found wandering in the open, with no sheltering brush or crevices in which to retreat, it will quickly coil and assume a threatening attitude as if realizing this is the only hope of survival. It is a calm and quiet captive, seldom sounding the rattle.

The Black-tailed Rattlesnake, *Crotalus molossus* (Plate 79), indicates relationship to the tropical rattlesnake of wide occurrence to the south, by its more than moderately high, keeled scales, and its markings. It is a handsome reptile, with dark rhomboidal blotches edged with yellow and enclosing lighter patches. The tail is black. The general body hue is rich yellow—sometimes darker.

It is fairly large, although restricted in size in some portions of its range, which in the United States is along the boundary region from Texas to Arizona. Southward in Mexico it appears to overlap the range of the Mexican Diamond-back, *Crotalus terrificus basiliscus.*

The most impressive member of *Crotalus* is the great Diamondback Rattlesnake, *C. adamanteus* (Plate 82), of the low coastal areas of the southeastern United States. It commonly grows to six feet, but attains a length of close to nine. The author has measured specimens eight feet and four inches and eight feet and six inches respectively. A six foot specimen will weigh from twelve to fifteen pounds, have a head nearly three inches in width and fangs three quarters of an inch long. The great amount of poison injected by the bite of such a creature may be surmised. It ranks among the world's most deadly snakes.

The pattern is bold and constant in the form of a chain of symmetrical blackish rhombs with light centers, or "diamonds," edged with paler hue, which increases the intensity of the marking. The background body hue is dark olive or olive-brown. The whole effect is one of striking symmetry of pattern, rather vivid when the creature is in the open and quite in contrast to the pale, bleached appearance of the Texas diamond-back. When coiled among grasses, however, or partially hidden by brushy vegetation this reptile is difficult to detect. The yellow margins of the rhombs blend with slashings of light and shadow or the weaving of stems and debris of the ground. I have more than once heard the deep intake of breath of these dangerous brutes and involuntarily leaped at just about the instant the warning rattle

was sounded, to find that I would have passed within a yard of the symmetrically round coil without seeing it. It is always well to wear leather leggings while tramping in the southern lowgrounds.

This powerful reptile inhabits the coastal areas of the Southeast, showing a preference for prowling through scrub palmetto or low brush. It is frequently noted along the wilder sea beaches in Florida where it lurks in the extensive stretches of tangled brush but a short distance from the line of the higher tide wash. The writer has also observed it in the sand hummocks, where the gopher tortoise digs its burrows. It is not a swamp species, although it may frequent woods close to water and does not hesitate to swim across small bodies of water. In the coastal strips it crosses fair-sized tide pools and has been noted several miles from shore, where it has been accidentally carried by the currents. It is also found along the keys. Its food when adult consists largely of rabbits, but I have also noted that these rattlers eat quails.

There are from eight to twelve young in a litter, these being born in August or September and precisely like the parent in pattern, though paler, almost sage-green in body hue, with whitish diamond markings.

It was with a litter of young of this type that I noted what appeared unique in actions for a snake—the first thing of the kind I have ever seen, either with a wild reptile or a captive specimen.

A six foot female diamond rattler from Florida gave birth to nine young, in August. John Toomey, the Head Keeper of mammals and reptiles, noted the litter as he inspected the collection during the morning. The mother was steadily rattling, which was unusual as she had appeared to be quite tame.

Later, when Toomey opened the cage to fill the water pan the big rattler glided rapidly at him and struck furiously from a lateral-S she carried in her neck as she advanced. This alone was astonishing as never before had we seen a diamond-back attack, or do more than defend itself from a coil. Toomey backed away from the cage to see if the snake would follow him, but she turned and retired into the cage. He returned to the door and she as quickly came at him again. This condition continued for a month and a number of persons observed it. We could form no other conjecture than a defence of the young—a manifestation we had never noted with a snake before.

The young rattlers were about 14 inches long when born and provided with a single button.   At the time of writing the author is rearing these young snakes.   Two of them have acquired five segments of the rattle in eight months' time and the others have four segments and the button.   The reason for this is that some feed more frequently than others.   A new segment of the rattle is uncovered at each shedding of the skin.   From their rate of growth I would estimate they should be of breeding size, or young adults when about two years old. Serpents reach a breeding age long before their growth has ceased.   My belief is that a snake of this kind grows rapidly up to two years' time, then slowly from three to five years more, and in particularly good feeding ground the latter phase of growth may be more extended, thus accounting for some old specimens being so much larger than others.

The Banded Rattlesnake, Timber Rattlesnake, Canebrake Rattlesnake, *Crotalus horridus* (Plates 78 and 79), has the most extensive distribution of any poisonous serpent in North America with the exception of the prairie rattlesnake and its various races.   It occurs from southern Maine to the easterly portion of the Great Plains, southward to northern Florida, and westerly into Arkansas and eastern Texas.

The average length of the adult Timber Rattlesnake in the northeastern states is slightly under four feet.   As with a number of species of serpents, however, an occasional specimen may well exceed the usual run.   The largest specimen I ever examined was two inches over six feet in length and nearly three inches in diameter.   It was taken near Sheffield, in the Berkshires of Massachusetts.   A specimen nearly as large (slightly under six feet) was taken near the top of the great rock slide near Hartsville, Massachusetts, which shattered ledge is alleged to have inspired Oliver Wendell Holmes' description of "the mountain" in his classic novel, "Elsie Venner."   Large specimens have been recorded from New Jersey and Pennsylvania.

Distribution of this rattlesnake in the northeastern states is associated with hills and mountains of moderate height, on which there are broken ledges with large, loose fragments on the slopes and top.   These flat fragments may be a foot or more in thickness and from a yard to six or eight feet in length, sloping back into a fissure, the bottom of which may be covered with soil or leaves, and which provides a position of security during storms.   It is the common habit of rattlesnakes to coil under the edge of these rock masses, protected from the too-hot summer sun, and ready to quickly retreat if disturbed.   If the intruder

goes on his way, the snake may lie in its motionless coil, without sounding the rattle, thus seeking to escape notice.

Near these natural homes, are specific crevices or "dens," where rattlers that have roamed over a considerable area during the summer, congregate each Fall preparatory to deep penetration and hibernation, beyond the frost line.   During the late summer the females return to such places and here the young are born, with a natural instinct to return to this specific spot each year for winter shelter.   From the areas of the ledges, many rattlesnakes prowl through the forests for food, and often into the farmlands.   Variations in weather conditions produce difference in numbers annually observed.   During particularly dry summers, they may come into the low grounds for water, in considerable numbers.   Their natural prey, small rodents and birds, sometimes shift their feeding grounds and this also affects the summer distribution of the rattlesnake.   If a farm is infested with rats and mice, and a rattlesnake den is not far distant, it will not take the reptiles long to discover the favorable feeding ground.   They may also be commonly noted during the haying season, due to the presence of numbers of field mice.

While a very dangerous snake from the standpoint of its large fangs and the amount of venom it is able to inject at a bite, the northern rattlesnake is rather inoffensive as compared with its larger allies in the southern states.   It also invariably gives warning of its presence by sounding the rattle, if disturbed when out of immediate contact with a sheltering crevice.   If closely approached, it will strike, but the full striking distance of the average specimen is barely eighteen inches —and usually shorter.   There are records of fatalities from the bite of this species, but generally considered, in the northeastern portion of its range, there is a surprisingly small number reported, less than with the copperhead, which gives no warning of its presence.   In an area of the southern Berkshires, where rattlesnakes are particularly frequent, the writer has records of but three bites during a period of about twenty years.   One of these was fatal.

Distribution is general in the wilder, hilly country of the East with the exception of the Catskill and Adirondack Mountains.   As far as I am aware, no rattlesnake has ever been recorded from the Adirondack Mountains proper, although the species is quite common on Tongue and Black Mountains, in the vicinity of Lake George.   Likewise, they commonly occur in some portions of the Catskills, but in

other equally ledgy portions of the same range have never been found. The species is abundant in the Ramapos (where, however, accidents are extremely infrequent), the Kittatinnies of New Jersey and Pennsylvania, and the Shawangunk range in New York. In central New Jersey it occurs in conditions rather curious for a mountain type. There is considerable flat, forested country back of the central coast, quite damp in spots and with large sections covered with heavy sphagnum moss. In these locations, the species attains a larger average size than the mountain type and exhibits a slightly different coloration. It is grayish, with strongly contrasted black bands, and a faint, rusty, dorsal stripe, several scales wide. There is a resemblance to the southern race known as the Canebrake Rattlesnake, which, in swampy coastal areas of the Southeast and the lower Mississippi Valley attains a length of close to eight feet and has a distinct reddish band along the back. These big specimens have much less bulk than the southern diamondbacks.

Rattlesnakes are extremely rare in the state of Maine, and that area is thus unique among all the states in the virtual absence of poisonous serpents. The Boston Society of Natural History has been unable to obtain a record specimen for its collection, from Maine. There appear to be a few records from New Hampshire, and specimens are reported on an island in Lake Winnepesaukee. Vermont seems to have few specimens, except along the westerly slopes of the Green Mountains and in the southern portion of the state. Both the copperhead and rattlesnake appear to be extinct on Long Island. That the latter was formerly found there is evident from skins and rattles among the trophies of old farmhouses. I have been unable to verify the occurrence of a specimen of either species during the past thirty years.

These serpents are particularly abundant in the mountains of Pennsylvania, the Virginias, the Carolinas, Kentucky and Tennessee. The species has actually become more abundant during the past twenty-five years in several portions of the East. This has been definitely noted in New York and New Jersey.

The typical coloration is yellow or tan, with wavy cross-bands of dark brown or black. Many specimens are well suffused with black, and some are almost entirely black (Plate 79). The black or darker examples are more commonly the males although melanistic females are also noted. It is rare, however, where black and yellow specimens inhabit the same areas, to find a male of the paler hue.

Avoiding Accidents and Treating Snake Bite

The timber rattler and its neighbor of the ledges, the copperhead snake, have brought me more queries as to precautions against accidents and what to do in case of snake bite, than any of the other North American serpents. This comes from their common occurrence in states of heavy human population, states in which there is much hiking and camping. Hence the present part of the narrative is a good point for insertion of suggestions about what to do in areas where poisonous snakes occur.

A pair of stout canvas leggings or leather puttees are positive protection to the legs against northern poisonous serpents. The leggings, however, should be worn with high shoes. If low cut shoes are worn, there are usually several inches of the ankle left exposed and this is usually the part of the limb most frequently bitten by venomous reptiles of moderate size.

Canvas leggings which become soft and pliable after having been wet or worn for some time are not positive protection against the bites of the big diamond-backs in the southeast or along the southerly (Mexican) boundary states, nor are knee-high leather boots to be confidently relied upon. The upper portion of such boots, from the ankle up, becomes soft from wear and motion and alternate wetting and drying. It is possible for the fangs of a big rattler, striking hard, to pierce such boots. The average height of stroke for the big diamond rattlers is from the lower to the middle calf of the leg, not higher. Stiff leather puttees, such as army officers wear, are the ideal protection besides being comfortable. And again they are more sanitary than high, laced leather boots as the overlap between them and the ordinary shoe insures ventilation of the legs. With such an outfit I have tramped for miles through the close-set and knee-high scrub palmetto of the Florida barrens and low tangle in Central America and Brazil, in places the fer-de-lance was said to be unpleasantly numerous. There is one point to be particularly remembered, however, especially in the southern states, and that is care in stepping over big trunks of fallen trees. There is every chance that the disintegrating trunk may have a hollow on the opposite side or there may be a shelf-like patch of matted brush. This would mean that a coiled snake on the opposite side would be well elevated from the ground and might strike one in the thigh.

I recall one fatal accident, from a large water moccasin, from this very condition.

Coming back to precautions in the northerly areas it is important to bear in mind that while the legs are protected the practice of using the hands in climbing rocky places or getting over a stone fence is dangerous, unless each hand-hold is investigated, with due thought of crevices or hollows that may secrete a coiled serpent. Any thick, brushy place, or pile of leaves, in the wilder country, should be considered a hazard, unless the eye is keen in noting where the hand is directed.

In establishing a summer camp, it is well to ascertain from local residents whether or not there is a particular prevalence of poisonous snakes. We have several times been consulted about camps which have unconsciously been located in the immediate vicinity of a den of rattlesnakes or copperheads, with the consequence that a number of city children, unfamiliar with woodcraft, have been turned loose in an area over-run with poisonous reptiles. There are many ideal locations for camps where poisonous serpents are seldom reported, and the finding of such areas is not difficult. There are also fine camping areas in most of the states under consideration, in which no poisonous snakes are ever to be found.

While the edification of young people in camps about the wild types of life found in the near-by country is highly desirable, instructional measures relating to poisonous snakes have been a bit overdone. This relates to the exhibition of numerous living specimens, and the handling of these in what is considered to be a safe way, to show the poison fangs, etc., the carrying of such specimens to lectures, and the like. Too much of such familiarity reduces respect for danger and it has been noted that a rather large following of boy students has been inclined to transport poisonous reptiles in anything but a competent and cautious manner. Several accidents have resulted from this undue familiarity. Camp instructors should be cautioned not to go too far in this direction, to caution boys not to collect poisonous serpents, and not to harbor such creatures for observations. A captive poisonous snake, except in the care of a matured and competent person, is a source of danger to the possessor and those around him.

Treatment of Snake Bite: Through the formation of the Antivenin Institute of America at Glenolden, Pennsylvania, and the guidance of Dr. Afranio do Amaral, Chief of the Brazilian government's Instituto

Butantan, at São Paulo, specific serum for the bites of the poisonous snakes of North America is being regularly produced.

It is only recently that any organization in the United States could be induced to undertake the production of specific antivenomous serum for use in North America. The cost of production is high and the market, from a commercial point of view, is quickly "saturated". On the average it appears that there are but slightly over one hundred fatalities a year in the entire United States—that is from statistics obtained with much difficulty. Work is now under way to check against results since the distribution of North American serum. The product of the Antivenin Institute of America "keeps" for at least five years. This means that when points of hazard have been supplied the demand for serum slows down, yet the expense of the producing organization in necessarily maintaining its series of horses under immunization processes, and its staff of scientific workers, goes steadily on. It is a very different situation from tropical countries—having their respective organizations—where the demand for serum is considerable and constant. The Mulford organization, in showing fine spirit in establishing a laboratory for the production of snake-bite serum, deserves much credit as the pioneer in this practical work for North America. They have been subsequently assisted by Harvard University and the United Fruit Company, and by the gratuitous services of a number of scientific specialists. All of this has resulted in the formation of the Institute, now issuing a formal publication which has become unique and of great value as a magazine on serum therapy, records of accidents, occurrence of poisonous reptiles and scientific discussions as to their relative toxicity.

Up to the time of the formation and functioning of the Antivenin Institute of America an efficacious serum for the bites of the North American Crotaline snakes was not available in the United States unless gratuitously distributed from the only point of production, which was Brazil. Certain laws of the United States treasury department, relating to tests and production, eliminated Brazilian serum from entry into American ports for distribution if sold. These technicalities are still existent. When it became generally known that the Brazilian serums were efficacious there was an insistent demand for distribution in the United States to points of particular hazard. The author brought several hundred tubes from São Paulo and distributed these gratuitously. The demand, however, was for several thousand and it was

out of the question to continuously impose upon Brazilian colleagues for a free supply to the United States. They had already gone to the expense and trouble of immunizing horses against the venoms of North American snakes. In Brazil there are specific serums for the bites of the fer-de-lance and its numerous near allies, for the quite different poison of the tropical rattlesnake, and for bites of coral snakes which secrete a neurotoxin. It was from these demonstrations that the Antivenin Institute of America was formed.

While it is encouraging to realize that this form of serum therapy has developed in the United States, I feel that there is still progress to be made in rendering North American serum more efficient. For instance, as it is now produced, it is still a polyvalent serum, that is, it is used for two rather different types of snakes, the rattler and the moccasin (water moccasin and copperhead). Polyvalent serums [1] have been found of value in other countries, but not so efficacious as specific types, produced by immunization with venoms of the particular kinds of snakes against which serum is to be used as protection. Thus, I think, there will ultimately be better results with two distinct grades of serum, one for rattlesnake bite, and another for the bites of the water moccasin and the copperhead. All of this means continued analysis of poisons at the laboratory and most important of all an exhaustive checking of physiological action of venoms and neutralizing properties of new grades of serum. The Pasteur Institute, under the guidance of the master hand of Calmette, the pioneer of serpent serums, also the Instituto Butantan under the direction of the brilliant Vital Brazil and Afranio do Amaral at São Paulo, have gone through these time-consuming steps of research. The United States is fortunate in having laid down the foundation stones and in having finally taken steps to produce a neutralizing agent generally obtainable without restriction.

Snake-bite serum is made by injection of horses with small doses of snake venom, the process continuing through a number of months until the animals have developed a high degree of immunity. Blood is then obtained from them, and is subjected to a number of processes. The red is separated from the serous portion, and the latter is filtrated. Simply explained, the action of this serum, injected into the human victim who has been bitten by a dangerous snake, is to neutralize the poison of the reptile. Its effect is rapid in relieving the dramatically alarming effects of snake bite.

[1] More technically indicated in the plural as *sera*.

Serum may be injected immediately after a bite, or up to the time the victim has approached a condition of collapse. It is then usually too late to be properly taken up by the circulation and thus neutralize the poison injected at the time of the bite.

The bite of a copperhead or massasauga is not ordinarily fatal, although it may be very serious. Serum may be injected as late as a day or even two days after symptoms of great swelling have developed. It is far better, however, to inject it as soon as possible, in order to quickly neutralize the poison and thus prevent great destruction of the red cells of the blood stream and the walls of the carrying vessels. This tends to prevent extensive necrosis of the bitten area.

A large specimen of the timber rattlesnake may inject enough poison to cause death within ten to twelve hours, and in a much shorter time if a vein is actually struck, which is a rare, but possible condition.

As the bite of a poisonous snake is no more nor less than a simultaneously double injection, by two hypodermic teeth (the fangs), the measures to meet the emergency should be quick and positive. A ligature of some type should be bound a moderate distance above the bitten part, to prevent the poison being absorbed into the upper limb. The ligature may consist of a strip of cloth, a large handkerchief, or even a piece of heavy cord. A rubber ligature is much the best. There is necessity of making the ligature sufficiently tight to indicate a stoppage of circulation. Even moderate pressure tends to localize the area of poisoning.

With the absorption of the poison retarded, the fang wounds should be opened by an incision across them to an estimated depth of three-eighths of an inch for a large rattlesnake, or a quarter of an inch for a copperhead. The incision should be made with care not to injure the delicate skin covering a bone, or to cut into a blood vessel. If no cupping device is at hand, drainage should be induced by sucking the wound, there being practically no danger from this if the lips and mouth are free from sores.

The mechanical drawing away of the poisoned blood in the vicinity of the wound is of the greatest importance. Every thought should be centered in making this measure as efficacious as possible and it should be repeated again and again after the ligature is slacked off about every ten minutes to reestablish circulation. It has been clearly established that the circulation of the major bulk of the venom into the system is comparatively slow—that much of it lingers in the vicinity of the wound. The more venom injected and the deeper the fang wounds,

the more poison is naturally taken up, but the immediate swelling that takes place appears to be Nature's provision to retard circulation of the lethal fluid. Also, there is an immediate rush of serum and lymph to the part, apparently another provision to dilute it in advance of its absorption. These fluids assist in mechanical drainage, in fact they are later liberally exuded from the drainage incisions. Ligation should not continue for much over half an hour—and always slacked off at regular intervals during this time—but intervals of mechanical suction should continue several hours after ligation has ceased.

Dr. Dudley Jackson has demonstrated in an extremely painstaking series of experiments with dogs, that lethal doses given fair time for absorption, yielded from the area of injection, by cupping, enough poison to kill a dog that received no treatment. The dogs receiving treatment by mechanical drainage or suction made recoveries.

Hence a cupping device, with small suction bulb should be part of a snake-bite kit. There should be two interchangeable suction surfaces, one of glass, for flat surfaces, and another of metal, with narrow, oval opening to fit against the surface of a finger or other rounded part. It is important that the first incisions made should be rather short and cruciform, so as not to extend beyond the suction surface of the device and admit air.

After the immediate measures for eliminating as much poison as possible, that is after the practically continuous suction during the period of ligation, the serum, if available, should be administered. It is better, of course, if assistance is at hand, to inject the serum immediately following the bite. The modern method of preparing it is in the form of loaded hypodermic syringes, and it is only necessary to attach the needle and the handle. The serum is not injected in the vicinity of the bite, but under the skin between the shoulder blades or on the abdomen, by what is known as subcutaneous injection. In this way it is quickly taken up by the general circulation. The entire contents of a tube should be injected for a bite. If symptoms are particularly grave, two or more tubes may be necessary. Intra-venous injection is advisable if the fangs have punctured a blood vessel, but this should be done only under the direction of a doctor who has actually diagnosed the condition.

It is well to wash the incision with a mild solution of permanganate crystals in pure water (to produce a pale amethyst hue), as this fluid will neutralize by oxidation what venom it may reach. The use of

strong solutions of permanganate of potassium, however, is not only unwise, but dangerous, as there is much tissue destruction by this chemical at a high strength.   This caution also points to the utter rashness of rubbing pure crystals of permanganate into a wound.   Moreover, such a wound should never be cauterized.   Nothing should be more foreign to the treatment of snake bite than such practice, which actually seals the destructive poison within the tissue.

As not only the immediate area of the wound, but a considerable portion of the neighboring tissue is much weakened and subject to bacterial invasion, and the bite itself is sometimes attended by specific infection with germs from the snake's mouth, the wounds should be covered with a heavy layer of wet dressing, and kept saturated with a mild antiseptic solution.   This not only retards or prevents infection, but induces copious drainage, through a discharge of quantities of serous fluids which always appear to be rushed to such a poisoned area.

Unless in a remote district not accessible within reasonable time to the aid of a physician, the snake-bite victim should, if possible, make contact with skilled hands to carry through all but the preliminary measures of treatment.

A first-aid kit for the treatment of snake bite should contain the following articles: Several one-sided safety razor blades; a small bulb and cupping glass for flat surfaces, with additional attachment for "round" surfaces, like a finger; a roll of rubber ligature; a small roll of bandage; and at least two tubes of antivenomous serum.   The serum will remain efficacious for several years.   A few permanganate crystals may also be carried.   Whiskey is useless as a cure, although a moderate dose of medicinal brandy does no harm and may greatly relieve the mind during a situation which may not be nearly so dangerous as it seems.

I have noted the bites of copperheads to produce great swelling which cleared up within a few days with no other treatment than a drainage incision across the fang wounds, some suction and the covering of the area with a wet dressing.   There are also cases of both copperhead and rattlesnake bites being treated with the serum and the patient going about his regular business the following day.   Again, there are records of grave manifestations, developing with great rapidity.   Consequently, poisonous serpents warrant the utmost respect, caution in investigating their lairs, and personal protection in going through the areas which they inhabit.

As many people are bitten by harmless snakes which may quickly glide away, leaving apprehension behind them, it is well to understand that the bite of a poisonous serpent is unmistakable. A harmless serpent may produce distinct wounds from its recurved teeth, and as but a few teeth may cause lacerations which bleed, the imagination of a nervous person may quickly classify two "fang" punctures. If nothing happens within ten minutes following a bite, the snake was harmless. A bite from a poisonous serpent develops rapid symptoms. A burning pain is apparent within three to five minutes, and within ten minutes there is distinct swelling. This rapidly increases, and is usually followed, within half an hour or less, with profuse perspiration and there may be reflex vomiting. By this time, of course, treatment should have been given, and if serum is at hand, its injection may prevent the more alarming symptoms.

CHAPTER XI

THE POISONOUS SNAKES OF CENTRAL
AND SOUTH AMERICA

SOUTH of the northerly and arid area of Mexico, the status of the rattlesnake group changes in the disappearance of species and through tropical Mexico, Central America and South America but a single distinct species is known. This has a symmetrical, rhomb-like pattern. The United States, therefore, is the headquarters of the rattlesnakes, with the greater number of kinds forming a radiating group in the southwesterly portion.

With the dropping out of the array of rattlesnakes comes the appearance in southerly Mexico of the characteristic type of poisonous snake of the New World tropics. This is the so-called lance-head type of pit viper of the genus *Bothrops*. Hence the tropical American vipers generally, with the exception of the bushmaster and a water moccasin, have been assigned to this genus, although the slender-bodied, tree-climbing species with a prehensile tail appear to warrant recognition within a distinct genus. We may take the fer-de-lance as a representative species of *Bothrops*. The name fer-de-lance (relating to the shape of the head—like an iron lance) is a Creole-French term coming from the southerly West Indies. In Central America it is commonly called the barba amarilla (yellow-beard) and in Brazil the jararaca—the latter word relating to an arrow and referring to the shape of the head.

It is the most abundant and widely distributed poisonous serpent of the New World, and represents the characteristic type most broadly developed in the American tropics. All told, approximately three dozen species of *Bothrops* are scientifically listed. The genus is to a certain extent monotonous in form and pattern of its members. Their venom is largely composed of a powerful haemotoxin, which destroys the red cells of the blood and breaks down the walls of the vessels. Rather dominating in its difference is the great bushmaster, extending from Nicaragua and Costa Rica well through Brazil. It is the giant

among vipers, attaining a length of twelve feet.　Its single species is assigned to a separate genus, *Lachesis*.

The poisonous serpents of Central and South America are rather similar, although a number of species occurring in the latter are characteristic to the more southerly country.　The prevailing and most widely distributed species are the rattlesnake, restricted to a single distinct species and on the higher ground, and the fer-de-lance or barba amarilla, *Bothrops atrox,* in the low, coastal areas.　Generally considering the great continental area of South America, the fauna of which fuses with that of the Central American tropics, a good viewpoint is obtained by stating that it shows as distinct development in its reptile life as does North America, and its characteristic genus of *Bothrops* has developed a greater number of species than the North American rattlesnake genus.　About thirty species of coral snakes are common in the humid forests of tropical America of which over twenty are indicated as being indigenous to South America.　A poisonous sea snake occurs in the bays and off the western coast of Central America and the northwestern coast of South America.

One phase of distribution—or lack of it—stands out prominently as a point of interest.　This relates to the absence of poisonous serpents in all of the large islands of the West Indies.　No dangerous reptiles occur in Cuba, Jamaica, Hispaniola (Hayti and the San Dominican Republic), or Porto Rico, nor anywhere in the West Indies except in the Windward Islands, where the fer-de-lance occurs in St. Lucia, Martinique and Tobago—and Trinidad, lying close to the mainland.　The coral snake also occurs on these islands, including St. Vincent.　This absence of poisonous reptiles among the large islands is all the more remarkable owing to the proximity of an infested Central American mainland, the luxuriance of flora of the islands, and climate conducive to reptile development.　The islands are fairly well populated with harmless reptiles.

The point is graphically illustrated by examination of a map showing the New World areas between north latitudes 15 and 30 degrees. The large islands appear to be nested in the great crescentic swing of the mainland from the point of Florida to Panama.　It even seems remarkable that with a mainland background of rattlers, *Bothrops* species and coral snakes, accidental importation has not occurred through the years, and it would be well for the authorities of these islands during importation of shrubbery, lumber or other products which might con-

ceal hidden specimens to have inspections vigorously conducted.   Such measures are in force in the Hawaiian Islands and those of the Madeira group.   There it is prohibited for travelling shows to bring in poisonous reptiles.   This is illustrated to be a wise provision when noting the accidental introduction of *Crotalus atrox* in the northerly United States —already described under that species.

The tropical American species are herewith considered in their systematic order:

The tropical Coral Snakes, *Micrurus (Elaps)*, grow considerably larger than the two species inhabiting southerly portions of the United States.   Some attain a length of nearly four feet and while they seldom strike will turn and bite if stepped on.   An unfortunate victim in bare feet may find the reptile imbedding its short fangs and retaining its hold.   Such bites of the larger species are often fatal.   Even in the tropics the members of this genus are the only New World representatives of the *Elapidae,* the family of cobras and allies which rate as the Old World's most dangerous snakes, owing to these large members being particularly alert and irritable.   Fortunately for the New World tropics, the members of *Micrurus* are of such brilliant coloration they are readily detected and moreover they are of burrowing habits, rather dull sight and not stirred to irritability unless restrained.

Micrurus, despite the brilliant coloration of its members, is at best of rather similar markings throughout.   In Mexico the common name for these reptiles is "Coralilla" and in Central America "Gargantilla", the latter meaning a necklace and relating to the similarity of the patterns to beads strung in color designs.   At least eight species appear to occur in Mexican and Central American areas, among these being *Micrurus fulvius* (Plate 32), ranging southward from the United States— but with proportionately wider red rings, *M. mipartitus* and *M. nigrocinctus* (Plate 32).   The latter is commonly seen from Guatemala to Panama.   The tendency of several harmless snakes to "mimic" the dangerous coral snakes is more pronounced in South America than in Central America.   Several of these non-venomous "imitators" are startling in their similarity to the poisonous species, as the South American coral snakes run to a greater variation in the width of the rings, and black on the outside of the yellow rings.   This makes it difficult to offer any fixed formula of gross differentiation in pattern to distinguish the inoffensive from the dangerous.   Some species of the inoffensive genera *Pseudoboa* (Plate 30), and *Erythrolamprus* (Plate 30), are

remarkable in their similarity of colors and ringed patterns to those of *Micrurus* (Plate 31).

Micrurus corallinus (Plate 31), of the Lesser Antilles and tropical South America; *M. frontalis* (Plate 31), of southern Brazil, Uruguay, Paraguay and Argentina, and *M. lemniscatus* of the Guianas and Brazil, are commonly observed and representative species.   Here are examples of the differences among the species as to the ratio of yellow, red and black rings, the width and arrangement of the latter being particularly important.   With *corallinus* the tendency is toward single black rings, narrowly margined with yellow or dull white; with *frontalis* there is black outside of the yellow rings (which are considerably broader), thus producing actually three black annuli; and with *lemniscatus* this is particularly pronounced, the yellow and black rings being so wide as to encroach upon and reduce the red, so typical of coral snake coloration.   A length of four feet is not rare among all of these.

Marine Serpents: The curious members of the *Hydrophidae* or Sea Snakes may be recognized by the vertically compressed or paddle-like tail.   There are many species, which abound in the Indian Ocean and the western tropical Pacific.   A single kind, however, occurs in waters of the New World—off the west coast of Mexico, Central America and northern South America.   All of the marine serpents are very poisonous and appear to be highly specialized allies of the Elapine group.

The Yellow-bellied Sea Snake, *Pelamydrus platurus,* may be recognized by its rather eel-like form, with quite long head, the body compressed and covered above and beneath with small, round scales.   Coloration is vivid and unusual.   The upper half of the body is black or dark brown, the lower half yellow, demarkation being very apparent while the creature is swimming, particularly if seen from the side. Length is seldom over three feet.   It is extensively distributed through the tropical Pacific, and into the Indian Ocean, and often observed in the Bay of Panama and off Punta Arenas, Costa Rica, where it may be watched for from steamers clearing the Panama Canal for west coast ports, north or south.   It also occurs in the lower Gulf of California.

Widely separated from its ally of the coastal swamps of the United States is a boldly marked water moccasin occurring south of the arid belt of Mexico.   This is the Tropical Moccasin, or "Cantil," *Agkistrodon bilineatus* (Plate 54), a far more dangerous reptile than that of

the North from a combination of a higher toxicity of its bite, a savage disposition and marked agility in striking. The large, symmetrical shields on the top of the head immediately distinguish it as a typical moccasin and offer a point of distinction from the members of *Bothrops*. It is strongly marked, in decorative pattern, as if embellished with touches of white enamel. Also it is a smaller water moccasin than that of the United States. The writer has noted no specimen over four feet in length. It should be looked for in swamps and in the marginal vegetation of streams.

Records indicate that it is confined to southern Mexico and the northerly part of the Central American tropics. Listings record it from Tres Marias Island, Colima, Guadalajara, Tehuantepec and Yucatan, also the Pacific coast of Guatemala. The writer heard of it near Belize in British Honduras, but in a careful search of swamps and waterways in the Republic of Honduras failed to find it, nor had Douglas March in his field work found it that far south.

The *Palm Vipers* are small members of the extensive genus *Bothrops* and produce a distinct phase of danger in the tropics as they are arboreal, blend with the foliage and may be encountered on bushes on a level with one's face. Reconnoitering through thick places should carry a thought of these reptiles which have excessively long fangs and powerful poison. The name "palm" viper is rather misleading, though usually applied. They may be found in any type of bush or low tree although they do show a liking for tightly coiling just where the base of palm stems join the trunk, the latter forming a good avenue for their travel if the stems are numerous and enabling them to seek various elevations or cross to encroaching branches of other kinds. They are persistently arboreal, have a particularly wide head and all are characterized by a prehensile tail, which as a rule is kept promiscuously twisted about some projection. The larger number occur in southern Mexico and Central America, in which combined area six species are listed. Two of these extend into northern South America and another is indigenous to the latter country.

Schlegel's Palm Viper; the Horned Palm Viper; the Eyelash Viper; "Bocaracá"; "Toboba de pestana", *Bothrops schlegelii* (Plates 67 and 68), is distinct in the development of several scales between the eye and the large plate above it. Two or three of these scales are directed upward to form spiny horns. There are two color phases. One is greenish or olive, speckled with black and red; the other, equally com-

mon, is yellow, often of pale lemon hue, speckled with black. The yellow examples are known as "Orapel." [1]

Prospectors should be wary about going into bushy places known to be frequented by these snakes. Under such conditions men have been bitten on the hands and face. A trail gang, cutting through the jungle in the Republic of Honduras had such accidents, several of them terminating fatally. While these snakes are small, the proportionately large head and long fangs render them very dangerous. Range of the Horned or Eyelash Viper includes Guatemala, south through Central America and well into South America.

The Mexican Palm Viper, *Bothrops undulatus,* also has a horn-like development over the eye, but this is produced by a *single* upturned scale. This snake is olive or brown, with large, rhomb-like spots, sometimes connected to form a zig-zag band. It is recorded from Guerrero, Orizaba, Vera Cruz, Actopan and Oaxaca. It probably ranges into Guatemala.

The Green Palm Viper, *Bothrops bicolor,* is uniform leaf green above and yellow beneath and recorded from western Guatemala.

The Yellow-lined Palm Viper, *Bothrops lateralis,* green above and beneath, has a yellow line along each side. Some specimens have yellow and dark cross-bands on the back. It is found in Costa Rica.

The Black Spotted Palm Viper, *Bothrops nigroviridis* (Plate 69), illustrates how observation extends the knowledge of a species. This snake was for a long time listed as occurring in Panama and Costa Rica. Through the field studies of Douglas March, in charge of the Serpentarium at Tela, Honduras, the species was found to be well represented in that country. This serpent is green, with black spots or speckled markings. The form discovered in fair abundance in Honduras by Mr. March, represents a subspecies based upon scalation.

The Yellow-spotted Palm Viper, *Bothrops nigroviridis aurifera,* occurs in Guatemala. It is green above and greenish yellow beneath, with scattered yellow spots.

Amaral notes the following about another palm viper *Bothrops leptura,* occurring in Panama thence into northern South America: "Seems to be very poisonous, as its fangs occupy half or more the length of the mouth and its venom glands are quite long and thick."

The only species of these arboreal pit vipers appearing to be confined to South America is *B. bilineatus,* and its range is essentially

---

[1] Meaning "false gold."

northern, or approximately north of south latitude fifteen, including Brazil, Bolivia, eastern Peru and Ecuador. It is leaf-green above, uniform or speckled with black. A yellow line or series of spots run along the outer row of scales. The native name is "Surucucū patiabo."

The *Hog-nosed Vipers* are small terrestrial members of *Bothrops,* three in number, recognized by upturned snout, very sharply so with one, moderately so with the second and pointed but little upturned with the other. These snakes in Central America are usually called "Chatilla" or "Tamagá." They occur over varied terrain, covering the greater portion of Central America and southerly Mexico. Two species range into northern South America.

The Nose-horned Viper, *Bothrops nasuta* (Plate 55), occurs in humid woodlands of eastern Central America, thence southward into Colombia and Ecuador. The snout bears an upturned, proboscis-like appendage. Coloration is brown, with thirteen to twenty small black markings on each side of the back, these usually in alternation and separated by a pale line. Length is seldom beyond twenty-four inches.

Landsberg's Hog-nosed Viper, *Bothrops lansbergii,* has the snout carried forward to a sharp point slightly upturned. Coloration is brown, with a double row of darker markings on the back, generally separated by a paler line and often united to form a zig-zag chain. The length is usually under twenty-four inches. Occurrence is largely confined to the drier areas from southern Mexico, through Central America and into Colombia, Venezuela and northern Brazil. Regarding its occurrence in Colombia, Amaral writes: "The 'Fer-de-lance' *(B. atrox)* which is the main problem in the plantations in Central America, seems to be comparatively uncommon in Santa Marta, its place being taken by another venomous species seldom found elsewhere but surprisingly common in the Santa Marta district. This is the dry-land Hog-nosed Viper *(Bothrops lansbergii),* which constitutes about 50 per cent of the Rio Frio catch. This species has been found among leaves in dry forests and also under bushes, dead trees, etc., so it is anticipated that with the progressive clearing of the jungle, it will probably invade the banana plantations and may become dangerous to the laborers in that section."

The Western Hog-nosed Viper, *Bothrops ophryomegas,* has the snout sharp, but not upturned. The markings are similar to the preceding, but there is a greater number of the dorsal blotches—twenty-six

to forty.   This little viper inhabits the arid districts of western Central America from Guatemala to Costa Rica.

So savage are these little hog-nosed vipers that they strike hard enough to slide a few inches when on comparatively smooth ground and at times actually *jump* several inches forward.   In this habit, however, they are far outclassed by a slightly longer, but very stout species of Mexico and Central America, a description of which follows:

The Jumping Viper; "Mano de piedra"; or "Timba", *Bothrops nummifera* (Plates 56 and 57), seldom reaches three feet, and averages closer to two feet, but it stands out among the *Bothrops* species in having the proportionately stoutest body and largest head.   The thick-set body is as incongruously heavy as the grotesque vipers of Africa.   Its scales are also peculiar, being exceedingly rough, like those of the bushmaster.   Mutilated specimens have led a few observers to the supposition that they had found young bushmasters in areas north of the actual range of that imposing species.

This snake receives its native name of "Mano de piedra" from its resemblance in form to a native implement used in the crushing of corn for tortillas.   It is particularly savage, and in striking can make a short jump.   The tales relating to the jumping of the "Mano de piedra" have been exaggerated, but specimens observed by the writer made a striking jump and slide that carried the serpent a full two feet forward.   In striking from the side of a log or from a bank, where there is good purchase to lurch its coils, it may be able to jump as much as a yard.   At any rate, a snake impelling itself bodily forward is startling, to say the least, and conducive to speculation and native exaggeration.

The fangs are proportionately short, and strangely enough, with all the native fear of reptiles and the branding of many harmless species as poisonous, this snake is but little dreaded, being declared harmless in some areas.   The venom has a haemolytic action, and is of lower toxicity than other species of *Bothrops*.

The body is gray or brown, with dark, black-edged, rhomb-like blotches, in a way, similar to the bushmaster, hence another reason for this species being sometimes mistaken for young specimens of the former.   Distribution is broad, from Mexico as far north as Tuxpan, south through Central America to and including Costa Rica, and probably northern Panama.

Godman's Viper, *Bothrops godmani* (Plate 55), seems to be closely

related to the preceding and is irritable enough, but does not appear to jump. It is rather stout, and in form and markings looks somewhat like a North American copperhead. The average length is under twenty-four inches. Distribution appears to be limited to Honduras and Guatemala; possibly southern Mexico.

With the groupings of the smaller members of *Bothrops* considered we come to the larger and more dangerous species, of which there is an imposing array.

The Fer-de-lance, Barba Amarilla, Jararaca, Terciopélo[2] and "Tomigoff,"[3] *Bothrops atrox* (*lanceolatus* now being relegated to the list of synonyms) (Plates 60 and 61), dominates the larger species in being the most widely distributed.

How the name "fer-de-lance" came to such broad use among English speaking observers, when it originated among the Creole-French in a couple of small islands of the West Indies—Martinique and St. Lucia —may be explained by the fact that this dangerous viper became famous—or infamous—on those islands in particular, owing to their proportionately generous human population and the former abundance of this poisonous serpent. There has been much dramatic writing about this snake. It has figured in romantic tales of the islands, where there is a legend that it was imported to induce slaves to remain upon the plantations and make no attempts to escape or hide. The fer-de-lance is now almost extinct upon these islands—although very common in Central and South America.

Among the native residents in the New World tropics, the term "fer-de-lance" is confined to those small islands. In Spanish-America the name commonly used for this reptile is "Barba Amarilla", meaning the yellow-beard, and coming from the chin and throat being yellowish.

During the construction of the Panama Canal, these snakes were frequently encountered and the workers, hearing the Spanish term of "tomigoff", meaning nothing more nor less than "snake", but not realizing its simple definition, felt it indicated something terse in the way of reptiles and applied the term to this viper—so that the appellation has become common in the region of the Canal.

The length is up to slightly over eight feet though in some areas it runs much smaller—three to four feet. Coloration is variable, from gray to olive, brown, or even reddish, with dark, light-edged crossbands or triangles, the apex of these extending to the center of the

[2] The common name in Costa Rica, and meaning "velvet snake."
[3] Pronounced "Tommygoff" and often spelled this way.

back. The form is moderately slender, with very distinct, lance-shaped head. Distribution is very extensive, beginning in southern Mexico, including the low-lying coastal areas of Central America, thence extending into Venezuela, Colombia, Ecuador, easterly Peru, Bolivia, the Guianas and southward in Brazil to approximately latitude 23 degrees south. The reason for its abundance is its large litters of young. The litters of three Honduran specimens were sixty-four, sixty-five and seventy-one. The young produced by a six-foot mother were twelve inches in length. They are born fully provided with fangs, and the bites of even these young examples are very dangerous.

The effects of the poison are dramatically sinister and rapid, the action being largely haemolytic, destroying the red blood cells, breaking down the walls of the carrying vessels, and producing great extravasation. This is evident from the reddening of the eyes, discharge of blood from the stomach and mucous walls of the throat and mouth, the same condition quickly developing through the kidneys and bladder. The tissue about the wound is practically dissolved by rapid necrosis. These effects are, however, efficaciously neutralized by serum produced by the several research laboratories in the tropics.

Douglas March of the serum station at Tela, Honduras, told the author about an occurrence illustrating the potency of fer-de-lance poison. In Honduras, as in other Central American countries it is the custom of the women of the small towns along the railways to meet all passenger trains for the purpose of selling fruits, tortillas and home-made candies. One woman's specialty was cocoanut candy. She grated the cocoanuts on an old-fashioned nutmeg grater and in consequence her finger tips had numerous small scratches through contact with the grater.

While she was engaged in candy-making, her husband who was employed as a laborer on a near-by plantation was brought home suffering from the bite of a barba amarilla (fer-de-lance), which he had received while at work. His wife immediately left her work to care for him, but as he was under the care of a native "snake doctor" her ministrations were confined chiefly to bathing the fang punctures on her husband's leg from which there was severe bleeding. Despite the frantic efforts of the "snake doctor" the man died within a couple of hours and his wife, appearing to have absorbed some of the venom through her lacerated finger tips, died the following morning. Her symptoms were typical of *Bothrops* poisoning.

Serpents of this type are liable to be more abundant near slovenly human settlements than in the wilder areas, as they are attracted to such places by the rats and mice which accumulate in areas of ramshackle buildings and trash heaps.

Bothrops jararaca (Plate 62), also called the Jararaca, commonly occurs in Brazil, from about south latitude 10 degrees to northern Argentina and northeastern Paraguay.

The Jararacucū, *Bothrops jararacussu* (Plates 62 and 63), is proportionately thicker-bodied, with a bigger head than the former. Its markings are likewise different. The paler outline markings of the blotches dominate the pattern, and there is a greater amount of the lighter colors on the sides. This is a quick and savage snake, and its big head, with excessive length of fangs, renders it extremely dangerous. The range is largely confined to Brazil.

Maximilian's Viper; "Jararaca"; "Urutū"; "Jararaca do rabo branco", *Bothrops neuweidii* (Plates 58 and 59), which in Brazil is one of the most widespread of the pit vipers, is another of the angularly marked "fer-de-lance" types and on gross examination might be immediately branded as the same kind that ranges into Central America. It is usually smaller, however, and while its colors are similar, a combination of olive or brown, with dark angular markings, the latter may be specifically described as a double row of dark triangular markings along the back, these being in alternation, though sometimes fused. They form actually a dorsal series, instead of extending downward to the lower sides, while toward the latter third they come together as notched blotches, like stout X's. There is a row of dark blotches on each side, while behind the head is a horse-shoe shaped blotch, the ends directed rearward.

No other poisonous snake in South America has been distinguished by so many subspecific names. Amaral has named ten subspecies, these showing a great variety in size of the blotches, their number and spacing. *B. neuweidii boliviana* (Plate 59) has a particularly attractive pattern as the blotches are closely crowded, very symmetrical and narrowly margined with a paler hue, producing, upon first impression, a pattern like bright tapestry. In Brazil this dangerous reptile occurs in all the northeastern, central, southeastern and southern states. It also extends into Argentina and northern Paraguay.

The larger members of *Bothrops* as clearly indicate a headquarters

in tropical South America as do the rattlesnakes in southwesterly North America. The genus of these lance-head snakes is far more extensive than generally understood except by technical workers in herpetology. Thirty-six species are now recognized and further exploration into the vast stretches of wilderness of the American tropics will probably bring to light a number more. The student will be interested to note a few of the names which by studies and comparisons now show them to be full species and which will appear new to his former checking of the lists. While this work has been held from technical treatment, a touch of systematic check-list methods may be of interest for the moment in showing the variety of the lance-head snakes. In addition to those already considered in detail, are the following, some representing very recent discoveries: *B. andiana* Amaral—(Peru); *B. barbouri* Dunn—(southern Mexico); *B. bicolor* Bocourt—(Guatemala); *B. chloromelas* Boulenger—(Peru); *B. erythromelas* Amaral—(Brazil); *B. iglesiasi* Amaral—(Brazil); *B. medusa* (Sternfeld)—(Venezuela); *B. melanura* (Muller)—(southern Mexico); *B. monticelli* (Peracca)—(Panama and northern South America); *B. neglecta* Amaral—(Central America) and *B. pirajai* Amaral, also from Central America. What an array of long-fanged species for a single genus! Fortunate it is for the New World tropics, particularly South America, that the rattlesnake genus has been held in check. The distribution of *Bothrops* continues all the way to northeastern Patagonia, where *B. ammodytoides,* a small species found also on the pampas of the Argentine, is characterized by a wart-like protuberance on its upturned snout.

Unique in appearing to be confined to a small and quite isolated island, the Island Viper, *Bothrops insularis* (Plate 65), occurs on what is little more than a great marine rock, of steep slopes, with separated patches of tropical vegetation.

This island has barely three-quarters of a square mile of surface. It is known as Queimada Grande and situated on the coast of the State of São Paulo, about forty miles southwest of the Bay of Santos.

This curious lance-head is pale brown, with rather widely separated cross-bands. Adult length is between three and four feet. It was discovered and named by Amaral.

There are many birds on the island, some of them resting there during incidental migrations from outjutting points of the mainland or the other islands in the vicinity. Hence these snakes, which occur

in abundance, have plenty of food, and appear to feed, when adult, upon nothing but birds, for the immediate killing of which they have developed a particularly powerful venom. Experiments have demonstrated that this isolated viper has the most highly toxic venom of any of its genus.

Bothrops insularis is largely arboreal and has a partially prehensile tail, but seems to be closely allied to the terrestrial and larger species of *Bothrops*.

Continuing the list are species which will be noted among the plate illustrations. As they range through country where the language is largely Portuguese or Spanish, the matter of "common" or "popular" names has been guided by designation in the native language where they commonly occur, with occasional digressions with those of particular prominence.

Bothrops itapetiningae (Plate 58), known in Brazil as "Boipeva" and "Cotiarinha", is rather small, of ruddy brown with a series of dorsal patches which may fuse with similar blotches on the sides. It is of rather scarce occurrence and restricted distribution.

The most handsomely marked member of the genus is a large species commonly known as "Urutū", *Bothrops alternatus* (Plate 65), attaining a length of five feet, quite heavy of body, and characteristic in the rich chocolate brown crescents on the sides, these vividly edged with yellow or white. This attractively patterned snake occurs in southern Brazil, Paraguay, Argentina and Uruguay.

The Bushmaster, *Lachesis muta* (Plate 70), stands in a genus alone and as the world's largest viper it warrants such distinction. Formerly, all the lance-head snakes were included within *Lachesis,* a distinctly improper grouping although it stood for many years. The Bushmaster is quite different from the lance-heads. It is more closely related to the rattlesnakes. In southerly Central America it is generally known as "La Cascabela Muda" (the mute rattler). In Brazil it is usually known as "Surucucū" [4] and in Trinidad as "Mapepire Z'Ananna."

Nowhere over its habitat, from southern Central America through tropical South America, does it appear to be abundant. It is more frequently found in Costa Rica and Panama than in the continental area to the south. Distribution extends into Nicaragua, but further observation must define just how far north it occurs. The writer was

---

[4] Pronounced *Surucusu.*

unable to locate records from Honduras, which thus appears to be too far north to be included in the distribution.

The Bushmaster grows to be twelve feet long. These very large specimens are, however, particularly rare. Two adults in the writer's possession were eight and nine feet, respectively. They both deposited perfectly formed eggs, indicating full maturity. It is the only American viper which lays eggs, all the others producing living young. Reports of the largest specimens come from southern Costa Rica, Panama, or extreme northern South America. This great Crotaline serpent is of moderately slender build. A nine-foot specimen shows no more bulk, when coiled, than a Texas or Florida rattlesnake slightly over five feet long.

Coloration is striking. The body hue is pale brown, often pinkish. A series of large and bold, dark brown or black blotches extend along the body. These are wide on the back and abruptly narrow on the sides. The pattern is the reverse of the fer-de-lance type, on which the blotches are narrow on the back, widening on the sides.

The Bushmaster is a bold and particularly dangerous snake, inclined to deliberately edge towards the intruder, bringing the lateral, S-shaped, striking loop to nearer and better advantage. Its great length of fangs and large amount of poison render a well delivered stroke of the utmost gravity. It often warns of its presence by rapidly vibrating the tail, as do a number of the other tropical vipers, but the vibration of the Bushmaster's tail is as rapid as the specifically provided warning tail of the rattlesnake. The tail of the Bushmaster among leaves produces quite a loud, buzzing sound.

Deducting observations and records of captured examples, it seems that this snake prefers higher and drier ground than the fer-de-lance. Dr. Herbert C. Clark, Director of the Gorgas Memorial Laboratory, showed the writer two fair-sized specimens which had been killed on the Alajuela Cut, not far from the Canal Zone, by the construction gangs working on the new damming project to provide more water for Gatun Lake.

Of all the captive specimens I have heard of, but one was ever induced to eat and that was a young example barely five feet long in the collection of R. R. Mole, in Port-of-Spain, Trinidad. It killed and swallowed a small rat. I have had about half a dozen specimens under observation and while they quieted down and we were careful not to frighten them they paid not the slightest attention to food. They

were unable to shed their skins and I am convinced that the Bushmaster does this under ground, while prowling into the burrows of small mammals.

In the resumé of the North American poisonous serpents it has been explained how the rattlesnake genus drops out and is limited to a single species in tropical America. No mention, however, was made of central Mexico where some manifestations of the genus flare into interest. Mexico has several characteristic species. There is the Mexican Blotched Rattlesnake, *Crotalus polysticus,* a small species, and a particularly interesting rattler which may properly be called Stejneger's Rattlesnake, *C. stejnegeri,* named by Dunn in honor of Dr. Leonhard Stejneger, the internationally known curator of reptiles at the United States National Museum. It is hard to decide, from the standpoint of change, what is happening to *C. stejnegeri,* but its sponsor has told the author that its appearance might indicate it was growing tired of using its rattle and starting to grow a long tail, like ordinary snakes. Certain it is that it has the proportionately longest tail and smallest rattle of its genus.

Found in the arid and desert area of central Mexico is a powerful rattlesnake of "diamond-back" pattern, which represents a northerly race of the tropical rattlesnake of southerly Mexico thence ranging to the Argentine. It may properly be called the Mexican Diamond Rattlesnake, and is technically listed as *Crotalus terrificus basiliscus.* (Plate 82). It is of deep yellow (sometimes golden hue) or yellowish-green, with a series of symmetrical rhombs that are boldly distinct owing to narrow, paler margins. Its scales are coarsely or tubercularly keeled. The rhomb-like pattern extends approximately to the neck. There are no bands on the neck, a condition which will be specifically described with the rattlers of Central and South America. This Mexican subspecies indicates a relationship between the blacktailed rattlesnake, *C. molossus* of northern Mexico and the boundary region of the United States and the races of *C. terrificus* of the tropics.

The Tropical Rattlesnake, *Crotalus terrificus* (Plate 83), is called Cascabel in Mexico and Central America and Cascavel in Brazil (Spanish and Portuguese terms). It is the most poisonous of the rattlers, as well as the boldest. The venom differs from that of northern rattlesnakes and other New World vipers in having a largely neurotoxic action, and is nearly colorless. It may be regarded as the most strongly toxic among the New World vipers, except that of the unique

and isolated island viper, *Bothrops insularis,* found off the coast of Brazil.   It is only by the considerably greater amount of venom discharged at a bite that the bushmaster may be rated as more dangerous than the rattlesnake.

This rattlesnake of the tropics has the widest range of any species of *Crotalus.*   It occurs from southeasterly Mexico to northern Argentina.   Moreover, it appears to be the only distinct species of rattler occurring over this wide area, with the exception of overlapping distribution of the Mexican species.

The pattern is of the "diamond-back" design, but there are elongate bands on the neck.   These are particularly prominent with southern Mexican, Central American and northern South American specimens. This marking represents the subspecies *durissus* (Plate 83), ranging into Venezuela and Colombia.   Over the area to the south the typical form occurs, the neck bands being shorter and less prominent. (Plate 83).

Like the bushmaster, this powerful snake will slowly work its way towards an intruder, even deliberately glide forward to attack, carrying the neck in a lateral loop, in readiness to strike.   The action is not a hostile rush, but an insolent and actual "edging in" to strike.   While the rattle is heavily developed, the species is particularly dangerous in infrequently using it.   It sometimes assumes a dramatic coil, with rattle buzzing steadily, but more often gives no more warning than a few quick side flings of the rattle, producing single harsh clicks. This is a sound well worthy of recognition in the higher ground of the tropics, as it may be immediately followed by the serpent's stroke— with no further warning.

The effects of the largely neurotoxic venom is described by March: "There is little or no bleeding from Cascabel bites; but death is preceded by blindness, paralysis and suffocation . . .   I believe that the idea holds over much of the range of the Cascabel that a bite will break a man's neck, regardless of the part of the body bitten.   This is probably due to some selective action of the venom which causes complete paralysis of the neck.   The man's head may, if he be held in a sitting position, slump forward on his chest, roll from side to side, or backward, in such a loosely connected way that the native cannot explain the condition as other than a broken neck."

Rattlesnakes in the American tropics frequent the higher, drier

areas and thus their distribution as a rule but slightly overlaps most of the *Bothrops* species which prefer the lower moist areas. They are abundant on the unwooded slopes of mountains back from the coast of Guatemala, Honduras, Nicaragua, and Costa Rica, or where the interior country may run into grassland or actually sterile areas. They are reported as particularly common in the mining areas.

Length is up to six and seven feet. The body is heavy and inclined to ridge at the back. The head is proportionately small for such a powerful serpent.

For anyone taking the east coast South American run to Rio de Janeiro, Montevideo or "B. A." as the capital of the Argentine is so frequently termed, it is possible to see an extensive and representative collection of the poisonous serpents of South America, and to observe them under novel conditions. This exhibition is at São Paulo, a fine city with a climate like California, situated on high land not far back from the coast. Here is situated the Instituto Butantan or Instituto Soro Therapico (Institute of Serum Therapy) a government plant for the study of tropical diseases, but having as one of its major departments, the special buildings, research staff and snake park for the study of South American poisonous serpents and the production of antivenomous serum to counteract their bites. It is this department that has brought the institution international fame. All the larger steamers touch at the coffee port of Santos, on their way up or down the coast, and as it is a short and delightful railway trip to São Paulo, the passengers almost in a body go up to see the snake park—and besides the park there is a fine museum of exhibits relating to work of the institute.

The snake park consists of broad paths between big ovals of well cut grass. On these lawns are gliding bushmasters, various species of *Bothrops* and rattlesnakes. Their escape is impossible as the ovals are surrounded by water moats with straight cement sides beneath the visitors' rails. Scattered among the ovals are cement shelters for the reptiles. These shelters are in form like large old-fashioned beehives. The orderly, park-like arrangement, the clean whitish cement of moats and shelters, and the well kept grass combine to make a most attractive and unusual picture. Yet coiled or moving before visitors' eyes are the varicolored scaled forms that long produced a high mor-

tality in the American tropics, until the work of the Institute greatly changed their status.

When the author first visited São Paulo, Dr. Vital Brazil was director of the institute. The method of obtaining the snakes was to send a box and a noosing loop attached to a long rod, to various places where reptiles were numerous. The snakes were then exchanged for tubes of serum. I was conducted through the rooms where the snakes were "milked" of their venoms, and inspected long lines of horses under treatment of injection to produce immunity. Afterwards we went through the department where the blood of immunized horses was going through processes to separate the serous portion. It is a thoroughly modern plant. Grades of serum were being produced for the rattlesnake, bushmaster, *Bothrops* species and coral snakes (*Micrurus*), all of which have their characteristic manifestations of poisoning.

During a later visit I inspected Dr. Brazil's new plant at Nictheroy —across the bay from Rio. He had been working on its design for several years. It is called the Instituto Vital Brazil. Thus there are now two serum establishments in Brazil and they have been of immense economic importance to that country, not only in production of neutralizing serum, but in directing campaigns of education regarding safety measures among the numerous fazendas, small farmers and construction workers. Placards are now sent to every part of Brazil, graphically illustrating the importance of wearing leggings in places where poisonous snakes occur. Dr. Afranio do Amaral, now director of the institute at São Paulo recently explained that before the establishment of the plant—some twenty years ago—the estimated death rate in Brazil from bites of poisonous snakes was around three thousand the year. During 1930, however, after careful tabulation, the total appeared to be well under one hundred.

North of the equator the Serpentarium at Tela, Honduras, is another research plant jointly maintained by the Antivenin Institute of America, Harvard University and the United Fruit Company, where venoms from the *Bothrops* types and the tropical rattlesnake are extracted. These poisons are sent to the United States where immunization of horses and development of the perfected antivenin are conducted. Thus the banana and coffee areas of Central America now receive economic benefit from this work. The mining areas have also sent in many requests for the rattlesnake serum. The Tela es-

tablishment like the snake park at São Paulo, is open to persons visiting Central America.

From this resumé of different types of serum, it will be understood that anyone going into a country where poisonous serpents are common, should use care in being provided with the proper kinds. All of these sera are hypodermically administered.

CHAPTER XII

THE POISONOUS SNAKES OF EUROPE AND ASIA

INSTEAD of following the continuity of classification in presenting the descriptions of poisonous serpents, it is more interesting to arrange the narrative from a zoögeographical point of view. The areas to be considered in this chapter extend inclusively from Europe to Malaysia, a vast sweep, but in considering it progressively a number of significant phases of distribution can be clearly brought out.

Europe: The only poisonous serpents of Europe are small vipers —true vipers or members of the *Viperidae.* All are members of the same genus—*Vipera.* There are no pit vipers, nor do these occur until we swing way to the East, into southern Asia, which region is unique in having representatives of all four families of the deadly snakes, the *Elapidae, Hydrophidae, Crotalidae* and *Viperidae.*

Seven species of vipers inhabit Europe, but this does not mean any abundant grouping of species in particular areas. Distribution is rather characteristic with most of these snakes. There are few areas in Europe where as many as three species occur, considerable areas where but two are found and some parts inhabited by a single kind. This is illustrated by viewing them collectively, as follows: *Vipera berus* (the common viper or adder and most extensively distributed) found commonly in England, ranging largely over Europe, but usually living in the mountains in the central portions and irregularly in the south, thence extending eastward through southerly Siberia to the island of Sakhalien on the Pacific coast; *V. renardi,* southern Russia thence into Central Asia; *V. aspis,* central France and southern Germany, Switzerland, Italy and Sicily; *V. ursinii,* southeastern France, Italy and lower Austria; *V. latastii,* Spain and Portugal, Morocco and Algeria; *V. ammodytes,* southern Tyrol and Hungary to Greece, Turkey and Asia Minor into Syria; *V. lebetina,* Greece and Syria into Persia, also Morocco and Algeria.

The Common Viper or Adder, *V. berus* (Plate 44), called in Ger-

many the Kreuzotter, is one of the smallest European species. It seldom grows to be longer than twenty-four inches. The color is variable, ranging through gray, olive and brown, sometimes reddish. This ground may be uniform or dotted with small spots. A bold zig-zag pattern of dark hue usually extends the length of the back thus distinguishing it from the harmless snakes. With darker specimens this is not distinct and some examples are entirely black. The zig-zag band is characteristic of the greater number of the European vipers, hence it is difficult to define the species without going into technical terms. With this species there is generally present a distinguishing mark at the back of the head. This is X-shaped, like a St. Andrew's cross. Hence the name commonly applied in Germany—Kreuzotter. The scales of the viper are roughly keeled and the eye has an elliptical pupil. There are two rows of plates under the tail.

Vipers (as commonly called Adders) are found in various conditions, in open woods where there are slopes and gullies exposed to the sun, on the heaths and moors. Heaps of loose stones or tumbled walls are favourite prowling places in hunts for food. Like the American rattlesnakes and copperhead they prowl into the farms during the late summer when the grain has ripened in search of small rodents and are often discovered under sheaves or trash piles. In the mountains they occur to elevations of at least five thousand feet. They return to specific places to hibernate, but in congregating at the dens in the autumn are not so easily seen as they hide under the early fall of leaves where body hue and pattern blend with the ground. The hibernating quarters are not of such specific character as those of the North American poisonous snakes, which are larger and seek deep crevices in ledges. The small size of the viper enables it to work its way through comparatively small holes. The base of an old tree with its labyrinth of passageways among the roots may be a long remembered winter "den", or a porous, shelving bank in the woods, which faces the south to catch the spring sun. Thus viper dens are not so easy to locate from the character of terrain. With the warm days of spring they issue in numbers, sometimes approximately a hundred at a den and coil sociably in clusters, the hands protruding in all directions. This is the breeding season. They remain at the dens until the early, erratic changes of weather are over, then scatter over areas for a mile or more to prowl and feed. The young are born during the late summer and to the number of about a dozen.

The broad distribution of this snake carries it farther north than any known poisonous species. From England and Scotland its northerly range extends to within the Arctic circle in Norway, Sweden, Finland and Russia.

As the viper is more abundant over considerable portions of its range than the harmless and common grass snake, it is a hazard to be reckoned with, although fatalities from its bite are not frequent. As a rule it is quick and savage, but warns of its presence by hissing surprisingly loud for so small a snake. It hisses with both intake and exhalation of the breath, the body energetically rising and falling in the operation. A bite is attended with much swelling, profuse perspiration and reflex vomiting and it is all important in successfully combating these symptoms to induce early and efficient drainage of the poison.

While becoming tame and quiet, possibly listless is a better definition, nine out of ten captive vipers refuse food and starve to death. They can not endure even the least amount of dampness as the skin becomes dull and develops numerous sores. This points to the habits of the majority of species of the *Viperidae,* which prefer dry places, some living in the deserts.

The European Asp or Asp Viper, *V. aspis,* occurs from about central France (from the latitude of Paris) in southern Germany, Switzerland, Tyrol, and Italy to as far south as Calabria and Sicily, Croatia and Bosnia.

It is hence a distinctly southerly reptile. The snout is rather sharp —slightly turned up at the tip. This is a slightly larger snake than the common adder. Its coloration may be defined: Gray, yellowish, brown or red with dark markings in the form of paired spots, which on some specimens fuse to form a zig-zag band as with *Vipera berus.* Some examples are entirely black. The principal point of identification is its sharp snout, slightly turned upward. Much greater development of the snout into a raised "horn" or fleshy knob will be noted with the two following species.

One of the European vipers is so distinct in the possession of a "horn" on the snout that it requires no detailed description for identification. This is the Nose-horned Viper, in Austria called the Sand Natter, and technically named *Vipera ammodytes* (Plate 45). The mention of a "horn" should carry the explanation that this protuberance is actually soft and covered with small scales. The *habitat* is southeastern Europe, whence it ranges eastward into Turkey and

Asia Minor. The author observed specimens on the Balkan Peninsula, living in rocky places and appearing to feed largely on lizards. In striking the prey the hold was retained, the lizard quickly succumbing to the poison. The swallowing was then particularly rapid, a continuous "walking" motion of both upper and lower jaw bones pulling the lizard into the throat with such dexterity that the prey, which appeared to be close to five inches long, was swallowed by a two-foot snake in not much over a couple of minutes' time. The spot was ledgy, with disintegrating stone crumbling to the consistency of coarse sand. There were numerous crevices and the snake had but half issued from one of these, seizing the lizard which had wandered by. The temperature was high, probably over eighty in the shade and the slope arid and dry. The alert and quick turning of the snake as it glided forward and into another crevice was quite at variance with the sluggishness of this species as a captive, although if kept very dry and warm it can be induced to feed. Its ground color is gray, some specimens being of ashy hue, and extending down the back in strong contrast to the body hue is the dark zigzag band common among European vipers.

V. latastii of southwestern Europe (Spain and Portugal), thence found across the Mediterranean in Morocco and Algeria, shows close relationship to the preceding in having a "horn" although it is shorter than with *ammodytes,* in fact not more than a scale-covered, wart-like protuberance. This reptile is thus intermediate between the European asp and the long-nosed *V. ammodytes.*

A particularly interesting little viper occurs in south-central Europe, from southeasterly France and northern Italy to Hungary, Bosnia and Montenegro. This is Orsini's Viper, *V. orsinii* (Plate 44). While possessing fangs and poison glands as well developed as other European vipers it is so gentle that it seems seldom to make any attempt to bite, even if handled. In areas of Austria, where this viper is particularly common, no accidents from snake bite are on record, although children often pick up these snakes and carry them around.

Professor F. Werner, of Vienna, has made a special study of this snake. He explains that it was first discovered by Count Orsini on the Gran Sasso d'Italia in the Abruzzos of Italy and described in 1839 by Bonaparte as the "Marasso Alpino" (*Peliseo orsinii*) to distinguish it from the "Marasso pulustre" or common viper (*V. berus*) of the marshy lowland. Years passed and the species had been com-

pletely forgotten, when it was redescribed as a variety of the common viper, from specimens collected from the Rakos plain, in Hungary. Shortly after Prof. Werner sent specimens from the same area to the noted herpetologist, Dr. Albert Boulenger, at the British Museum. They were identified as belonging to the older species of Bonaparte, thus bringing the species again into prominence and permanently so, as an abundant snake confused with the common viper from which it differs in having nineteen rows of scales around the body instead of twenty-one (as with *berus*), and markedly in habits. More remarkable, however, is a subspecies of this viper frequenting the barren mountains of the northwest Balkan Peninsula, in Bosnia, Herzegovina, Albania and Macedonia, and more rarely in Istria and Dalmatia. It is distinguished by its larger eyes and hence called *V. orsinii macrops*. While the typical form has ceased using its poisonous fangs in defence, *macrops* has relinquished food requiring the use of fangs injecting strong venom. It feeds upon grasshoppers, which sometimes fill its stomach in a compact mass. It is so gentle it may be picked up when wild, showing no inclination to bite. Nevertheless, in form and zigzag pattern it looks much like the common adder of irritable temperament. It is well for collectors to have the fine points of definition clearly in mind before picking up vipers in the areas where distribution of species may overlap.

Summing up the vipers of Europe, which in the text have been presented in continuity to more or less indicate human contact and familiarity with them, it is well to indicate their relationship or systematic grouping. *V. orsinii, renardi* and *berus* are closely related. *V. aspis, latastii* and *ammodytes* show near relationship in the upturned snout of the former, the wart-like protuberance of *latastii* and the elongated appendage of *ammodytes*. All have a similar pattern —a zigzag dorsal band or dorsal row of dark blotches inclined to fuse and form an undulous band. With the exception of *latastii* and *ammodytes* they are subject to much variation of the ground or body color, even extending into melanism. *V. lebetina*, ranging from Greece to the frontier of India, also occurring in northern Africa, and largest of the species coming into Europe, shows relationship to the big *Vipera russellii* of Asia and Malaysia. *V. raddii*, occurring in Armenia, and not previously mentioned, shows a development of the large plate over each eye to form a pair of horns.

Asia and Malaysia: Clearly, in swinging eastward into the vast

territory under consideration, we are going more distantly from the headquarters of the typical vipers. The fair array of similarly marked and related forms in Europe seems to be but a northerly extension from their place of origin, which is Africa, and there their largest and most diverse members occur. In the swing to Asia the European vipers drop out and a few others are encountered. *Pseudocerastes persicus* is one, a sand viper, a yard long, found in Persia. Then again, *Echis,* a small genus with its two little "carpet vipers," has extended into the arid areas of southwestern Asia, but its distribution is far more extensive in Arabia and Africa north of the equator.

Throughout the far flung areas of India and Malaysia there is a scant representation of viper species, the large and dangerous Russell's Viper or Tic Polonga, *Vipera russellii* (Plate 45), and the small *Azemiops feae* confined to the hills of upper Burma. While species are scant, the Tic Polonga makes up in broad abundance. It is found in India, Ceylon, Burma, Siam, Sumatra and Java, even extending through the Dutch East Indies to Flores, and is common even on the little island of Komodo, recently accorded fame from the discovery of the world's largest living lizard, the Komodo Monitor.

Thus with the vipers insistently commanding recognition in Asia, and all the other families of poisonous snakes represented, this region is unique in the world's snake inhabited areas in having every known family of venomous serpents. And again, all of these representatives are widely distributed, and as serpents normally occur, of abundant occurrence.

Reverting to technical continuity the following families are both Asiatic and Malayan: [1] The *Elapidae,* the cobras, kraits and allies; the *Hydrophidae,* sea snakes with vertically compressed, paddle-like tail; the *Viperidae,* or typical vipers and the *Crotalidae,* the pit vipers. These families will be considered in this continuity.

The *Elapidae* is well represented in the Asian and Malayan regions, in fact its members here attain their largest size. But this does not point to any cradle of development as Africa, from Cape to the northern coast, has a fine variety of them, including a dozen species of cobras and the deadly mambas, while Australia is the area of greatest variety. There they predominate in a country unique in having comparatively few harmless serpents.

---

[1] The Opisthoglyph or rear-fanged snakes are not included in this chapter, as they are not considered as generally dangerous.

The star snake of the Indo-Malayan area is the King Cobra, *Naia hannah* (Plates 38 and 39), for not only is it the world's largest poisonous serpent and the most deadly of all reptiles owing to the great amount of the particularly powerful neurotoxin its venom glands secrete, but it is the most dangerous of all living wild creatures. Combined with the deadliness of its fangs, it is extremely active and commonly inclined to attack. Coupled with insolence, sometimes prompted by curiosity, but more often by anger, is an intelligence that renders it unique.

Not many years ago—and observations of reptiles have greatly broadened—the maximum length of the King Cobra was thought to be about twelve feet. Adult specimens are more commonly a bit under this size, but the writer recently received three specimens that were thirteen, fourteen and approximately fifteen feet long respectively. They weighed thirteen, fourteen and sixteen pounds each. These may seem light weights for serpents of such length, not more than for a six- to seven-foot rattlesnake, but the King Cobra is a slender, racer-like type. The fifteen-foot specimen in the author's care is barely two and a half inches in diameter at the thickest part. Recently a friend returning from the Malay Peninsula brought me data of a sixteen-foot specimen. Dr. Thomas Barbour has the measurements of what is probably the record example, which was slightly in excess of eighteen feet.

The coloration of the King Cobra is olive, or yellowish-brown, often with ring-like cross-bands of black. Some have a tinge of ruddy hue about the chin and throat of much the same color as a tangerine orange. The eyes are bronze, with round pupil, brilliant and disconcerting in their intense stare. This giant Elapid inhabits Burma, the Malay Peninsula, southern China and the larger islands of Malaysia, including the Philippines.

The king cobras which have come to the Park for exhibition have traveled all the way from Chinese animal shops in Singapore in strong cases with a strip of mesh for air and but little or no provision for anything else. I have for a number of years taken exception to these dangerous reptiles being carried on steamers without someone competent in charge to see that there was no chance of boxes being broken by shifting of near-by objects. There is far less carelessness than in the past, when I refused to have any dealings with persons reckless in shipping poisonous reptiles in flimsy containers. I have received

specimens in cases so constructed there was no possibility of them even being given water on a trip half way around the world. But a king cobra doesn't seem to mind a six weeks' trip with no care whatsoever. I have opened a box in which a snake had traveled that long and the reptile reared out of it with a hiss and alacrity as if freshly captured.

After such a journey they usually have trouble in shedding the skin. This may have been partially shed in the shipping case, but as is a common trouble with all cobras, the transparent caps over the eyes remain adherent. If the snake has been several months in captivity and receiving little care, several of these caps may cover the eyes. The reptile can see, but as if through a haze. In this condition it usually refuses food.

We received one fine example in this shape. It turned out to be four inches in excess of thirteen feet, by actual measurement which was made possible by an experience worth describing.

This big cobra was induced to go into a tank and bathe for several hours, but there was no sign of its being able to rub off the old eye caps, which it tried its best to do. I decided to get hold of it and remove them with a pair of tweezers. This was no easy task and required some planning. The snake had already shown a preference for a certain corner of the double cage—there being a sliding partition door between the two compartments.

Waiting for a chance to find it prowling into the adjoining compartment, we slid the door, then suspended a net on a heavy iron ring a yard in diameter, over the spot where the snake most frequently coiled. The partition door was reopened and not long after the snake coiled on the anticipated spot. The net was dropped over it and it reared within it like a giant candelabra. It now seemed safe enough to go into the cage, force the reptile to the floor with a long staff and by rolling this towards its head firmly pin that member and grasp it by the neck, through the mesh of the net. I removed three old eye caps from each side, but never have I had hold of a snake so difficult to manage. It had uncanny agility and strength in twisting, but as long as we were at it, we raised the net and the head keeper and an assistant stretched the reptile out and measured it, noting the dimensions already given. All difficulty in safely getting out of the cage was eliminated by tucking the long olive folds within the net again, imbedding the ring in the gravel and spryly retreating before the cobra thought of digging under the gravel. When the net was hoisted clear

the snake presented a dramatic picture.   There had been little character to that previously rearing form with eyes so dull they appeared
sightless.   The eyes were now clear and glittering.   And it was rather
remarkable to note that the snake did not appear to be much disturbed
but deliberately glided to the observation port of the door—about
three feet from the floor—and with spread hood looked out at us.
In that inscrutable gaze it was hard to detect whether it felt relieved or
desired to bite us.

I have observed many demonstrations of the singular intelligence
of the king cobra—and am using the word "singular" because other
snakes do not act this way.   A newly arrived captive soon detects the
character of glass, which covers the front of its cage.   For a day or two
it will strike at visitors and thus bump its nose, but soon does nothing
more than rear and feint at striking.   Captive examples appear to
recognize the persons who care for them, yet evince antagonism towards
strangers.   They become active at feeding intervals, usually a week
apart, will come to the rear door of the cage and if there is a small
crevice will peer up or down a passageway watching for the keeper.
Moreover, I have noted that specimens discovered which side of the
door was the opening portion as the head keeper often rolls the door
back slightly to insert a long wire to pull out fragments of shed skin.
All of this demands caution in door manipulation as the inclination of
these snakes would be to immediately come to an open door, "boss"
the keeper out of the way by rearing and feinting a strike, then glide
into a passageway.   Interference would be met by bold attack.   I
have never seen them show much fear or nervousness.   They have their
favorite corners in which to coil and sleep and a king cobra I took from
New York to Washington, that had invariably coiled in the left hand
rear corner of its cage, prowled its new quarters and went to rest in
a left rear corner.

Despite their dangerous insolence they are easily manipulated if
one knows their ways.   When we decided to transfer this fourteen-
footer from its boarding quarters in the New York Park to the new
reptile house in the National Zoological Park in Washington the head
keeper and I had a short conference and made simple arrangements.
The partition door between the double cages was closed, thus giving
us an empty side to work in.   A large bag of tough canvas material
was selected as the carrying medium.   This bag was about five feet
deep.   An oblong frame of thin wood was constructed and attached

to the mouth of the bag with thumb tacks.   This tunnel-like arrangement was then fastened to the lower portion of the partition door frame.   The next step was to take a piece of soft sash cord, fasten it to the front of the cage, take one turn around the bag slightly below where it was attached to the wooden frame and carry the rope through itself to form a tying loop, the free end being carried through the slightly opened door.   The partition slide was pulled and we awaited the inevitable result of curiosity on the cobra's part, terminating in its coiling within the bag as a restful retreat.

About an hour later Head Keeper Toomey calmly walked into my office with the bag, now securely tied and the wooden frame removed. The bag was placed in a sole-leather case which was locked and strapped.

While the king cobra has elongated anterior ribs it cannot spread its "hood" to anywhere near the proportionate width of the smaller and abundant Asiatic cobra.   Nor as a rule does it rear in such dramatically posed positions.   Occasionally, it will rear four feet high and stand as motionless as a great candlestick, staring fixedly.   There is none of the nervous swaying or marked arching of the neck of the common cobra.   The attitude is one of intense scrutiny.

King cobras can seldom be induced to eat anything but snakes.   My observation has been that they can detect poisonous serpents, have great respect for them and will not attack them.   Our specimens have been fed mostly upon Texas gopher snakes (*Drymarchon*) four to five feet long.   The head keeper kept a record of the footage in serpents devoured by a fourteen-foot specimen from July to the following March, the reptile feeding on the average of once a week.   He handed me a memorandum showing that the cobra had devoured one hundred and forty-five feet of snakes during this period.

Throughout its range, from eastern India to the Philippines, the king cobra was for years considered to be rather rare.   Recent records are changing this status.   Numerous examples come into the animal shops of Singapore, their necks badly scarred from noosing.   In the recent and excellent work by Edward H. Taylor, issued by the Department of Agriculture and Natural Resources of the Bureau of Science, at Manila, and entitled "The Snakes of the Philippine Islands," the following appears: "This snake (the King Cobra) grows to a large size in the islands. . . .   It is reported as being very common on Lubang Island, north of Mindoro.   I have not been able to

verify this report. It probably occurs on all the larger islands. It is striking, however, that I find no specimens recorded from the western Visayan Islands (Bohol, Cebu, Negros, and Panay). In fact, no cobras of any sort have yet been recorded from these islands."

From the Academy of Natural Sciences of Philadelphia came the following notes by Rodolphe Meyer de Schauense about the king cobra in Siam:

The largest poisonous snake in the world is found quite commonly in Siam. The record specimen for the country is in the neighborhood of 16 feet.

Regarding the power of this formidable reptile, an incident which had just taken place near Chieng Mai in Northern Siam a short time before I arrived struck me quite forcibly.

The best trained tusker elephant in the teak forest, belonging to one of the big foreign companies had died from the bite of a King Cobra. He was working in the forest when one of these brutes bit him on the foot.

At first I must confess I rather doubted the story, because to me it seemed impossible for a snake, no matter how large, to pierce the skin of one of these huge beasts. I asked how it was possible and was told that the mortal bites are inflicted either on the end of the trunk, or just at the juncture of the nail and the foot, in both of which places the skin is tender. An elephant is said to die in about three hours after being bitten.

The death of an elephant from a bite of one of these reptiles is not a very unusual occurrence. As a matter of fact, the teak companies count on losing at least two or three elephants a year as a result of the King Cobra. As good trained tuskers are very hard to replace, they are highly valued and command prices between four and five thousand dollars. Any loss caused by snake-bite is therefore quite considerable.

When we returned to this country we had with us a collection of live specimens destined for various Zoological Gardens in the East. Included was a 12-foot King Cobra, which went to the Philadelphia Zoological Society.

There was no receptacle for water in the box of the King Cobra and I hardly cared to open it and put one in. The result was that the water was given to it from a pitcher and the snake soon learned to raise its head against the wire and drink from the nozzle. It got quite used to this method of drinking and I really believe he got to know the pitcher. This is an observation which confirms the accounts of the high grade of intelligence displayed by this reptile.

Clifford Pope, associated with the reptile department of the American Museum of Natural History extends the distribution of the king cobra in China and speaks from first hand information. Mr. Pope spent considerable time in that country collecting reptiles for the museum. He recently told the author that the king cobra ranges

well northward into China to about the latitude of Shanghai and that in the area between Canton and Foochow it is fairly common.

With well authenticated general occurrence in fair numbers of this giant of the Elapines, the question naturally arises as to how hostile the species really is in attacking humans.   There is no doubt about its fearlessness, nor about its disposition to quickly advance and attack if interfered with, but it seems rash to form the conjecture that the average king cobra pursues man on sight.   It seems more probable that if the snake is not molested it may be passed unseen, or else over portions of its range a few sinister stories of attacks and death from its bites spread.   The explanation of attacks of this serpent appears to largely revert to the breeding season, the early-year months following the rains when small groups or pairs congregate on certain grounds for mating.   In such places, it is reliably stated, these snakes are extremely savage and hostile at human intrusion, will rise from the ground four to five feet, angrily hiss, and some among their numbers come straight at the person blundering upon their lairs.   This is probably the basis for this reptile's extremely bad reputation, coupled with its insolence in preferring to fight rather than flee if man or domestic beast brushes actual contact with it when prowling.   In any event, its size and deadliness, its activity and intelligence, warrant passage through its known domains being made with the greatest caution.   To the author this is the world's most interesting snake and while not actuated by any but what I consider normal reaction in observing it, I have always felt a curious respect for it, akin to awe.

There are but two cobras in the entire Asiatic-Malayan region, the big species previously described which has proportionately shorter spreading ribs to form a "hood" and hence deserves generic recognition, and the "Indian Cobra."   The latter name for the smaller and far more abundant species is anything but appropriate, in fact misleading, as this snake has an exceedingly wide range.   It occurs from the easterly shores of the Caspian Sea throughout southern Asia to China, its distribution including the entire Malay Archipelago, sweeping northward into the Philippines.   Its races or varieties are many, extending through different body hues, markings and even outline of form, which varies from slender to moderately stout.   A number of subspecies are thus indicated, but they are difficult to define owing to intergrading forms.   The Philippine cobras, of dark brown, or black,

with no hood markings seem to represent no more than a melanistic subspecies—*samarensis*. Some Philippine examples have a dull V-shaped mark on the hood.

Hence we consider the Common or Asiatic Cobra, *Naia naia* (Plates 36 and 37), also known as the Indian Cobra or Cobra de capello, the latter title again misleading as cobras generally spread a hood, and a name pointing to a snake with a cape or hood might as well be applied to any of the numerous species of cobras inhabiting Africa—which is their actual headquarters in variety of kinds.

A large example of *Naia naia*, the Asiatic cobra, is six feet long. The coloration of the typical form is yellowish to dark brown with a black and white spectacle-marking on the hood (seen when spread) and a black and white spot on each side of the lower surface of the hood. This form is more commonly found in southern India and Ceylon. However, there are varieties in India with no hood markings. Another Indian variety is called the Monocellate (one spot) Cobra. It has a large black ring on the hood enclosing a paler area, this having a large black spot in the center. It occurs in the more northerly portions and in China.

The Common Cobra is a nervous, excitable snake, quickly rising when disturbed, spreading the hood and arching the neck. It will make intimidating strikes at the object of its anger, accompanying each dart of its body forward and downward by a sharp, sneeze-like hiss. This striking, which is simply a forward sweep of the anterior or raised portion of the body, is not nearly so quick as the stroke of the vipers, which in lightning-like fashion dart the head from a lateral loop of the neck. The cobra seldom resorts to such a loop, depending upon pulling its head backward by the up-curved, vertical action. Moreover, when it bites it is inclined to retain its hold, the temporal muscles bulging in contraction over the poison glands and thus imbedding a considerable amount of the powerful neurotoxic venom from the short fangs. Often cobras are irritable enough to come forward in attack, but their action is not spectacular or particularly dangerous. There is no deliberate rush to be avoided with difficulty, but an angry gliding forward with hood spread and anterior body erect. Such a specimen can easily be kept at bay with a light stick and the action—if one knows anything at all about cobras—is more amusing than thrilling.

It is in chasing rodents or frogs that the cobra shows uncanny dex-

terity, its glide flashing from side to side as a small mammal darts one way or the other in an endeavor to escape, or in pursuing a frog, catching up with its jumps and from a slight kinking of the neck darting its head to grip the prey with aim as unerring as directing a bullet at an object. Fortunate it is that this widespread and abundant reptile uses no such tactics toward humans.

With such clearly established agility it seems curious that the cobra is almost invariably killed when attacked by its enemy the mongoose—which is not immune to the serpent's poison. If it would revert to its sinuous rush, in turning this on the mongoose, there would be quite a different story. But the cobra in these fights assumes nothing but the posture of defence. It is a fair defence, so far as it goes, as the snake does its best to reach its enemy by sweeping strike. But such sweeps are not quick enough to reach the lively mongoose which in each instance jumps out of immediate reach, to return on the other side, causing the reptile to change its position and strike again and again. Such efforts are tiring and discouraging and the mongoose knows it and adds to the breakdown of morale by darting in from a momentarily safe quarter and nipping the cobra's tail—and as quickly jumping back. That action is always close to the end of the fight and the enraged, blinded serpent, now tired and striking wildly, turns supposedly toward the adversary, but is leaped upon by the mongoose from the opposite quarter. The small mammal's canines are buried in the reptile's neck. While the ensuing action is fast and furious there is no doubt about the result if the mongoose hangs on, which it usually does. Its particularly strong, sharp teeth sever the joints of the cervical vertebrae.

Serum for cobra bite has been highly perfected in the Orient, thanks to the magnificent work laid down by Calmette. The difficulty lies with the East Indian races. It is to induce victims of snake-bite to benefit by treatment before it is too late to use a serum. There is the Haffkine Institute with its invaluable work at Bombay; and in Siam, where cobras are particularly numerous, the Pasteur Institute maintains a large establishment at Bangkok—at the base of the Malay Peninsula. One of the major departments of this plant is the production of serum for snake-bites which are frequent in the jungle areas and rural surroundings. The main building is a handsome domed structure, behind which is the snake park where living specimens are kept in shallow pits surrounded by a concrete wall. The institute is

similar in its organization and surroundings to the Institute of Serum Therapy at São Paulo, maintained by the Brazilian government. Like the latter it is saving the lives of many victims.

If the natives of India could be educated to protect their feet and legs—an extremely forlorn hope—the death rate from snake-bite in that country would drop fifty per cent. Official statistics tabulate approximately twenty-thousand deaths from serpent bites in India every year, and this very materially is caused by the native habit of walking about at night bare-legged. On the plantations, where disciplinary measures are possible and serum is available, snake-bite fatalities in the Asiatic and Malayan areas have been greatly decreased.

There is a mistaken idea that the appalling figures of fatalities from serpent bites among the swarming, fanatical races of Asia are to be blamed directly to the cobra. Recent tabulations disprove this and point to the truth of the matter being that the kraits, the Russell viper, half a dozen species of *Agkistrodon* (similar to the New World moccasins) and several kinds of *Trimeresurus* (like the tropical American *Bothrops*) combine to form the high death rate, with the Russell viper a large offender.

The Kraits, forming the genus *Bungarus* to the number of half a dozen species, are largely nocturnal and dangerous from their habit of prowling into human habitations or lying in the dust of the roads at night, where despite the evening's chill the surface gives off the warmth absorbed by the sun. In such places they are often stepped on. These creatures in their habits—although much larger—are somewhat similar to the American coral snakes. They do not strike or attempt to bite unless restrained. Then they deliberately turn and bite, retaining a hold with the short fangs and "chewing" in an effort to imbed the poison. Their venom approaches the potency of the cobra.

Kraits occur in India, Burma, southern China and Malaysia and are more common in the populated areas than cobras. They are four to five feet long, with smooth, lustrous scales, dark brown or black with pale cross-bands, some quite vividly marked with yellow "rings"—the effect being of alternate rings of the paler hue, and ground color. They are distinguished by a curiously emaciated outline, the back rising to a ridge on which there is a row of enlarged scales. The head is small and not distinct from the neck. They feed largely upon smaller snakes, but also hunt for small mammals, frogs and lizards.

The Common Krait, *B. candidus,* has wide distribution, from the

plains of India through the Malay Archipelago. The Banded Krait, *B. fasciatus,* is a ringed species occurring over the same area. As captives they are inoffensive, listless and short-lived. While they substantially add to the toll of deaths from snake-bites in Oriental areas accidents from such reptiles could be largely reduced through simple precautions.

Consideration of three additional genera, *Hemibungarus, Callophis* and *Doliophis,* closes the list of Elapine snakes in the Asiatic and Malayan regions. These genera contain respectively, four, five, and four species. All are small, their dimensions running from eighteen to twenty-four inches on the average. They are likewise slender and secretive, not inclined to bite, hence not figuring among the dangerous kinds. *Doliophis* is the most interesting genus, its four cylindrical, lustrous-scaled representatives inhabiting Burma, Cochin-China and Malaysia. Specimens are usually well under two feet long and if it were not for a remarkable internal development these little snakes might be passed with mere mention or altogether omitted in a general review. The development referred to consists of a remarkable enlargement of their poison glands, which, instead of being confined to the temporal region as with other Elapine snakes, extend backward into the body a third its length as long cylindrical processes terminating in club-shaped fashion. The development is so highly specialized that some of the viscera have been "rearranged" in adaptation, the heart being farther back than with other snakes. This excess of venom does not point to any particular danger from these snakes as they appear too small to be able to use their fangs except upon their natural prey. And this they seem to realize—for if bothered they go through curious manoeuvres seemingly calculated to inspire fright. They crawl slowly away, keeping the head close to the ground. The retreat, however, is a rear-guard action in which the *tail* solely figures. It is reared upward, then bent slightly in the direction of the object of fright. Being blunt, curved in at just the right angle, then slowly waved—though the picture is a miniature—it awesomely looks like a threatening head awaiting a chance to bite. And as a keen touch to the spectacle, the "throat" of the simulated head is bright red. The effect is of something decidedly "poisonous" and man or animal would hesitate to be too familiar with such a threatening object. Strangely enough, several harmless snakes inhabiting the same regions, and being of similar size and form, as well as coloration, affect the same antics as if seeking

defence in imitating their poisonous neighbors. The commonest species of *Doliophis* is *D. intestinalis,* brown or blackish, with narrow yellow stripes.

So far in these pages there has been mention of but a single species of sea snake and that was brought up in the chapter relating to the poisonous serpents of the American tropics. The reason for this is that the New World is out of the area of occurrence of the numerous representatives of the *Hydrophidae.* A single species is found off the west coast of tropical America. Yet there are over fifty species in this family, which swarm in some portions of the tropical seas. In considering the seas bordering southern Asia and the waters of Malaysia we wander directly into the zones of maximum occurrence of these unique reptiles.

The Sea Snakes, accorded full family recognition as the *Hydrophidae,* are marine allies of the cobras and kraits. They have developed wide paddle-like tails vertically compressed. They are as much at home in the sea as fishes and frequently seen a thousand miles from shore. They must frequently come to the surface for air. They will live for days if taken from the water, and they are also able to remain under the surface for a long time, possibly for hours, owing to their ability of literally swallowing and ejecting water, in easy, rhythmic fashion, which seems to provide them with oxygen from the water itself to "aerate" the blood. Thus they are creatures of extreme specialization, although their fangs and poison glands are of the Elapine type. Their poison is very deadly. Its action is similar to, though stronger than, that of the rear-fanged snakes in quickly benumbing the prey which consists of fishes.

The general range of the sea snakes is from the Persian Gulf to the western tropical Pacific. They are particularly abundant in the Indian Ocean and Bay of Bengal, where their varied size and colors, some being brilliantly ringed, form an interesting study from steamers plying these waters. *Hydrophis* is the largest genus with about two dozen species, a few of which reach a length of eight to ten feet and have an incongruously long, slender neck and small head for the heavy body. With several the diameter of the body is four to six times the width of the head, imparting very unusual outlines for a snake.

The average length of sea snakes is four to five feet. They give birth to living young. Previous to the young being born they seek tide pools and shallow flats of deserted shores. The greater number

have no enlarged abdominal plates and never actually leave the water. Members of the genus *Laticauda* (Plate 41), of easterly parts of the Indian Ocean and the westerly Pacific, are exceptions in having broad abdominal plates like terrestrial snakes although the tail is wide, flat and paddle-like. These snakes are often found prowling in tidal marshes. The body is cylindrical and the creature crawls slowly but with graceful ease out of the water. They are quiet and inoffensive if not actually annoyed, but quickly turn and bite if held down with a stick. A dozen specimens under the author's observation came all the way from the Caroline Islands to New York, in large tin cans with netting covers. They were given daily baths of sea water, but were not kept in it. They were vigorous and in good condition on arrival and although provided with a large tank in which was an "island" of blocks of coral, and while provided with sea water, steadily refused to take the different kinds of fish offered them. They were listless, but survived about six months' time.

Sea snakes have never constituted a great hazard to man. Fishermen of the Malayan areas are sometimes bitten, in some instances fatally when hauling in well-laden nets. Under such restraint these reptiles furiously bite. There are few reports, even among the natives where exaggerated tales are common enough, of swimmers being bitten by these snakes. The disposition of such reptiles is not to attack, but quickly swim away. Passengers boarding steamers from small tenders in the Oriental tropics are sometimes startled at seeing sea snakes swimming nearby, but such examples are merely attracted by the gangway lights and have not the faintest hostile intentions.

The *Viperidae,* while scant in Asiatic species, is all too prominently represented by the large and deadly Daboia or Tic-Polonga, which occurs in India, Ceylon, China, the Malay Peninsula, Java, Sumatra and Borneo, and small islands of the Dutch East Indies.

There is a small viper in the hills of upper Burma, which is curious in having the head covered with large symmetrical plates and the body clad in smooth scales. This is *Azemiops.*

The Russell Viper, Daboia or Tic-Polonga, *Vipera russellii* (Plate 45), with a maximum length of about five feet, ranks with the cobra as one of the dreaded snakes of the Orient and rivals the Elapid in taking fully as high a toll of human life. It is a particularly handsome snake, as colors and patterns go. The body is pale brown, but of rich hue, and extending the entire length are three rows of large black rings,

bordered with white or yellow, enclosing darker brown, or even red. On some specimens the rings of the back unite to form a chain.

This is a savage creature, but usually gives warning of its presence by loud hissing, producing a sound readily heard twenty-five feet, the hisses being rapidly intermittent as the reptile makes as much noise with the intake as expulsion of the breath. It strikes with such agility that it sometimes slides a foot or more and thus appears to jump. While its poison is largely of haemolytic action, its toxicity is very high. Owing to its large fangs and the amount of venom expended at a bite some toxicologists regard it as more dangerous than the common cobra.

One reason for the widespread abundance of the Russell Viper is the generous litter of young, usually about two dozen. The little serpents are immediately ready to shift for themselves. The adults prowl mostly at night, and as rodents are the favorite food are lured into the neighborhood of human settlements, in fact may be more numerous in such places than the open country. The presence of the tic-polonga under such conditions is similar to that of the fer-de-lance in tropical America. As long as slip-shod human methods in the warmer latitudes are conducive to the multiplication of rodents, poisonous snakes, thus provided with abundant food, will automatically thrive in striking a balance.

Asia and the islands form an Old World mecca for the *Crotalidae.* There are no rattlesnakes, which are characteristically of the New World, but the genus *Agkistrodon,* or moccasins with symmetrical plates on the head, is represented to the number of seven species, and *Trimeresurus,* similar to the tropical American *Bothrops,* in fact for a long time carried under the same generic heading (then *Lachesis*) as the New World species, occurs to the number of nearly two dozen kinds, thus coming close to the New World aggregation in scope of listing, although not in variety of form or size.

The Asiatic members of *Agkistrodon* are mostly similar in habits to the North American copperhead snake and range from two to five feet in size, although the greater number, when adult, are not much over a yard. They do not extend as far east or northeastward through the chain of islands as most of the other Asiatic poisonous snakes, not occurring in the Celebes or smaller Dutch East Indies; nor are they found in the Philippines. The species indicated in the technical lists, follow: *A. acutus,* upper Yang-tse, China; *A. halys,* borders of the Caspian Sea and the Ural River to the upper Yenisei; *A. intermedius,* Central Asia, eastern Siberia, Mongolia and Japan; *A. blomhoffi,*

eastern Siberia, Mongolia, China, Japan and Siam; *A. himalayanus,* Himalayas from 5000 to 10,000 feet elevation and the Khasi Hills of Burma; *A. rhodostoma,* Siam and the Malay Peninsula, Sumatra and Java; *A. hypnale,* Ceylon and the western Ghats of India as far north as Bombay.

Some of the species are very abundant. The Roy Chapman Andrews Expedition in Mongolia, in search of fossil specimens for the American Museum of Natural History, found the species known as *intermedius* unpleasantly curious and numerous in visiting the camping sites, coiling on boxes or hiding under heaps of luggage. Fortunately these reptiles appeared to be mild mannered and not inclined to bite. Clifford Pope also collecting for the American Museum of Natural History observed *A. acutus* to be common in inland China in approximately the latitude of Shanghai. *A. rhodostoma* of Malaysia, is of particularly striking coloration, the pattern in rich mottling of angular, dark brown, black-edge blotches on a reddish-brown background. The labial plates are pinkish. As this species has smooth scales the colors are all the more prominent. The snout is particularly pointed and the head very wide at the rear imparting the outline of a javelin tip. The sinister conformation does not belie its looks. This snake has powerful fangs and its poison is noted as being of higher toxicity than that of the northern species, there probably being a similar difference as noted in the New World northern *A. mokasen* and the tropical *A. bilineatus*—the latter semi-aquatic. However, the Malayan pit viper is not a water snake and as its habits are calm rather than irritable the natives do not greatly fear it. The principal danger is from stepping on such reptiles with bare feet. As with many snakes of what may appear to be vivid patterns in shades of brown this creature deceptively blends with the varicolored leaves of the forest floor.

In the extensive genus *Trimeresurus,* which is characteristically Asiatic and Malayan, there is considerable monotony in form and size. The head is always broad and distinct from the neck, of typical viperine outline. The body is but moderately stout and in some instances rather slender. Most of the species are about a yard in length—the average being slightly under. Their habits range from terrestrial— with some the frequenting of damp places like the marshy borders of streams and lakes—to persistently arboreal. The terrestrial kinds show no indication of prehensile power in the tail. With the arboreal species the development of the prehensile tail is as marked as with the New World palm vipers. Moreover, the arboreal kinds are quite

slender and have proportionately wider heads, like tropical American tree-climbing or palm vipers. Coloration of the ground prowling types is brown or gray with darker markings. Most of the arboreal species are green, some with fairly defined markings, but others of rich leaf-green are difficult to detect amongst foliage. Though of moderate bodily size, the fangs of these snakes are proportionately very long and all should be rated as highly dangerous. The toxicity of their venom, however, appears to be lower than that of the Russell viper.

They range throughout southern Asia and the Malayan region, their numbers generously extending into the Philippines, where seven kinds occur, several characteristic to those islands. Several appear to be found only in the Loo Choo Islands, south of Japan. One is found only in Borneo. At least nine occur in India. They may be readily recognized from the Asiatic species of *Agkistrodon* in having small scales upon the top of the head.

As to *T. halieus,* a Philippine species, named and described by Griffin in the Philippine Journal of Science in 1910 from ten specimens collected at Polillo, the sponsor says: "The head is broadly triangular. . . . The specimens were all collected along the banks of streams or in damp localities. This snake seems to leave the ground very rarely. When the natives of the island go at night along the streams to catch mudfish by torchlight the snakes are commonly seen near the edge of the water and the fishermen say they are there for the same purpose as themselves and for this reason call the snake Manda-dalag, which, literally translated, means 'the fisher of the dalag (or mudfish) !' "

Edward H. Taylor, in an examination of preserved examples, found a frog in one, the scales of what appeared to be a fish in another, and in a third a mass of hair indicating the remains of a rat.

The Green Tree Viper, *T. gramineus,* is the most broadly found over India and Malaysia to and including the Philippines. It is a scant yard in length, leaf-green with a pale yellow stripe on each side. The tip of the tail is red. This is one of the strictly arboreal species and has a prehensile tail. Its name might as readily be applied to several of the others, of green coloration, but with differences of scalation or minor markings. One of the Loo Choo Islands species is of particularly vivid blue-green hue.

CHAPTER XIII

THE POISONOUS SNAKES OF AFRICA

AFRICA has an extremely interesting variety of poisonous serpents. From the viewpoint of explorer or sportsman this aggregation is of importance on account of the number of large, active and highly irritable reptiles. Some are particularly dangerous owing to excessive fang length and high toxicity of venom; and among others there is a manifestation practically unique among African serpents. This is the ability and deliberate intent of certain cobras to "spit" their poison in the direction of the eyes of intruders.

There are no pit vipers in Africa, but the Elapines and typical vipers are elaborately represented. If Australia (where the Elapines predominate) were eliminated, Africa could properly be called the headquarters of the *Elapidae*. There are eight genera and twenty-four species. Here, apparently is the land of origin of the typical vipers—*Viperidae*—as they exist in great variety, from heavy terrestrial kinds to forms adapted to move over or burrow into the loose sands of desert areas, and again slender-bodied, big-headed arboreal species in shades of green that are highly specialized to climb and to "mimic" their surroundings. One genus, *Atractaspis,* has seemingly gone wild in development of poison apparatus, acquiring fangs of such enormous comparative length they nearly defeat their free use and purpose. Another genus, *Causus,* is Colubrine-like in form, with shielded head. Its members lay eggs, as is also the case with *Atractaspis.* But one African viper, a large species called the River Jack (*Bitis nasicornis*), seems to be semi-aquatic. Altogether there are seven genera of African *Viperidae,* with a total of twenty-nine species.

The Elapine Snakes: In clearing the way for the Elapine stars of Africa, the cobras and mambas, several genera of small species should first be checked. These are commonly known as Garter snakes or Coral snakes. They are small and slim with glossy scales and rather similar to the New World coral snakes, in looks and habits. Their inclination is to burrow, but they are often seen wandering on the surface.

They are not inclined to bite unless restrained or injured. As they average under twenty-four inches in length there is little fear of them. *Elapsoidea* has six members, most of them prettily marked and occurring in tropical and South Africa. *E. guntheri* is beautifully ringed in coral-pink and white. While belonging to a group commonly known as "garter snakes" it is as frequently called the "coral snake". There is a variety in the Usambara Mountains which is black, with narrow white "rings". This is the subspecies *nigra* and known as the "Black Garter Snake". These little serpents are actually banded, and not ringed as the markings do not encircle the body. The two members of *Homoroselaps* or Striped Garter Snakes are seldom over a foot long. Both are South African. The body is yellow or yellowish-white with ring-like or delicate chain-like markings, but these miniature Elapines are characteristic in having a reddish or bright orange stripe along the back.

Boulengerina is a remarkable genus of aquatic Elapids or "Water Cobras" inhabiting Lake Tanganyika. They reach a length of at least six feet.

The Cobras, *Naia,* range from the arid North coast to the Cape, the regions between these boundaries being their true headquarters. The Asiatic or spectacled, or Indian cobra, and the great Indo-Malayan king cobra appear to represent but a northeastern extension of the hooded clan. At least two African cobras have expertly developed the effective defense of ejecting their venom in a shower of fine drops toward an enemy's eyes. This is done with definite intent. As this type of poison is at once absorbed through the conjunctiva, the spray, if reaching its mark, and it is directed with force and accuracy, throws the victim into a condition of pain and confusion, enabling the cobra to escape.

There are at least eight full species of African cobras and several subspecies distinct enough to warrant about a dozen "kinds" being generally spoken of. Following is a summary of these snakes:

The Egyptian Cobra or Asp, *Naia haie* (Plate 35), has long carried a name that is misleading as this common snake has the widest range of any cobra in Africa. On the north coast it occurs in Morocco, thence generally eastward into Egypt—except in the coastal area of Algeria. In ranging over the northerly areas, where it is the only, but a frequent species, it carries the range of *Naia* throughout the continent—except the absolutely sterile, central desert portions. It

is, however, particularly numerous in the countries bordering the
Sahara.   Southward it extends through easterly Africa all the way
to Natal.

This snake prefers hot and dry places and its dull lusterless scales
are in keeping with the sand and dust through which it loves to prowl.
Its usual coloration is a medium brown, with or without faint markings.
With such extensive distribution there are naturally color variations.
These run into paler brown or olive, sometimes with the head of darker
hue.   Moroccan examples are commonly blackish-brown.   The length
is four to six feet.   It is a quick, irritable reptile rearing upon the
slightest disturbance and repeatedly striking with sharp hisses.

This is the cobra so often seen with snake charmers in Egypt.
Most of the reptiles under such conditions have had their fangs extracted, but occasional and particularly skillful "charmers" carry
fanged cobras, seeming to have keen knowledge as to how far they
can go in handling such dangerous exhibits and really appearing
to have control of the serpents' actions.

As a captive this snake is alert and displays considerable intelligence.   It cannot endure anything but positively dry and steadily
warm quarters—and under ordinary conditions survives but a few
months.   This is in marked contrast to some of the other African
species, living in the more humid areas.   The author has records of
the latter kinds extending over periods longer than sixteen years,
with no provisions made to keep their quarters at a minimum of
humidity.

The Spitting Cobra or Black-necked Cobra, *Naia nigricollis,* comes
close to being the most dangerous snake of Africa.   The author hesi-
tates to accord it this rank, as he has in mind the active and deadly
mambas which sometimes viciously attack, and another spitting cobra
confined to the southerly portion of the continent.   These points, however, should be considered: *N. nigricollis* has a wide range, occurring
from upper Egypt thence southwesterly to Angola on the west coast,
thence southerly to the latitude of the Transvaal.   Thus it is found
over extensive areas in many of which it is common.   Coupled with
this distribution are its size and power to effectively eject its venom to
a distance of eight feet or more and thus reach the eyes of a standing
person.   It is the type of attack which usually strikes the victim as a
complete surprise.   Moreover, it is administered in an instant, the
snake rearing and "spitting" upon slight provocation.

With a reptile as dangerous as this, it is well to have identity clearly established. This is one of the dull scaled cobras, that is the scalation is satiny, not polished. A blackish example has the luster of the surface of a gunbarrel. The species grow to be seven feet. One variety is blue-black without any markings whatever above, although a pair of large crimson blotches of quite startling contrast show beneath the hood when this is spread and the snake faces an opponent. At Nairobi an olive-colored form is found with yellow markings beneath the hood. This cobra varies into brown and Loveridge says that at Longido there is a salmon pink variety. With olive, brown or any of the lighter hued examples there is a black band across the throat, within the lower portion of the hood, this band six to seven scales wide. It is this marking which gives the serpent its name—the black-necked cobra. Black, or dark olive specimens show red or yellow patches under the hood and these may be as bright as the markings on a butterfly's wing.

The term "spitting" does not correctly indicate the manner of ejecting the poison, as the performance is accomplished with the jaws slightly parted and the venom comes directly from the openings at the tips of the fangs. The performance is very quick, but watching it repeatedly (from behind glass) my diagnosis is as follows: The snake rears—and it may instantly spring to the pose. Facing the object of anger it looks intently at one's face; and this we have tested from both crouching and standing positions. If it seeks to direct the poison upward it curves its rearing pose backward, thus directing its head upwards. The ejection of poison is an instantaneous operation. The jaws are slightly opened and closed so quickly as to appear like a snapping motion and during this action the poison leaves the fangs. There is no dribbling or spilling of the fluid. It issues in twin jets and the jaws of the snake are clear of it when the feat is accomplished. There is every indication that at the instant the snake prepares to eject the poison it contracts the temporal muscle over each poison gland, thus producing pressure to force the toxic fluid a considerable distance. This flies with such force that its impact can be distinctly heard against ordinary glass five feet away. At the instant of ejection the snake emits a sharp hiss. This ejection of air may be an accompanying token of anger, or it may assist the travel of the poison.

Astonishing amounts of poison are expended. Considerable drops may flow down glass after a single demonstration, but the snake may

repeat the performance a half dozen times. With two specimens on exhibition in the Zoological Park, it was necessary to remove the cobras every five or six days as the glass was so showered during their "spitting" at visitors it was impossible to see through it. These demonstrations continued fully six months, when the snakes gradually became accustomed to passing observers and sent only occasional jets in their direction. The area of the glass most thickly spattered was on a line between the heights of the snakes' heads when reared in irritation and visitors' faces.

We made a number of experiments on a smooth concrete floor, where any small drop of moisture was clearly apparent. The cobras were large examples, close to six feet in length. By making threatening motions at them from what we considered to be a safe distance it was noted that about the maximum distance from the snake to the last sprinkling of tiny drops was twelve feet. It was my estimate that to stand within six feet of one of these snakes would be unsafe—that from this distance, in its reared pose, a large example could accurately direct poison forward and upward to one's eyes.

After a vigorous demonstration and the discharge of four to six jets of poison the glands rapidly refill. This seems to be a particular provision. The snake will produce a similar manifestation the following day, but we have found by scraping the glass and analysis of the poison that the new fluid is of much lighter specific gravity than older storage and consequently of lower toxicity. My friend Dr. Adolph Monaelesser very carefully demonstrated this. Both he and the author also found, with startling discomfort, that microscopic flakes of even the newly secreted venom liberated in the air during scraping from the glass or pouring into test tubes, can produce results temporarily organic when absorbed through the moist lining of the bronchial tubes.

Under observation in captivity the spitting cobra lives for years. One example, now some five years captive, is in perfect condition and "tame" enough to glide to the door of the cage at feeding time. We never trust them and always wear goggles when cleaning the cage.

Arthur Loveridge, of the Museum of Comparative Zoology, at Cambridge, Massachusetts, has had considerable experience in capturing spitting cobras. In some notes in the Bulletin of the Antivenin Institute of America, he says: "Owing to this habit of discharging their venom the capture of a cobra is almost invariably an exciting matter. Unless the venom happens to fall upon a cut or abrasion

of the skin, there is no danger apart from it entering the eyes. The immediate result, should this happen, is intense pain and temporary blindness caused by the superficial blood vessels absorbing the venom. This conjunctivitis subsides in a few days if prompt treatment is applied.

"A friend of mine was crawling through some grass to obtain a final shot at a hartebeest which he had wounded. Suddenly up rose a cobra before him. He had presence of mind to tightly close his eyes and received the venom upon his eyelids. Lying back he awaited the arrival of his syce, whom he instructed to take his water bottle and pour its contents upon his face. Then after a careful sponging with a wet handkerchief he opened his eyes and was none the worse for his unpleasant experience.

"A keeper in the garden of the Zoological Society of London received a box of snakes from West Africa. Seeing there was netting beneath the lid, he started to pry up the slats, when he received a charge of poison in his eyes at very close range. A year later he was still suffering from the effects, his eyes looking weak and watering at the slightest strain. He informed me that he could never read by artificial light in consequence."

The author has heard of several instances where the immediate application of water from a canteen or a nearby stream or puddle saved the eyes from serious consequences after receiving a charge of poison. It is well for the African traveler to bear this in mind and to carry a small package of mild antiseptic, like boric acid, that may later be converted into dilute solution in water to treat the eyes during inevitable weakness that temporarily, or more persistently develops. It is probable that if nothing were done to dilute or wash away the poison from the absorbent membranes, serious impairment of sight, or blindness would result. Not enough of the poison appears to be absorbed through the conjunctiva to produce fatal organic symptoms, in fact the poison of this snake—possibly through the provision of rapid secretion within the glands—does not seem to be so toxic when injected into tissue as others of its genus.

The Black Cobra, *Naia melanoleuca* (Plate 34), is a slightly larger and heavier reptile than the spitting cobra and might readily be confused with it. It does not so eject its venom and is less inclined to take a reared pose when threatened, but this is in no way a redeeming trait. It is quickly stirred to anger and may unexpectedly make a short rush

forward in an effort to deliberately bite. It grows to be seven feet long and the black scales are as polished as glass. Its glossy surface thus forms a distinguishing character. Like most of the cobras it has developed racial color differences. A variety in Central Africa has the anterior half of the body pale brown and the posterior portion black. This big cobra is confined to tropical Africa. It extends farther northward on the west coast than *nigricollis,* occurring in considerable portions of the central area where the latter is found, but not ranging into southerly Africa.

A batch of captives remained quiet enough, not even rearing to spread their hoods. While stirring them up a bit with a bamboo stick to make them spread their hoods, I was surprised to see two of them rear slightly, hiss and expand in true cobra fashion and come straight at me. I am inclined, however, to regard this species as the least nervous of the African species we have had under observation; but having a dangerous insolence when stirred to anger.

The Cape Cobra, *Naia nivea* (*flava*), is confined to southerly Africa. Its distribution includes the whole of Cape Colony, thence northward as far as the southerly portion of the Tanganyika Territory. Here again is a very variable species in coloration. It is more frequently yellowish, but may be reddish, brown or even black. It is difficult to sharply define these cobras without going into technical details, these largely relating to rows of scales across the hood and around the body; also differences in the head plates.

Common in the Cape Colony, this cobra gives way in numbers in Natal and the more northerly parts of South Africa where *N. nigricollis, N. haie,* and *N. anchietae* overlap its range and thence take its place. It grows to a length of five and occasionally seven feet, is quick and savage and there are numerous deaths from its bites. It is attracted by rats around barns and native houses and may thus be more frequently found in such locations than in the wilder areas.

Naia goldii is a West African cobra inhabiting the region of the lower Niger, extending westward to the Gold Coast and eastward to the Cameroons and largely arboreal. It is a large reptile, blackish above and greenish yellow beneath. Together with *N. guentheri* (also of West Africa) it may be distinguished by its particularly large eyes. *N. anchietae,* of Angola and the central area, has no hood, but rears in oblique postures and waves its head from side to side. *Goldii* likewise is nearly hoodless. From specimens of both examined by the

author these appear to be astonishingly quick and highly dangerous cobras, inclined to bite from a short rush, rather than a strike. Whether or not these "hoodless" cobras will long remain in the genus *Naia* depends upon future deductions of technical workers. In bodily outline and size they otherwise resemble their allies. *Anchietae* is dark brown or black. The end of the snout and sides of the head are yellow.

The Ringhals, or Keel-scaled Spitting Cobra, *Sepedon haemachates,* creates the necessity of providing a genus in which it stands alone. This comes from its scales being keeled, rendering it unique among the cobras. Otherwise it runs true to the most vigorous of the hooded snakes, matching the dangerous habits of the big black spitting cobra occurring farther north and which its distribution overlaps. Thus the menace of spitting cobras is carried down to the Cape.

The name Ringhals has been applied by the Boers from presence of a whitish ring (sometimes two) across the throat. Another name is Spoewslang, applied from the reptile's "spitting" its poison.

This is the smallest of the cobras. The average length is around four feet. Owing to the keeled scales the back is lusterless and of dingy black or brown. The underside is blackish (with exception of the pale ring or rings on the neck) and the broad, highly polished abdominal plates are in glittering contrast as this serpent rises in combat attitude.

The ejection of poison is performed as described with the larger, black-necked cobra. Captives shower the glass of their cage, but this snake is not so dangerous owing to its smaller size and inability to throw its poison much over six feet, and probably not so far if directed obliquely upward. The great danger from the Ringhals is to persons stooping toward the ground near brush or rockpiles where an alert specimen may be lurking. The Ringhals departs from the usual cobra habit of laying eggs and produces the young alive. As the litters range from two to five dozen it holds its own in unpleasant abundance close to inhabited areas.

The Mambas, *Dendraspis* (Plate 33), of which there are several species of similar form, are the most famous snakes of Africa. Their venom appears to be particularly deadly; and as they sometimes attack, are amazingly quick and fatalities from their bites are reported under dramatic conditions, a sinister reputation has been built around them.

If statistics for large areas could be clearly presented—a difficult matter in Africa—the Mambas would probably be found responsible

for no greater amount of accidents than the cobras, yet they range over practically the same broad area, except the extreme northerly portion. Actual pursuit of humans and attacks are indicated to be largely limited to the breeding grounds, during the specific mating season, which also applies to the king cobra. During the balance of the year the average Mamba, unless cornered, cautiously glides from man's presence.

The Mambas are unique among really deadly snakes in being of extreme slenderness. The outlines of a seven-foot example can be aptly compared to the slenderness of a carriage whip of similar length. The head is narrow, but moderately distinct from the neck, and in form that of a typically harmless serpent. The mild appearance is enhanced by the large eyes. Thus in looks a Mamba is a close match to the innocent tree snakes of the *Dendrophis* type, being of course longer. The comparison is strengthened by the pale green hue of many Mambas. A seven-foot specimen resting among branches, gives little indication of its considerable length, and to the uninitiated no hint of its deadliness. But Mambas grow far longer than this common length. There are two phases of coloration. One is green and the other dark olive, so dark that unless in the sunlight the snake appears quite black. This latter phase is the so-called Black Mamba growing very much longer than the green phase. While the green variety is six to eight feet long as a rule, the Black Mamba attains the unusual length for an Elapine serpent, of twelve feet. In this respect it rivals the king cobra, but slender as the latter is, foot for foot it would be close to twice as thick as the largest Mamba.

When the Mamba opens its mouth in threatening, if it considers itself cornered (as does the harmless *Dendrophis* of similar form), the respect of a person understanding the anatomy of snakes builds up tremendously. The fangs are situated so far forward in the mouth they might be said to be practically under the serpent's nose. They are particularly large for an Elapid and point almost directly downward. A visual flash of this lethal provision is enough to entirely counteract former thoughts of the Mamba's light build and mild-looking head—when the jaws are closed. The toxicity of Mamba poison tests very high. While series of comparisons of the various African cobras and viper poisons are not available the author believes that the Mambas secrete the most powerful poison of any of the fanged serpents of that country. This does not mean that they are the most

deadly, as some of the cobras with their larger heads secrete much more poison, and then again the big vipers (*Bitis*) carry powerful poisons and their huge fangs are capable of deeply injecting large quantities of it.

Supposition points to the Mambas being cobras which have become arboreal and thus acquired slenderness of form for quick travel among the branches. The anterior ribs are slightly elongated and can expand or flatten the neck to a slight extent. I have noted this when they are intently watching something and are nervously alert yet not stirred to anger. In striking they can so laterally double back the neck and anterior body that a lunge carries the head close to forty per cent the length of the body. They are more commonly observed in bushes or rather low trees where they watch for birds, but often come to the ground in search of small rodents. In such locations, the gliding rush of large specimens is startling and bewildering. Under such conditions interference may be dangerous. Certain spots are favorite lurking places or breeding grounds and during the mating season they are bold and inclined to attack. At other times they appear anxious to evade humans by dashing away. Mambas have an unpleasant habit of entering houses in the outlying areas in search of rats and occasional accidents from such occurrences are reported. Four species are scientifically recognized, of which the South African Mamba, *Dendraspis angusticeps,* is the most familiar. Its range is from coast to coast, from the Tanganyika Territory to West Africa south of the Congo, and southward to Natal. There are two color phases, the green and the black. A second extends northwestward to the Niger and another into Abyssinia.

The author remembers opening his first box of Mambas at the Zoological Park. The case was about four feet long and a yard wide. It contained eight specimens. Accompanying it was a box containing half a dozen "boomslangs", a rear-fanged snake rated capable of a dangerous bite.

Each box was placed close to the sliding door at the rear of the respective big cages the specimens were to occupy—and the doors of the rear passageway closed as is our custom in transferring newcomers. It was our intention to lift each of the boomslangs out of the box on a light iron rod bent over at the end like a poker. They cling to this.

Those boomslangs were seething with activity and deviltry. At a touch of the rod they rushed out of the box, bit and struck at us and

rushed into corners where they put up a great show of threat by swelling their throats until the scale rows were widely separated. We figured that such actions displayed by mildly poisonous South African snakes were a warning in handling the highly dangerous mambas—all of the green variety. This happened in years past. It was our initial experience with mambas.

The cover of the mamba case was carefully pried loose, then we shoved the whole box inside of the big snake cage. When the end of the long rod was gently shoved under one of the serpents and it was lifted to the gravel floor of the exhibition cage, the head keeper remarked that he was disappointed in the much vaunted mamba. I felt the same way after we had six of them out and their almost stringy bodies were gliding around the cage. We similarly removed the seventh, and likewise the eighth, but held this last one up on the rod to get a good look at it. Two of the others had gone prowling into a tree extending six feet upward in the cage. The last mamba started to slide off the rod, which had been gently manipulated. In attempting to balance this snake, the end of the rod accidentally poked one of the tree climbing members. I have never noted a quicker movement on the part of a snake. It was about seven feet long. Its full length came through the door with a speed looking like the shaft of a travelling arrow. We blinked, for the mamba had seemed to vanish, but turning we saw him on a shelf fully five feet from the ground, which he had gained by following up the projecting corner of a door frame. His anterior length was in several loops ready to strike and we then noted the location of mamba fangs, right under the snout, where the merest nip would imbed them. Then and there we decided the mamba deserved its reputation. The rod was gently inserted under a loop of this touchy specimen and it was slowly lifted back to the cage, in which it glided up the tree.

Our mambas however soon became quiet and really tame. They would take dead mice from the end of a bamboo staff. Later I trusted one of them enough to take him into my motion picture studio where some low trees had been set up, and made some good scenes. The snake gave me no trouble and showed no nervousness beyond a slight flattening of the neck when the powerful quartz lights were turned on. I had no difficulty in guiding it into a fibre case when the work was over. An accompanying illustration is an enlargement from a motion picture clip made during this work.

These mambas lived for about a year when they stopped feeding, suddenly grew listless and died. This has been the case with several additional batches of them. Mr. J. L. Buck, of Camden, New Jersey, who obtained these snakes during an African west coast collecting trip told me that in the region where they were found the water everywhere looked rusty and without doubt contained some mineral to which the snakes had been accustomed. We endeavored to create such a condition by rendering the drinking water of our specimens of mildly iron solution, but the attempt was unsuccessful. Later experiments produced the same results.

As it seems cruel to import living things which cannot endure captivity and as frequent shipments of mambas should be discouraged, I have notified all sources that we no longer wish to exhibit them.

The *African Vipers:* With close to thirty species of the *Viperidae* inhabiting Africa, these representing seven genera, there is naturally much variety of form and size among these long-fanged types. *Causus* is a particularly interesting genus as its four members are rather like Colubrine snakes in form with but moderately distinct head, covered with symmetrical shields. Moreover, the members lay eggs. Together with the species of *Atractaspis* (small burrowing vipers) they are thus unique among the African long-fanged snakes. The eye has a round pupil.

The Cape Viper, *Causus rhombeatus,* is also called the Night Adder. It grows to be two, rarely three feet long and is particularly common over the greater portion of South Africa. Coupled with its moderate size is a relatively lower toxicity of venom. It is gray, with a chain of dark, light-edged rhombs along the back. There is usually a triangular or V-shaped mark at the rear of the head pointing forward. It has a habit of lurking in rubbish heaps, discarded heaps of lumber or rock piles and emerges at night to hunt. In noting its occurrence well up the east coast Loveridge says: "It is one of the commonest snakes in Nairobi, and the surrounding district. . . . When molested it coils and displays a vicious disposition, and having intimidated the aggressor to its satisfaction it moves off with neck flattened in cobra fashion, its head raised some five inches from the ground."

With this genus of vipers there is a parallel development in extension of the poison glands into the neck, as noted with the Elapine *Doliophis* (of Asia). The peculiarity is not so marked as with the latter, but *Causus* has elongated glands reaching several inches into

the neck. These vipers feed largely on toads and frogs and in this selection of cold-blooded prey also differ from most members of the family. They extend northward through the tropical portions and to both coasts. They are similarly patterned with rhomboid or chevron-like markings. Their body hue ranges from gray to greenish. Two of the species have an upturned snout, presumably for burrowing.

Vipera, so well represented in continental Europe, has but two species in Africa. One of these, *V. superciliaris,* occurs in the coastal area of Mozambique; the other is East African. *Bitis,* with eight mostly big species, is the most spectacular genus of the family. Its members are really frightful looking creatures, the personification of deadliness, and as dangerous as they look. Their distribution covers the continent almost as broadly as that of the cobras. These snakes are excessively stout for their length with very wide head. Their fangs are enormously developed. They strike with a lightning-like flash, injecting their poison by a combination strike and bite as do the pit vipers.

The Puff Adder, *Bitis arietans* (Plate 46), outranks the others in breadth of distribution. It is found from southern Morocco and south of the Sahara into southern Arabia, thence southward generally to the Cape of Good Hope. Its length is up to four and a half feet and an example of this size would be nine inches in girth. Its brightly laid colors consist of black chevrons separated by yellow crescents. It receives its name from a habit of loudly hissing when molested, with each inhalation and exhalation of the breath. This habit is more or less evident with all true vipers, but particularly emphatic with the puff adder.

The Berg Adder, *B. atropos,* and the Cape Puff Adder, *B. inornata,* occur in extreme southerly Africa. *B. caudalis* and *B. cornuta* have a wider range in the southerly portion. The former has an upright horn-like scale over each eye. *Cornuta* has several sharp scales uniting to form a pair of quite high horns above the eyes.

The Gaboon Viper, *B. gabonica* (Plate 47), is the world's most frightful-looking snake. An example less than four feet long is three inches in diameter with a head as broad as across the four fingers of a man's hand. The incongruously stout body suddenly tapers to a stubby tail and anteriorly tapers enough at the neck to cause the head to look enormously wide and sinister. Upon this awesome form the symmetrical pattern and really beautiful hues repel, rather than soften

the picture. The design looks more like a pattern in bizarre weaving than markings of a serpent. There is a series of precisely oblong buff markings on the back, which are inclosed within long ovals of rich brown. This combination is again enclosed by a chain of purplish markings. On the sides are triangular blotches of purplish or deep brown directed upwards. The background hue behind this pattern usually has distinct tints of pinkish brown. A dark brown blotch begins as a point beneath each eye and runs backward and downward to the jaw to form a vivid triangle. The eyes are silvery. Some specimens have a blunt horn on the nose and a few have a forked horn.

The poison of this viper is of remarkably high toxicity. Its prey is killed almost instantly by injections driven deeply with the long fangs. Until recently the author was not critically familiar with the ratio of the toxic elements—the proportions of haemotoxin and neurotoxin and the power of these respective components. Usually, with viperine serpents, both typical vipers and the pit vipers, the haemolytic (blood destroying) element predominates. In the New World there is an exception in the case of the tropical rattlesnake. We were to learn that the poison of the Gaboon Viper not only produces a furious blood and tissue destruction, but has nearly as much power besides in attacking the nerve centers, particularly the vasomotor system controlling the muscles of breathing, as does that of the cobra; and that the wound from a single fang, only moderately imbedded and injecting a far lesser amount of poison than would be imbedded at a normal bite, can produce results dramatically severe which would probably terminate fatally unless every measure to combat the injury was at hand.

One morning Mr. George P. Vierheller, Director of the Zoological Gardens at St. Louis, Missouri, called me by long distance telephone to obtain quick advice as to serum treatment for the bite of a large Gaboon viper. The injury was to Mr. R. Marlin Perkins, Curator of Reptiles at the gardens. Knowing that the institution had an assorted series of sera for different types of snakes, but also realizing that no specific serum existed for the Gaboon viper, I suggested to Mr. Vierheller to immediately administer the American polyvalent antivenin, to observe the patient closely and watch for difficulty in breathing which would indicate that the poison contained a powerful neurotoxin.

About an hour later Mr. Vierheller again telephoned that Mr. Perkins was struggling to breathe. There was now no mistaking the

presence of a dangerous neurotoxic element and I advised the immediate injection of cobra serum, thus adding a further specific neutralizing agent.   During midafternoon hemorrhagic symptoms were so extremely pronounced that I recommended the administration of a third type of serum specifically prepared to neutralize the poison of the fer-de-lance and other *Bothrops* species, which produces such marked haemolysis that bleeding occurs from the eyes, mouth and stomach. It is my conviction that if these specific grades of serum had not been available, Mr. Perkins would have died.   Thanks to the foresight of the St. Louis officials the requisite sera were at hand to combat the respectively grave symptoms and thus produce from products obtained through immunization with the poisons of entirely different kinds of snakes a polyvalent treatment for a reptile with a combination venom of great power.

The following case report, prepared by Dr. Forest H. Staley of St. Louis, is of great value in delineating the developing symptoms and the treatment Mr. Perkins received.   He was fortunate indeed to have been under Dr. Staley's competent attention.   The report is from the Department of Surgery, St. Louis University School of Medicine, and I am indebted to Dr. Staley for permission to use it.   With omission of the more technical details, the report reads:

". . . The action and the destructive properties of this venom are well illustrated in the case of Mr. R. Marlin Perkins, Curator of the St. Louis Reptile House, who was recently bitten by one of these serpents.   While treating this snake for parasites, with the assistance of his associate, Mr. Moody Lentz, he was struck with only one fang on the dorsal surface of the index finger of the left hand.   This occurred at 9:50 a.m. on December 31, 1928.   Immediately, Mr. Perkins felt excruciating pain in the finger, followed in a few seconds by similar pain in the hand.   An incision one-half inch long at the site of the fang puncture was made as soon as possible and Mr. Perkins himself began sucking the wound.   He then started to walk to his office which was sixty feet away, becoming dizzy on the way, and nearly fainting.   He sat down in a chair, feeling extremely giddy.   On reaching the office a tourniquet consisting of a towel was applied, but was not drawn tightly.   Both he and Mr. Lentz continued sucking the wound.   At 10:00 a.m., ten minutes after the bite, Dr. Kammerer, the Zoo veterinarian, arrived and injected one tube of our American Anti-Crotalic serum, injecting about 2 cc. on the dorsum of the left hand, 2 cc. at the

wrist and the remainder in the left pectoral muscle.　At 10:05 the entire arm was paining him greatly and there were shooting pains in the left side of the chest radiating toward the heart.　He also complained of severe headache, limited to the top of the head.　The finger began to swell immediately after the bite and to show a dark discoloration. The swelling rapidly progressed to the hand and up the forearm and arm.

"I arrived at 10:10 a.m., twenty minutes after the accident had taken place.　As I entered the room I did not have to be told what had happened, as I saw Mr. Perkins very pale and blood oozing freely from the end of the finger where the incision had been made.　His pulse was 80, and very weak.　We carried him at once to my automobile and hurried quickly to St. Mary's Hospital.　On admission to the hospital he was extremely pale, but quite rational and conversed freely about his injury, although complaining of great pain in the finger, hand and arm, also of the pain previously described in the left side of his chest.　He was already passing into shock.　No more than five minutes later he said he was having difficulty in getting his breath, and described his condition as though the chest wall would not expand, and as though a heavy weight were pressing downward on his chest.　This difficulty in breathing gradually became more marked.　He was admitted to the hospital between 10:25 and 10:30.　Owing to the weak heart action and difficulty in breathing, he was given hypodermically 7½ grains caffeine sodium benzoate and 1/30 grain of strychnine sulphate.　The arm was placed in a hot bath of normal saline solution, but this did not relieve the pain.　The difficulty in breathing increased in spite of treatment.　During this time the blood was flowing freely from the wound on the finger.

"Ten minutes after admission the pulse was 70 per minute.　The temperature was 97.4 degrees F. on admission and respirations 20. Ten minutes after admission the respirations had gone up to 28 per minute.　The pulse rate continued to get weaker and slower and at 10:50 the rate had dropped to 64.　At 10:55 a.m. patient was breathing with great difficulty and began to complain of additional pain, severe in character, in the back over the region of the kidneys.　At this time he voided urine highly colored with blood and was seized with further great pain along the entire course of the urinary tract.　The pulse quickly dropped to 50, was very weak, and by 10:58 had become imperceptible.　The respirations were now rapid, labored and of short

excursion. The patient looked very bad, deathly pale and was bathed in a cold sweat. At 11:00 a.m. he became unconscious. The pulse could not be felt. The pupils of his eyes were widely dilated and would not react to light. It was thought he was dying. In spite of this, however, he was then given ten cubic centimeters of the American Anti-Crotalic serum slowly in the right median basilic vein. At the same time he received another hypodermic injection of 7½ grains of caffeine sodium benzoate and 1/15 of a grain of strychnine sulphate. He was also given ten cubic centimeters of Cobra Anti-venin (Pasteur Institute, Calmette's) in the right pectoralis major muscle. The respirations soon after the administration of the sera and drugs began to quiet down, although the pulse was still imperceptible.

"At 11:20, after novocaine infiltration, incisions were made on the greatly swollen arm, one two inches long over the dorsum of the hand; the other two inches long over the dorsum of the forearm near the elbow. These incisions were made to relieve the tremendous swelling, allowing the broken down blood and lymph which had passed out into the tissues to escape. The left upper extremity was swollen to at least twice its natural size. The index finger was nearly black. This discoloration extended to the back of the hand which was very dark blue. The bluish and purplish discoloration extended up the arm, and, on the inner side of the arm extending upward into the arm pit, the discoloration was almost black. It is to be noted that even at this time wherever hypodermic injections had been given, as well as the serum, hemorrhagic areas three to four inches in diameter had formed. At 11:25 the original incision on the back of the index finger was lengthened. The tissues began to herniate through the incisions made just a few minutes before. At 11:30 both eyes were extremely bloodshot and the pupils were only moderately dilated, the right pupil being more dilated than the left and the lips and ears were not quite so pale. At 11:45 the patient showed signs of consciousness and asked for water. The pupils were of normal size and equal. The tourniquet was applied soon after admission to the hospital and was released for 20 seconds every ten minutes. At 12:02 patient was complaining of headache, but said he felt a little better. . . . 12:11, patient having a severe chill, shaking. 12:17, still chill. 12:30, pulse weak, rate 112 per minute; respirations 28 per minute; color cyanotic; patient still cold, but not chilly. 12:45, arm removed from bath and placed in hot packs

of normal saline. 1:00 p.m. patient having another chill; still cyanotic; pulse 120 per minute; pupils normal size and equal.

"1:30, temperature 101 degrees F., pulse 116; respirations 28; patient perspiring freely; urine very bloody, in fact consisting of almost pure blood. Most of the red blood corpuscles showed normal contour, although many were disintegrated. Wounds oozing and bleeding freely; necessary to apply compression to wounds to check bleeding; wound on finger not touched. 1:50 to 2:30, patient resting, taking fluids freely, but still complaining of great pain in the affected arm; still very pale and cyanotic; pulse very weak. 3:00, pulse 134 per minute and thready; respirations 28. 3:15, 10 cc. Anti-Bothropic serum given hypodermically in right deltoid muscle. . . .

"Owing to patient's marked anemia, general weakness and resultant shock, a blood transfusion was given at 4:45 p.m. using a number four donor. Five hundred cubic centimeters of citrated blood were given slowly in the vein of the right arm. As the transfusion was going on patient began to look better and to feel much better. His lips and cheeks gradually became pink, losing their pallor. The pulse became stronger. Patient had no reaction following the transfusion."

The report continues through the period to January 20th when Mr. Perkins was discharged from the hospital. During the first few days of January he remained very weak, the hand greatly swollen, and the arm discolored from extravasated blood, this condition extending to the chest. These symptoms slowly subsided and the patient's organic condition steadily improved. After extensive details as to treatment inducing complete recovery, the report concludes with the following summary—in part:

"The extraordinary toxemia seen in this case, which almost culminated in the death of the victim, was undoubtedly a lethal one, but apparently was controlled by the anti-snake-bite sera, by the incisions, suction and drainage, and by the blood transfusions given. The intravenous administration of our Pit-Viper serum, Antivenin, seemed, at least, to bring our patient out of a condition that otherwise would have soon resulted in death, had immediate improvement not taken place. The anti-Cobra serum given at practically the same time seemed to check the respiratory failure that was coming on. The anti-snake-bite serum of the South American Fer-de-Lance (Antivenin Bothropic) given in the afternoon, one hour before the first blood transfusion, unquestionably improved the patient's general condition. It was

given for the purpose of neutralizing the toxins still present, hoping to lessen the great destruction of the erythrocytes still going on and the damage to the capillaries, and thus to allow more beneficial results from the blood transfusion.   The blood transfusions were certainly indicated.   Judging from the marked improvement obtained, it would seem very important, if not imperative, to give blood transfusions in all severe cases of snake-bite poisoning with great hemorrhage, shock and toxemia. . . ."

The development of specific sera is now going on in Africa as in other countries, and credit for this work should be extended to F. W. Fitzsimons, Director of the Port Elizabeth Museum, who is a keen student of serpent life.

It has been asserted that the venom of the Rhinoceros Viper, *Bitis nasicornis,* is even more highly toxic than that of the preceding species. This snake is often found along streams, hence is also called the River Jack.   Its body is just as ponderous as that of the Gaboon viper, but its head is smaller and narrower.   This deficiency is fully compensated by two high double horns standing erect upon its snout, and sometimes several smaller ones at their base.   Ordinarily, as the creature crawls in and out of silty water its exceedingly rough scales show nothing but a dingy pattern.   Freshly shed, it is the most amazing snake of Africa.   The effect is of a body of velvet softly blending a dark carmine and olive, with a pattern laid over that seems utterly out of place for a living creature.   Down the back is a row of large and nicked oblong markings of pale blue.   Each of these has a lemon yellow line down the center.   The blue markings are enclosed in irregular black rhombs.   On the lower sides is a series of dark crimson triangles, narrowly bordered with blue.   The top of the head is blue with a vivid black javelin-shaped mark pointing forward.

The Rhinoceros Viper grows to be four feet and inhabits tropical West Africa.

The Sand Vipers, *Cerastes,* form an interesting little group adapted to the sterile areas along the northern borders of the Sahara.   Their ordinary length is two feet or under and all are of pale hues of yellow or pink to match the sandy areas.   They are as particularly adapted to a life in dry, shifting medium, as are specially developed water snakes, or aboreal serpents.   The ribs are capable of greatly flattening the body and the muscles so arranged that the snake may use the sharp edges of its depressed form to shovel sand over its back, or

communicate a wave-like motion along each side which enables it to quickly sink beneath the surface.   Such a provision is necessary to a creature living in the open with no place to hide.   The usual habit is to imbed the body just beneath the surface and leave the top of the head protruding.   As the eyes are directed upward for this very provision and are of the same color of the sand, the snake is practically invisible.   Another development relates to swift progress over the yielding sand.   A gliding gait would be laborious as the reptile would sink to a certain extent in the sand.   Then again such progress would thus be slow and labored.   Instead, it throws lateral loops, one after another, in such agile fashion that its spry progress is more like "walking" than the movements of a snake.   All the members of the genus quickly move about in this manner.   Some of the big species of *Bitis,* living in sandy areas, do likewise, and on the other side of the world, the "sidewinder" rattlesnake, living in the deserts of the southwestern United States, uses the same gait.

The Horned Sand Viper, *Cerastes cornuta* (Plate 48), needs little description, as this bleached, sand-colored desert creature has a sharp, upright spine over each eye.   The maximum length is two and a half feet.   The Common Sand Viper, *C. vipera* (Plate 48), is smaller, and proportionately stouter.   It has no horns, but its body is of the same pale yellowish, or pinkish hue.   To see one of these creatures run as fast as a crab over the sand dunes at the desert edge, then seem to sink from sight, leads the observer to decide that these are remarkable actions for a snake, but necessarily so in such environment.   *C. vipera* has a smaller range than the horned species.   It is found in northern Africa from Algeria to Egypt, while *C. cornuta* not only occurs in this area, but is found in Arabia and southern Palestine.

The little Carpet Viper, *Echis carinatus,* of the northerly parts, also prefers sandy places, but is not so characteristically a desert type as the former, though it sometimes burrows to hide.   It is prettily marked. This snake ranges through Syria and Persia into India—and in this way differs from other African poisonous reptiles, which are confined within the continental area, except moderate extension into Arabia and the sandy countries immediately adjacent.

There have been various references to interesting phases of parallelism, similarities in eccentric habits or structure to be noted among unrelated snakes.   We have an instance of this—in structure—with the genus of small Tree Vipers or Bush Vipers, *Atheris,* the several

species inhabiting tropical Africa. These slender-bodied, wide-headed serpents quite match the distinctive palm vipers (*Bothrops*) of tropical America. They are leaf-green, barely a yard long, and live in low trees or bushes. They appear to occur along mountain ranges. They may strike in defence, but seem more commonly to try tactics to escape observation and stiffen the neck at odd angles in an endeavor to imitate a twig. In these manoeuvres they simulate the actions of the walking stick insects. Evidently, they are easily frightened—or like most snakes have an inborn fear of man. In his field notes made during the Harvard African Expedition of 1927, in Liberia, Dr. Glover Allen speaks about the Green Bush Viper, *Atheris chlorechis:* "The snakes remain perfectly still in low vines or bushes and allow one to approach quite close. One was seen coiled up in a bush about four feet from the ground. I struck it a powerful blow with a stick thinking to break its back, but for several minutes could not find it, though the ground was open and nearly bare. At length it dawned in my sight posed in stiff and motionless attitude among a few spears of grass which it exactly matched in color."

The closing genus of African vipers is of particular interest as it is hard to surmise what has influenced the members in acquiring enormously developed poison fangs, as they are burrowers. They have small eyes and poor sight, appear to feed upon small prey, and short fangs would seem far better adapted to their purpose. These snakes form the genus *Atractaspis*. They are a foot and a half to two feet long, slender, with heads no wider than their bodies and covered with symmetrical shields. The body scales are smooth. The eye is minute, with round pupil. There are about a dozen species. All of them lay eggs. Distribution covers the greater portion of tropical and southern Africa.

In his notes from East Africa, Loveridge says:[1] "These snakes are known as the burrowing vipers and all the three species with which I am acquainted are black or plumbous in color. Six others occur in east Africa. . . . Like the blind snakes they come to the surface after rain and in traveling over the ground hold their sharply-pointed (in some species rounded) snout at a peculiar angle as if ready to dig down into the soil at a moment's notice. They are surprisingly quick and in attempting to pick one up at Lumbo, it having wandered into a tent, it struck at my thumb. I withdrew my hand quickly, but just

[1] Bulletin of the Antivenin Institute of America, Vol. II. No. 1.

felt a prick on the tip of my thumb which happened to be protected with somewhat horny skin at the time; no venom was visible. . . .

"It has been suggested by one writer that the fangs were so long the snake could not gape widely enough to bring them into play, but in one *(Atractaspis rostrata)* I captured at Morogoro the fangs were brought down on either side of the lower jaw (like the teeth of a musk deer) in the act of striking.

"Owing to their burrowing habits they are rarely met with. At Kilosa and Morogoro two were found near my quarters, another was unearthed by natives digging a pit, a fourth was beneath a mass of earth and stones representing a demolished building. A fifth was reported by natives as seen near a log but it had wriggled down a hole. On digging down into this old termite colony it was discovered about a foot below the surface and four feet from where it had been lying. It squirmed convulsively like a blindsnake or worm, when disturbed. When picked up with a pair of forceps it struck out viciously, discharging a quantity of straw-colored venom upon the instrument."

Snake Bites in Africa: From the statistics the author has been able to gather, Africa has never been notorious for high fatality from snake bites. Of course, it is impossible to collect accurate data from the numerous tribes of the interior, but it is doubtful if there has ever been a death rate from this cause which was very high as compared with the population. There is keen woodcraft among the tribes and this is always associated with caution. To imagine that Africa is everywhere teeming with poisonous snakes, is to gain a false perspective. That has also been a common idea with tropical Asia, particularly India. There is no country in the world that generally teems with dangerous reptiles. And to revert to an assertion already made, I will repeat that it is my conviction that poisonous snakes are no more numerous anywhere in the world than in some of the mountainous portions of New York and Pennsylvania, with their rattlesnakes and copperheads—and possibly again the coastal swamps of Georgia and South Carolina, where the water moccasin abounds. In the actual tropics, poisonous snakes are not so frequently seen as in the temperate zones. One can explore the jungle a week and see not a single snake. This has been my experience in most of the Central American countries, and in Brazil. There are vast stretches of upland and open Africa where snakes are as infrequently seen as upon the prairies of the United States.

Nevertheless, from the review of fanged species within this chapter explorers and sportsmen may note that Africa has its hazards for the careless and the unwary.   It is a vast region and in it are many areas conducive to abundance of reptile life.   The vivid patterns of the big vipers are no more nor less than camouflage markings to blend them with the forest floor or leaves and debris along the trails.   Such conditions should be matched by watchful eye and proper attire and travelers should carry the protective accessories indicated for the country, not only with a thought of themselves, but for the native assistants they employ on their respective missions.

CHAPTER XIV

THE POISONOUS SNAKES OF AUSTRALIA

AUSTRALIA is a land of animal oddities. Differing from all other continental areas its mammals are largely restricted to the representatives of a single Order—the *Marsupialia*. This very Order, in other regions much larger than Australia, is but scantily represented.

But the Australian marsupials have counteracted the absence of the characteristic forms of other Orders in assuming their outlines and habits. This parallelism has resulted in a mammalian masquerade. Thus the pouched animals, which give birth to the most minute and helpless of young, thence carry them in a pocket containing the nursing glands, have developed forms to "represent" various true carnivores, rodents, insectivores and edentates lacking in the small island continent.

In a region where the mammalian fauna is so markedly eccentric one would naturally look for differences in other forms and it is not necessary to go far to find further eccentricity. The serpents of Australia furnish this. With them there is a similar restriction—as to representation of *families*. Australia has plenty of snakes, generous as to number of species, and many of these of abundant occurrence, but unlike other countries they are largely restricted to the members of a single family, and utterly unlike any other country the great majority are poisonous. Australia is a land of Elapine snakes, but unlike the mammals they have not branched out in development to simulate members of other families lacking in their country. If this had been the case there would have been arboreal, aquatic, constricting, burrowing, thick and thin members, but such is not the case—except with one. A germ of influence evidently lodged in the Death Adder—for here is an Elapine snake assuming the form of a viper in a viperless country and developing fangs out of proportion to a dealer of neurotoxic venom. Not only is the *Elapidae* more extensively represented in Australia than in any other country. It is the sole family of poison-

ous serpents found in that country.   There are over eighty species and these are divided into fourteen genera.   None occurs outside the area that may be called "Australasia."   Hence they form a distinct group of the *Elapidae*.   Figuring the Moluccas, New Guinea and the nearby Solomon Islands, we view their widest range of distribution.   Yet the greater number occur in Australia.   Six genera of the fourteen are represented in New Guinea, but not by all of the species of these genera.   At least two of the genera are represented in the Solomons, and again at least two have species in Tasmania.   But few occur in the Moluccas.

This abundance of Elapines may thus be checked against small and burrowing members of *Typhlops,* which are seldom to be seen, three genera of pythons and less than a dozen innocuous Colubrine snakes. It should be understood, however, that the waters of the warm, northern coasts of Australia are inhabited by a number of species of the poisonous marine serpents already considered in detail in the Asiatic and Malayan chapter.

With the exception of a single species, the death "adder" (which is not a true adder), the poisonous snakes of Australia have the outlines of the graceful Colubrine serpents of other lands.   This is not a puzzling matter on the island-continent as snakes generally (except the pythons) are regarded with suspicion.   While the fangs of these Elapines are short, those of the larger species are stout and these snakes bite savagely.

Dr. N. Hamilton Fairley, in a series of valuable papers published in the Medical Journal of Australia during 1929, sums up records of fatal bites, and explains:

One hundred and fifty-four out of two hundred and eighty-one persons were bitten below the knee and the vast majority of these could have been prevented by the use of boots and leggings or putties.   The fangs of any of the Australian colubrides [1] can pierce one layer of material satisfactorily and a snap bite by a tiger snake on a sheep whose foreleg was covered by a thick woollen stocking proved fatal within one hour and twenty-five minutes.   Immediately the snake struck, the sheep pulled its foot away and the whole bite only occupied a fraction of a second.

When the same sock was employed covered by two layers of a regulation army putty, natural bites in the case of both the tiger snake and the death adder

---

[1] Author's note: Reference to "colubrides" in Dr. Fairley's text indicates the disposition of some writers to classify the elapine snakes as a subfamily of the *Colubridae*. This status, however, is now quite generally going over to full family recognition.

proved ineffective, the poison being injected into the sock and not into the skin which showed no fang punctures.   The death adder employed in this experiment had average sized fangs and showed an interfang measurement of 1.75 cm. Despite this finding, however, leggings are in my opinion preferable to putties in country where adders abound.   In a natural bite the fangs of the death adder were found to penetrate through the side of an ordinary shoe, but one of the fangs was lost in the process and an effective bite was improbable.   With thick boot leather penetration becomes impossible.

Snakes bite man by accident more often than by design and though both brown and tiger snakes enter houses, this is not a common event.   Death adders are found on paths and roads at night and it is very advisable to carry a lantern or torch in death adder country.

Tiger snakes and brown snakes frequent logs and copper-head and black snakes rabbit burrows.   The common practice of thrusting the hand into such places is to be deprecated and only a month ago one youth was fatally bitten on the face while crawling into a hollow log after a rabbit.   Attention to the natural habits of the ophidia and commonsense would prevent many bites.

A number of the Australian Elapines are not considered dangerous to man, owing to their being small, having very short fangs and either being inoffensive and timid or of secretive habits.   The larger species stand out from points of abundance, insolence and quick disposition to bite, or remarkably high toxicity of their venoms.   The latter point is of particular interest.   There is a great range in the toxic power among the really dangerous species.   While the action of the poison is more largely neurotoxic—as is world-wide among the *Elapidae,* there are some haemolytic effects, with greater extravasation than with Elapine snakes of other countries.   This variation in toxicity brings us to the consideration of some of the representative and larger kinds.

The Black Snake, *Pseudechis porphyriacus* (Plate 40), belongs to a genus of eight species, at least one of which occurs in New Guinea. This fairly large and really beautiful reptile is the most abundant of the larger and dangerous Australian snakes.   It is widely distributed except in the North, but does not occur in Tasmania.   It prefers damp, often marshy places, often goes into the water and swims well. Its length is about five feet.

The Black Snake is gracefully formed, not unlike a racer, although there is a tendency for three or four inches of the neck to show a slight widening or flattening owing to moderately elongated ribs of cobra type and these laterally move forward at the least feeling of doubt or alarm spreading the neck into an elongate "hood", proportionately half as wide as that of a cobra.   The snake does not rear in combat

attitude like a cobra, but may elevate the anterior portion on a slanting plane with the head a few inches from the ground. The scales are smooth and the upper parts of the body are satiny blue-black. In contrast to the purplish sheen of the back is the lower row of scales on each side. Extending from the neck to the tail, these are of bright scarlet or carmine, often narrowly margined with black. The abdomen is of the same beautiful color, the cross plates edged with purplish black.

Black Snakes are omnivorous as serpents go, eating small mammals, birds, lizards and frogs. My captive specimens were extremely quick if pursuing living prey, darting after frogs with such a rush they would catch them after two or three jumps. The swallowing motions are rapid and the prey barely passes into the throat when the reptile, with darting motions of the head from side to side, scans the nearby area for additional prey. Captives become tame, which is not generally the case with Elapids, but upon unusual disturbance there is a nervous flattening of the neck. The satiny skin is extremely susceptible to attacks of parasites from other reptiles having resistance against such pests. In fact, I have found that all the Australian snakes suffer greatly from the skin mites and red "bugs" commonly carried by South American reptiles, even by some of the snakes of the southern United States. It is indicated that these parasites in burrowing under the edges of the scales and biting produce irritation, against which the Australian reptiles have no immunity. Vesicles form, which develop hard, "cheesy" centers. As these become numerous, some of them increase in area, and a toxaemia is produced which is invariably fatal. Such snakes should be kept isolated from reptiles of other countries if they are to be successfully studied. Under conditions free from parasites the Black Snake is hardy and contentedly lives for years. A beautiful example was on exhibition in the reptile house of the Philadelphia Zoological Society for a period of slightly over seventeen years.

Despite its fair size the bite of the Black Snake is not nearly so dangerous as some of the other larger species, owing to the lower toxicity of its venom. It produces up to two dozen living young. Here again is an Australian variation from the rule commonly relating to Elapine species. Members of the *Elapidae* of other countries are quite generally oviparous.

There is much in prospect to be learned about Australia's poison-

ous snakes, as indicated by a new and excellent work brought out in concise form under the authorship of J. R. Kinghorn, Zoologist of the Australian Museum, at Sydney. This is entitled Snakes of Australia. In this the author speaks of a giant species of *Pseudechis*, attaining a length of nine feet with proportionately long fangs and large poison glands. It appears to inhabit central Queensland. More surprising, however, is a description of a recently discovered species closely related to the former, but called the Giant Brown Snake, *Oxyuranus maclennani* Kinghorn. It seems to be restricted to the Cape York Peninsula and is the largest venomous snake yet to be found in Australia, attaining a length in excess of ten feet and, as the author of the description explains, having fangs almost half an inch in length. A skin in the Australian Museum nearly ten feet long and a skull from a specimen ten feet and three inches long are the only known specimens in scientific collections, although W. McLennan who first noted the species at Coen, Cape York Peninsula, states that this formidable creature, a close rival of the king cobra, is not uncommon.

The Copper-head Snake, *Denisonia superba,* differs from the black snake in occurring commonly in Tasmania. Its range in Australia is in the southeasterly portion. This dangerous reptile attains a length of five (occasionally six) feet and in color ranges through shades of brown to black. The head is usually of a coppery tinge, this being particularly marked with younger examples. It is a stouter species than the black snake. When angry it rears a few inches from the ground, the neck arched slightly, like the first motions of a cobra when aroused. Watching these creatures I have often thought that here may have been the ancestral indications, the beginnings of the cobra's supreme combat attitude.

The genus *(Denisonia),* to which the copper-head snake belongs, is the largest in Australia. There are close to two dozen species. Several are very slender and others very small. The former are called whip snakes. The White-lipped Whip Snake, *D. coronoides,* is on the average eighteen inches long, and the Little Whip Snake, *D. flagellum,* fifteen inches long. Kefft explains that the bite of the small species produces no greater effect than the sting of a bee.

Demansia, with about a dozen species, has similar variations in size. Several of the members are called whip snakes. The Brown Snake, *D. textilis,* broadly distributed and usually four to five feet long is rated as highly dangerous. The color is light brown above and white

beneath.   The young are pale brown and prettily ringed during their first year.   The members of this genus are oviparous.

Owing to its small head the amount of poison injected by the bite of this snake is small, yet it is of very high toxicity.   No better example of innocence in outline could be selected than an adult Brown Snake. Its form is like that of a typical racer, such as described among the harmless Colubrines.   The head is high and narrow, with large eyes, and a student might walk past a case containing specimens and from a glance surmise that they were specimens of innocuous West Indian racers (*Alsophis*) or North American coach-whip snakes (*Masticophis*).   A glance at the side of the mild-looking head tells the story. That is the scientist's first step in "running down" deceptive members of the *Elapidae. The loreal shield is missing.*   This is a squarish shield between the orbitals (the shields forming a margin about the eye) and the nasals (between which the nostrils are situated).   It is missing in a few harmless serpents, but not many.   Its absence is a sinister warning.   This carries through the cobras, kraits, mambas, coral snakes and their allies.   It is a point which the reptile student should understand early in his observations.

The Tiger Snake, *Notechis scutatus* (Plate 40), receives its name from bands of dark color on a tawny body hue, although occasional examples are so dark the bands are indistinct.   It is commonly four to five feet long.   The form is moderately stout.   Owing to inhabiting quite dry country the range is particularly extensive, not only in Australia, but in Tasmania.

This is the most savage and dangerous of the Australian reptiles. Investigations of its venom indicate its being of such extremely high toxicity as to be unmatched by that of any other known serpent.   Applied against this, however, are smaller poison glands than a number of the world's better known deadly types.   It appears to produce more fatalities in Australia than the combined bites of all of the other poisonous serpents in that country.

Tiger snakes are quick to bite, spreading the neck by enlarged anterior ribs and lunging with a flashing stroke so vigorous that the body may slide forward.   With a particularly enraged specimen that action looks like a short jump.   The aspect, even when at rest, is not reassuring.   It is not of the graceful, whip-like form of the brown snake. The head is rather wide and the swollen temporal area hints of the glands secreting the powerful poison.   It is not Viperine in outline,

but rather like the more heavily-bodied Colubrine snakes that possess a temper in keeping with their looks. These snakes feed upon both small mammals and lizards. Unfortunately, with such a dangerous reptile, it is highly prolific, producing as many as fifty living young.

The Death Adder, *Acanthophis antarcticus* (Plate 41), represents a characteristic Australian development on a parallel with the masquerading mentioned among the Marsupialia. With those warm-blooded creatures there has been a remarkable tendency to develop forms like carnivores, rodents and insectivores. With the Death Adder we have the personification of a viper in a modified Elapid. This snake is short and thick with a wide head, hence its name in an actually adderless country.

It is seldom more than two feet long, but its large head has fangs longer than those of a big tiger snake. With such weapons to deeply imbed the powerful neurotoxin of its race, and with the toxicity of its venom so high, the danger from a bite of this unique reptile may be surmised. It is not so flashing in its rage, so quick to strike as the tiger snake, but is rated as extremely dangerous as it is liable to be stepped on. Its colors closely match the dry, usually sandy soil where it lives, and in areas where the sand may be gray, brown, pink or even reddish, the death adder matches the hue of the surface. There are bands of darker hue crossing the body. The scales of the anterior portion are very roughly keeled, even the shields of the head having coarse striations. There is a spine on the tail. The young are produced alive in litters of approximately a dozen.

The death adder occurs in the dry areas over the greater portion of Australia except southern Victoria. It occurs in New Guinea and the Moluccas, in fact has the widest range of any member of the Australian *Elapidae*.

As to the relative toxicity of the venoms of the larger and more dangerous Australian serpents, and a comparison of their poisons with snakes of other countries, Fairley has brought out some extremely interesting points. He has very kindly given me permission to draw from his material [2] in this summary of the Australian snakes. In part, he says:

In Table I will be found a record of the deaths occurring within the Commonwealth from venomous bites and stings. It will be noted that in the seventeen year period from 1910 to 1926, 244 people died from these causes. . . .

[2] Articles appearing in the Medical Journal of Australia, March 9, 16, 23 and June 8, 1929. Besides the papers by Dr. N. Hamilton Fairley, there are several by Dr. C. H. Kellaway.

TABLE I

DEATHS IN THE COMMONWEALTH FROM VENOMOUS BITES AND STINGS
(1910 TO 1926)

	DEATHS FROM VENOMOUS BITES AND STINGS		
YEAR	MALES	FEMALES	TOTAL
1910	8	4	12
1911	14	7	21
1912	10	6	16
1913	11	5	16
1914	16	5	21
1915	6	0	6
1916	11	2	13
1917	11	2	13
1918	4	3	7
1919	5	3	8
1920	18	5	23
1921	21	8	29
1922	19	4	23
1923	6	0	6
1924	1	5	6
1925	10	2	12
1926	8	4	12
Total	179	65	244 [3]

Stings as well as venomous bites are included in these figures and if the snake-bite mortality is taken as 80 per cent of this total, it means that in the seventeen years under review 195 persons have died from this cause.

Though by no means formidable such a series of deaths does suggest the advisability of reviewing the present position regarding snake-bite and the snake-bitten in this country. . . .

The important Australian venomous snakes are the death adder (*Acanthophis antarcticus*), the tiger snake (*Notechis scutatus*), the copper-head (*Denisonia superba*), the brown snake (*Diemenia* [4] *textilis*) and the black snake (*Pseudechis porphyriacus*).

Another table follows, showing a mortality rate produced by the more dangerous kinds, from the records of Tidswell and Ferguson:

[3] The great proportionate difference between these figures and those of India, with numerous and active poisonous serpents in both countries, is readily explained by the variance in habits of the residents of Australia from the predominating, ignorant and careless nations of the Orient who everywhere go barefooted both by day and night.

[4] Recently changed to *Demansia*.

Species of Snake	Number of Persons Bitten	Deaths	
		Number	Percentage
Death adder	10	5	50
Tiger	45	18	40
Brown	70	6	8.6
Black	125	1	0.8
Totals	250	30	12

From the preceding table it will be noted that the black snake, which most frequently bites man, is rarely the cause of death, while the death adder and tiger snakes rate higher in producing fatalities than any other of the Australian species.

The article explains that Tidswell recorded the average yield of poison, after an extraction and it had been dried, from a death adder as 56.7 milligrams, from a tiger snake as 26.2 mgm., the black snake as 19.2 and the brown snake as 4.8. Thus the death adder was revealed as the largest venom producer, while the brown snake proved much the smallest. The figures are significant in showing the much higher toxicity of the brown snake's poison if examination is again made of the table. It will there be noted that despite the small amount of poison yielded at a bite by the brown snake (approximately one quarter that of the black snake) the percentage of death from its bites is 8.6 against .8 of the black snake. Larger yields are obtained from occasional specimens of all of the kinds mentioned.

As examples of fluid yields in milligrams [5] it is interesting to compare well known species to the Australian snakes, as follows: North American Diamond-back Rattlesnake, *Crotalus adamanteus,* 600 mgm.; North American Copperhead Snake, *Agkistrodon mokasen,* 55 mgm.; Indian Cobra, *Naia naia,* 317 mgm.; Indian Russell's Viper, *Vipera russellii,* 108 mgm.; Australian Death Adder, *Acanthophis antarcticus,* 84.7 mgm.; Australian Tiger Snake, *Notechis scutatus,* 47.2 mgm.; Australian Copper-head Snake, *Denisonia superba,* 35.6 mgm.; and the Australian Black Snake, *Pseudechis porphyriacus,* 47 mgm.

These figures again bring out some very interesting points. They show the large amounts of poison secreted by reptiles that are famous for their deadliness and the comparatively small amounts of the Aus-

[5] The venom loses much of its bulk and weight in drying, the reduction being as much as sixty per cent or even two thirds, this depending upon its specific gravity or viscosity, or length of time it has been secreted in the glands since biting. Venom long secreted has higher specific gravity than from glands recently refilled after biting.

tralian serpents.   Figuring out an example in ratio for the Australian Tiger Snake to include the amount of venom it secretes and the human death rate from its bites, it appears that drop for drop this Elapid secretes a more deadly poison than any other known serpent of the world, even ranking the curious tree viper, the New World's most lethal species, found on an isolated island off the coast of Brazil.   Here are examples of how the proportions of complex elements composing serpent poisons vary, not only in quantities but in relative toxicity.

INDEX

(*Upper*).   Mexican Dwarf Python, *Loxocemus bicolor*.   Unique in being the only known species of the subfamily of Pythons in the New World.   This example was captured near Colima.   The range is small and the species is rare or so secretive it is seldom seen.   Tabulation indicates the scant number of approximately a dozen examples to have reached scientific collections.

(*Lower*).   Head details of Mexican Dwarf Python.   The pointed snout is used in burrowing.   Double plates under the tail create a distinguishing character from the small burrowing boas of similar form.

PLATE 2   Non-venomous Snakes

(*Upper*). Ball Python, *Python regius*. Inhabits tropical West Africa. Attains a length of four to five feet. A number of the pythons are of little more than fair size compared with general serpent measurements, in fact the really huge species of the subfamily are in the minority.

(*Lower*). Ball Python in "defensive" attitude. When frightened these supple constrictors draw the body into compact folds with the head tucked in and hidden. This habit may be noted with wild or particularly timid examples. Most captive specimens become tame and relinquish such antics.

(*Upper*).   Indian Python, *Python molurus*, (light phase).   There are two distinct color phases of this species, which is recognized by the arrow-shaped blotch on the head.   This paler variety occurs from Kurrachee to Madras.   It is smaller than the darker, typical form occurring easterly in India, the Malay Peninsula and Java.   *Molurus* is one of the world's largest snakes, attaining a length of twenty-five feet.

(*Lower*).   Carpet Python, *Python spilotes variegata*.   A variety of the Australian Diamond Python. Usually under ten feet although recorded to a length of fourteen feet in northerly Australia.

PLATE 4   Non-venomous Snakes

(Upper). Reticulated or Regal Python, *Python reticulatus*. The world's largest species of snake. Readily distinguished from the Indian python by a narrow black line on the head. The range is Burma, Indo-China, the Malay Peninsula and Archipelago to the Philippines, inclusive. The example in the illustration is twenty feet long.

(Lower). Anaconda or Water Boa, *Eunectes murinus*. The example shown is nineteen feet long with weight of two hundred and thirty-six pounds. This great constrictor of tropical America is proportionately stouter than a python. Its maximum length is about twenty-five feet.

(*Upper*). Yellow Anaconda, *Eunectes notaeus*. There is a more mottled effect of the markings than with the more abundant *E. murinus*, which is dark olive, with round black spots. The specimen shown is from Minas Geraes, Brazil, an area noted for its big serpents.

(*Lower*). An Anaconda's Skin. The total length was twenty-one feet and four inches. A serpent of this size could swallow a peccary or a third-grown tapir.

PLATE 6   Non-venomous Snakes

(*Upper*).   South American Boa; "Boa Constrictor," *Constrictor constrictor*. The term "Boa Constrictor" is sometimes improperly applied to the big snakes of Asia and Africa—which are pythons.   The larger boas inhabit tropical America.

(*Lower*).   Central American Boa.   This represents the same species as the upper figure.   The example was twelve feet long.   Maximum length of the "Boa Constrictor" is about fifteen feet.   Its range is from southern Mexico well through tropical South America.   Several races, or subspecies, are recognized.

(*Upper*). The Boa Constrictor at Home. Coiled on the tropical forest floor this handsomely marked boa is difficult to detect. Its blotched pattern of light and dark hues breaks its outlines. This is the case with many snakes that under artificial conditions appear to be vividly marked.

(*Lower*). West Indian Boa, *Constrictor orophias*. The length is seldom over eight feet. The blotches are more crowded than with the mainland species. It appears to be normally confined to St. Lucia and Dominica although young specimens are occasionally found in near-by islands where they have been transported after hiding in cargo.

PLATE 8   Non-venomous Snakes

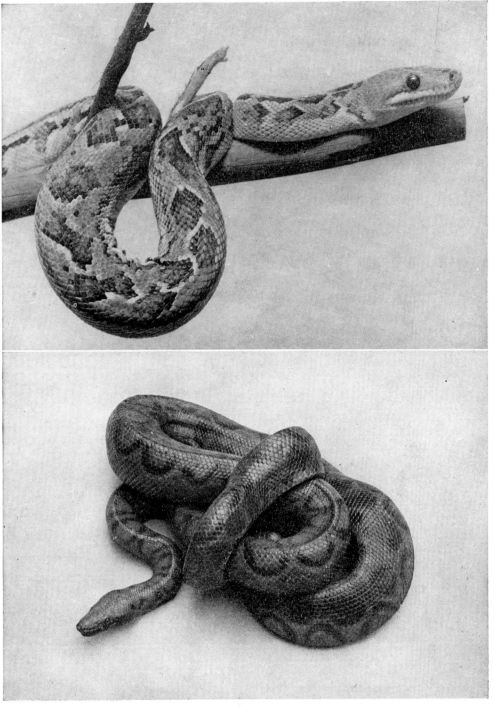

(*Upper*).   Cuban Boa; Majá, *Epicrates angulifer*.   Cuba and the Isle of Pines.   A stout and powerful boa attaining a length of about ten feet, but large examples are rare.   Cane cultivation has resulted in its extermination over considerable areas.

(*Lower*).   Rainbow Boa; Ringed Boa, *Epicrates cenchris*.   Northern South America is the home of this five-foot boa of brownish hue with blackish rings.   Gliding into the sun the reptile is transformed.   As the light catches the upper surface at certain slants, patches of iridescence glow in green and blue, like the wings of the morpho butterfly inhabiting the same country.

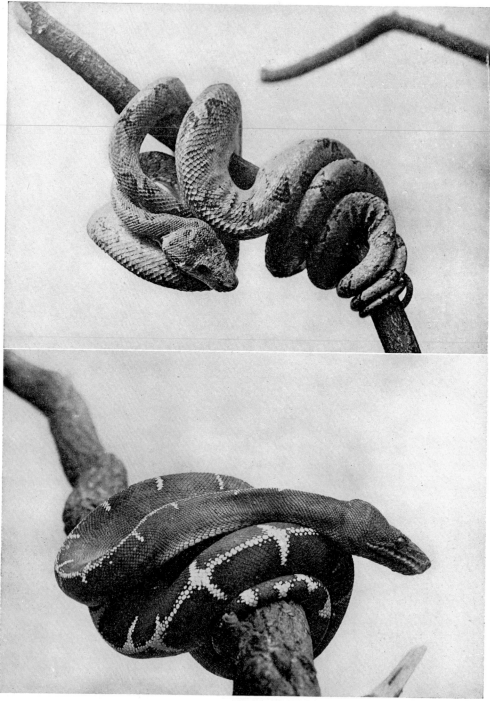

(*Upper*).   Gray Tree Boa, *Boa enydris*.   Tropical America harbors several kinds of these slender boas, with chunky, wicked-looking head in strong contrast to the thin neck.   Their length is from four to six feet.   The tail is strongly prehensile.   They have particularly long teeth and savagely bite when disturbed.

(*Lower*).   Emerald Tree Boa, *Boa canina*.   The green body, with its decoration of enamel-white pattern, combines to make this the most vivid serpent of South America.   In the trees, however, the markings serve as "camouflage" and break the outlines in simulating patches of light coming through the foliage.

PLATE 10

Non-venomous Snakes

(*Upper*).   Head of Emerald Tree Boa, *Boa canina*.   These non-venomous reptiles have a head fully as sinister in outline as the deadly species of *Bothrops* or lance-head snakes.   Like all members of the *Boidae* the pupil is elliptical and most of the prowling is done at night.

(*Lower*).   Skull of Tree Boa.   Excessive length of anterior teeth in both upper and lower jaws is of great value in piercing the feathers and obtaining a firm hold of birds, upon which these reptiles largely feed. They also inflict painful injuries when used in defence.

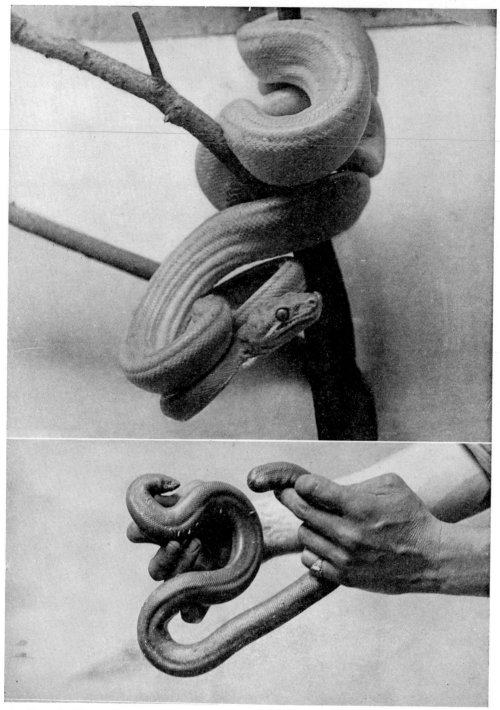

(*Upper*).   Tree Boa, *Boa enydris*.   (Albinistic example.)   Lemon-yellow (albinistic) specimens of this arboreal boa are not uncommon.   This tendency is also noted with another tropical American tree snake—a pit viper—the yellow specimens as frequent as the typical form.

(*Lower*).   Indian Sand Boa, *Eryx johnii*.   Several small burrowing boas inhabit southerly Asia and northern Africa.   This species grows to about a yard in length.   The tail is remarkably blunt, as is the case with several of these pygmies of the *Boidae*.   The wedge-shaped head is used in burrowing.

PLATE 12   Non-venomous Snakes

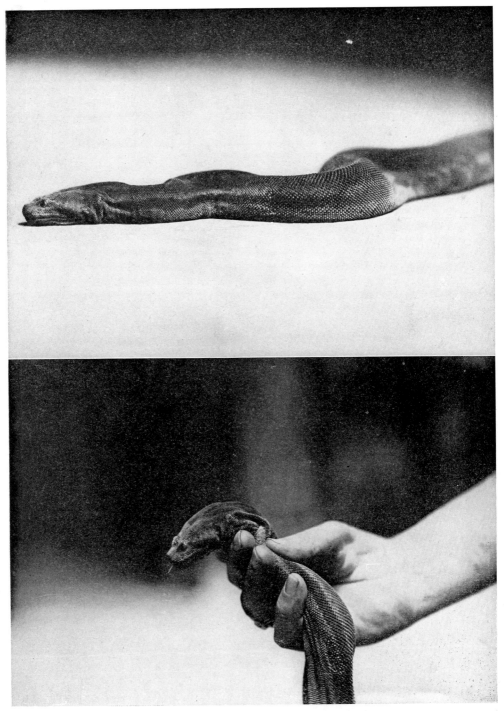

(*Upper*). Karung; Indian Water Snake, *Achrochordus javanicus*. A member of the great series of Colubrine snakes. The extremely ugly and clumsy-looking water snakes form a small subfamily inhabiting Oriental swamps and rivers. Their tough and mottled skins are the high favorites among reptile leathers, the scales being crushed to smooth and glossy surface between powerful rollers.

(*Lower*). Karung. Showing the collapsed condition of the skin when the reptile is removed from the water. These snakes are slow and awkward on land, but strong and graceful swimmers.

(*Upper*).   Garter Snake; Striped Snake, *Thamnophis sirtalis*. The most generally abundant snake
of eastern North America.   The genus of Striped Snakes is distributed throughout North America and into
Mexico.   Some species are semi-aquatic.

(*Lower*).   Red-bellied Water Snake, *Natrix sipedon erythrogaster*.   Water snakes of this type can travel
rapidly on land and hence are quite different from the Karung on opposite plate, which belongs to a different
subfamily.   About a dozen kinds of water snakes inhabit the United States.   These non-venomous reptiles
are often confused with the Water Moccasin, an unrelated poisonous species (Plate 54).

PLATE 14   Non-venomous Snakes

(*Upper*).   American Blacksnake; Black Racer, *Coluber constrictor*.   A characteristic, very active and familiar reptile of the eastern United States.   Its satiny black form gliding swiftly through meadow grass is startling to anyone not familiar with snakes.   It feeds largely upon small rodents and is hence of economic value.

(*Lower*).   Coachwhip Snake, *Masticophis flagellum*.   Inhabits the southeasterly United States, but similar species occur westward to the Pacific coast.   Western whip snakes are marked with bands running lengthwise.   These serpents attain a length of about seven feet.   They are very timid and can glide at astonishing speed.

(*Upper*).   Tropical Whip Snake, *Masticophis mentovarius*.   The range is southerly Mexico and Central America.   Whip snakes, racers and their near allies occur in both North and South America, also the Old World.   They have no power of constriction hence feed upon comparatively small prey.   Some devour other kinds of snakes.

(*Lower*).   Green-spotted Snake, *Drymobius margaritiferus*.   Member of a genus with mostly tropical species.   This attractive reptile ranges from Venezuela to southern Texas.   There is a green, or yellowish-green spot in the center of each scale.   Some of the members of *Drymobius* reach a length of eight feet.

PLATE 16   Non-venomous Snakes

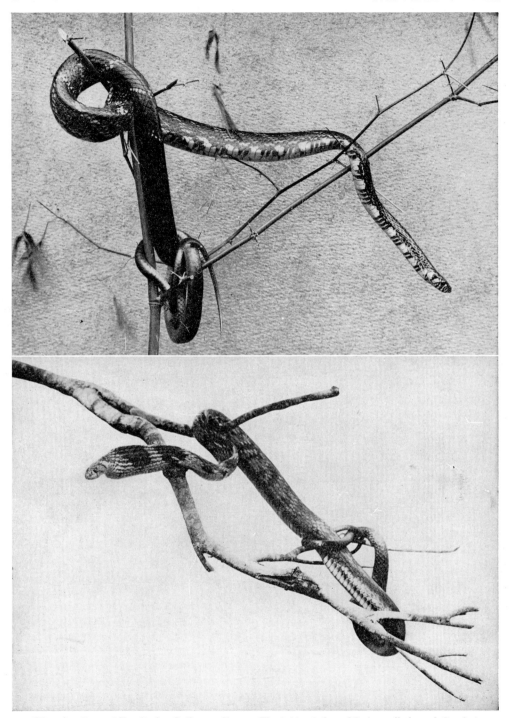

(*Upper*).   Spotted Rat Snake, *Spilotes pullatus*.   The *habitat* is from Mexico well through South America.   Although having slight bulk this is probably the longest tropical American serpent with the exception of the boa and anaconda.   It attains a length in excess of twelve feet.   Its vivid yellow and black pattern is very striking.

(*Lower*).   Spotted Rat Snake in threatening attitude.   Many harmless snakes seek to intimidate an enemy.   The habit of dilating the throat with air is noted among a fair number of New and Old World non-venomous serpents.   Others flatten the neck laterally, while a few dilate the neck vertically.

(*Upper*). Corn Snake, *Elaphe guttata*. The southeastern United States. Its genus contains a number of large, attractively-patterned species, occurring in both the New and Old Worlds. The Corn Snake is grayish or tan, with crimson blotches. It receives its name from prowling into planted areas in search of rodents.

(*Lower*). Tropical Rat Snake, *Elaphe triaspis*. Central America. The blotches are proportionately larger than with the corn snake (seen above). The body is silvery gray, the blotches darker. All the members of this genus are powerful constrictors. They are agile climbers and partially arboreal.

PLATE 18   Non-venomous Snakes

(*Upper*).   Pine Snake, *Pituophis melanoleucus*.   One of the largest serpents of the eastern United States. The species of *Pituophis* are characteristic in taking deep inhalations when annoyed, opening the mouth slightly and producing a loud hissing sound by expelling the air against an erectile filament in the lower jaw.

(*Lower*).   Bull Snake, *Pituophis sayi*.   The plains region of the United States.   Growing in excess of eight feet, it is one of the largest North America serpents.   It loudly hisses like the pine snake (above).   A particularly valuable destroyer of injurious rodents in the wheat belt.

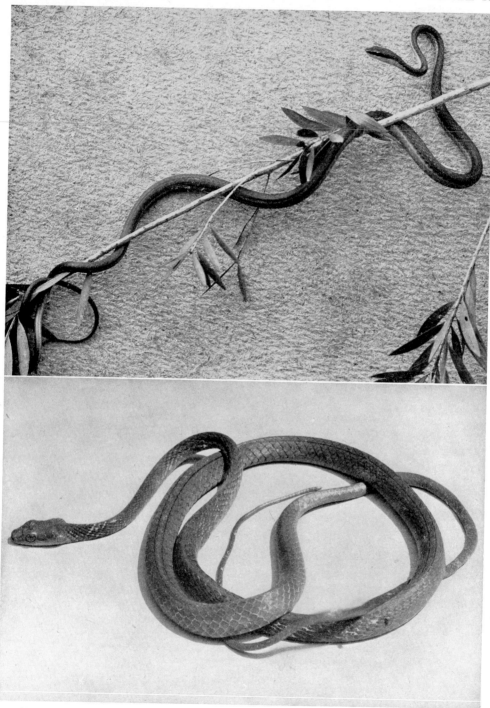

(*Upper*). Green-headed Tree Snake, *Leptophis mexicanus*. Mexico to Costa Rica. Over a dozen kinds of these dainty tree snakes inhabit the American tropics. The back of this species is of lustrous bronze hue. The head is bright green. It threatens by widely opening the mouth and staring at an intruder.

(*Lower*). Green Tree Snake; Chocoya or Parrot Snake, *Leptophis occidentalis*. Found from Guatemala to northern South America. Uniform leaf-green with two hair-like stripes on the back. The food consists of lizards and tree frogs. These slender arboreal snakes seldom feed upon warm-blooded prey.

PLATE 20   Non-venomous Snakes

(*Upper*). Hooded Snake, *Ophis merremi.* The name is applied from the habit of flattening the neck
by means of elongated ribs. A common Brazilian species. Related forms are abundant throughout the
American tropics. All flatten the neck in this fashion. Owing to similarity in markings they are sometimes
confused with the poisonous pit vipers.

(*Lower*). Banded Ground Snake, *Liophis decoratus.* Represents an American (tropical) genus of
moderate-sized, secretive species given to habits of burrowing into damp ground. They are mostly seen
crossing trails or roads after heavy rains.

(*Upper*).   Green Snake, *Liopeltis vernalis*.   This delicate, grass-green creature of eastern North America is interesting in extending northward into Canada as far as serpents are ever found — the other scant representatives of reptile life being an occasional striped or ring-necked snake.   It frequents overgrown meadows and feeds upon soft-bodied insects.

(*Lower*).   Milk Snake; House Snake; Checkered "Adder," *Lampropeltis triangulum*.   The common names of Milk Snake and House Snake come from the habit of entering barns in search of rodents, where the serpent is alleged to "steal" milk from the cows.   Inhabits eastern North America.

PLATE 22   Non-venomous Snakes

(*Upper*). King Snake, *Lampropeltis getulus*. Represents a genus of constricting species inhabiting North America, Mexico and Central America. Several are of fair size. All attack and eat other snakes. The larger kinds are known to be immune to the bites of the pit vipers and often overpower and swallow these poisonous reptiles.

(*Lower*). Tropical King Snake, *Lampropeltis polyzonus*. Mexico and Central America. This example is from Honduras. The wide spaces are of scarlet, separated by yellow rings bordered with black. While cannibalistic all the king snakes also eat rodents. The species are of economic value and should be protected.

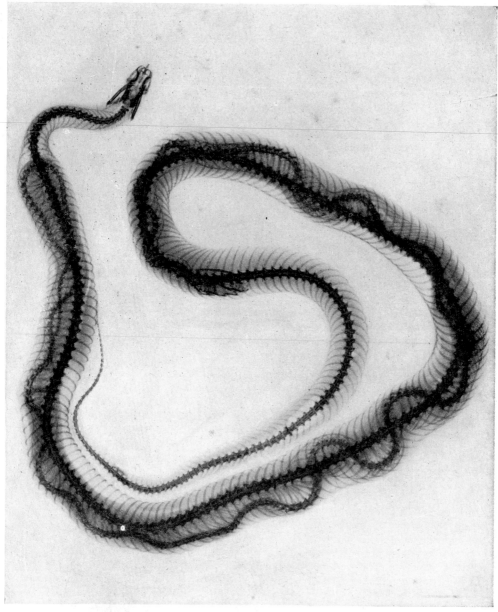

Florida King Snake, *Lampropeltis getulus floridana*. X-rayed after having swallowed a non-venomous serpent longer than itself. The "walking" motions and pulling power of the independently movable jaw bones with their recurved teeth, also the wave-like force of the thoracic area in swallowing are indicated by the undulated disposal of the prey. In this instance it is probable that during the latter portion of the meal the snake managed to grip the tail of the victim while engulfing the last twenty per cent of its length. This resulted in a readily swallowed "hair-pin" section.

PLATE 24   Non-venomous Snakes

(*Upper*).   Cuban Racer; Whip Snake, *Alsophis angulifer*.   Abundant in Cuba.   Closely allied to the North American racers and whip snakes, but shown here in comparison of head-markings and patterns. Flattens the neck and rears the head when angered.

(*Lower*).   Neck-banded Snake, *Sibinophis annulatus*.   Occurs in southern Mexico and northern Central America.   Here is an example of extremely eccentric markings.   The anterior half of the body is red, the pairs of black rings on the neck enclosing lavender areas.   The rear portion of the body is gray.

(*Upper*).   Mangrove Snake, *Boiga dendrophilus*.   A rear-fanged and mildly poisonous species, but very gentle in its manners.   It inhabits the Malay Peninsula and the greater portion of Malaysia.   Its six-foot body with lustrous black scales decorated with orange-yellow rings produces an attractive combination. Species of its genus are persistently arboreal.

(*Lower*).   Mangrove Snake.   Comparing this figure with the head markings of *Alsophis* on the opposite plate imparts a clear idea of the decorative patterns commonly to be noted among snakes.

PLATE 26   Mildly Poisonous Snakes

(*Upper*).   Night Snake, *Leptodira annulata*.   Fairly common in southern Central America and tropical South America.   A rear-fanged species receiving its name from prowling to the edge of swampy areas at night.   Its pupils are elliptical and cat-like.   It is seldom found far from damp places and feeds mostly upon frogs.

(*Lower*).   Guarda Camino ("Road Guarder"), *Conophis lineatus*.   A savage little Central American rear-fanged snake.   Its habit of lying at the edge of roads and trails in watch for lizards and the young of other snakes has produced its common name in Honduras and Guatemala.

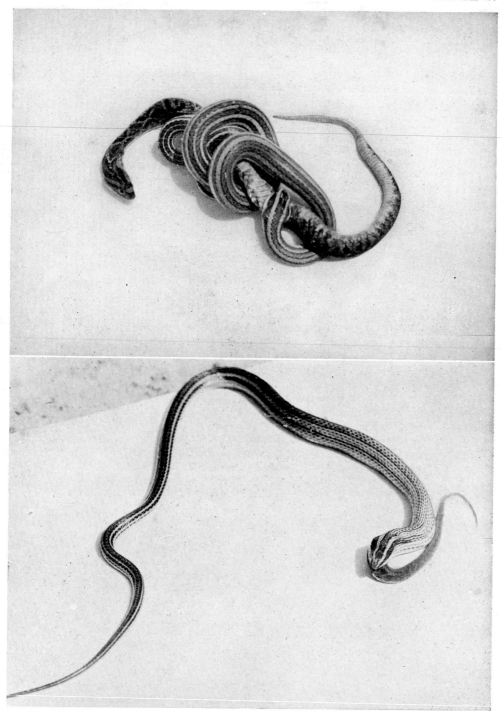

Guarda Camino ("Road Guarder").   This is the species figured in better detail on the opposite plate. The savage nature of this reptile is seen as it imbeds its fangs with their benumbing poison into a young *Ophis colubrinus*—a very common snake of tropical America.   Douglas March while in charge of the Serpentarium at Tela, Honduras, was bitten by one of these snakes barely eighteen inches long.   There was an immediate burning pain and a localized swelling rising abruptly from the hand, about an inch in diameter and half an inch high.   The symptoms continued for several hours.

PLATE 28   Mildly Poisonous Snakes

(*Upper*). Mussurana; Sumbadora, *Pseudoboa cloelia*. Six to eight feet long, lithe and powerful, and glossy black, this enemy of poisonous snakes inhabits Central and South America. It seems to be uncommon everywhere. It feeds largely upon the deadly lance-head snakes and is immune to their bites.

(*Lower*). The Mussurana and its Prey. While it has rear fangs and poison to benumb its victims the Mussurana is a powerful constrictor. Its coils, rather than venom-conducting teeth are the more effective. Central American specimens are white beneath. Those from South America are uniformly black.

Vine Snake; Long-headed Snake, *Oxybelis acuminatus*. Members of this tropical genus and the allied species of the Indo-Malayan *Dryophis*, are remarkable for their excessive slenderness of form and elongated heads. All are arboreal, green or the color of bark and particularly interesting as examples of reptilian mimicry. They are difficult to detect owing to their resemblance to stems, tendrils or vines. All are rear-fanged but practically harmless to man. Their scanty and mild poison is utilized in paralyzing lizards upon which they mostly feed.

PLATE 30   Mildly Poisonous Snakes

(*Upper*).   False Coral Snake, *Pseudoboa trigeminus*.   The pattern of red, black and yellow bands is remarkably similar to that of the dangerously poisonous coral snakes.   This tropical American serpent belongs to the same genus as that containing the Mussurana.

(*Lower*).   False Coral Snake, *Erythrolamprus aesculapii*.   Inhabits Brazil and is marked with red, black and yellow bands.   There is similarity to the deadly coral snakes in coloration, but the yellow rings are single and margined with black, a reverse from the usual pattern of the dangerous reptiles.   Harmless "mimics" of coral snakes are found wherever the latter occur.

(*Upper*). Poisonous Coral Snake, *Micrurus frontalis*. Southern Brazil to Argentina. The wider spaces are rich red separated by black rings bordered with yellow. While not apparent on the illustration, the yellow is again narrowly bordered with black. These snakes are the only New World allies of cobras and kraits.

(*Lower*). Poisonous Coral Snake, *Micrurus corallinus*. Tropical South American and the Lesser Antilles. The yellow rings are narrow but vivid. In contrast to the black rings they enclose, and the broad red areas, they combine to form a very beautiful pattern.

PLATE 32   Dangerously Poisonous Snakes

(*Upper*).   Coral Snake; Harlequin Snake, *Micrurus fulvius*.   There are approximately two dozen species of these deadly snakes.   Their length is from two to four feet.   Two occur in the southern United
States.   The species figured inhabits the southeasterly area thence extends into tropical America.

(*Lower*).   Central American Coral Snake, *Micrurus nigrocinctus*.   The average length is close to three
feet.   These slender-bodied, narrow-headed serpents with their pretty patterns look anything but dangerous.
They do not strike, but deliberately bite if touched or stepped on.   Their venom attacks the nerve centers
and bites are often fatal.

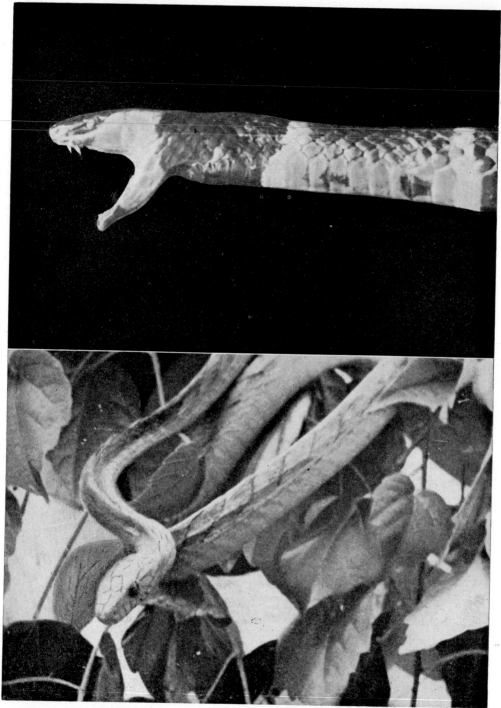

(*Upper*).   Head of Coral Snake, *Micrurus*.   Showing the short poison fangs, which are permanently erect.   For studies of fang development among snakes note Plates 39, 42, 43, 50 and 51.

(*Lower*).   Mamba, *Dendraspis angusticeps*.   The most dreaded snake of Africa.   There are several species, two of these commonly seen in green and black phases.   Mambas are extremely slender, with narrow head and do not look like poisonous snakes.   They glide at great speed, both upon the ground and in trees.   During the breeding season they are inclined to attack in such rapid and bewildering fashion the victim has little chance for defence.

PLATE 34   Dangerously Poisonous Snakes

(*Upper*). Black Cobra, *Naia melanoleuca*. Tropical Africa. There is a common idea that India is the land of cobras, but actually Africa is the headquarters of this type of snake. Here, owing to at least eight distinct species and several subspecies, a dozen "kinds" of cobras produce representation of the hooded clan in all parts of the great continent.

(*Lower*). Black Cobra, *Naia melanoleuca*. Attains a length of six to eight feet. Its scales are highly polished and from this condition it may be distinguished from cobras with the dorsal scales having a satiny luster.

(Upper). Egyptian Cobra, *Naia haie.* The commonly applied name is misleading as this cobra occurs from Egypt to Natal. The scales are of satiny luster—not polished as with the reptile on opposite plate. The example seen is at rest, with no indication of a "hood."

(Lower). Egyptian Cobra, *Naia haie.* With this illustration compared to the one above, the significance of the cobra's hood becomes clear. The hood is formed by laterally spreading elongate, anterior ribs as the serpent rises in combat attitude. In passive mood these ribs lie folded against the sides.

PLATE 36   Dangerously Poisonous Snakes

(*Upper*). Indian Cobra; Spectacled Cobra, *Naia naia*. The title of "Indian" cobra is misleading as this species occurs throughout India, Indo-China, the Malay Peninsula and Malaysia to and including the Philippines. In these areas, this, and the larger king cobra, are the only members of the genus *Naia*.

(*Lower*). Indian Cobra; Cobra de capello; Monocellate Cobra, *Naia naia*. This example illustrates nothing more than a pattern difference in the hood markings — a ring enclosing a single spot. The common name of "cobra de capello" (snake with a cape) might just as appropriately be applied to the cobras of Africa.

(*Upper*).   Indian Cobra; Spectacled Cobra, *Naia naia*.   Hood markings appear as nothing more than an elongate blotch unless the neck is expanded by laterally extensible ribs.   A gliding cobra, or one at rest, as shown on Plate 35, is an ordinary looking snake.

(*Lower*).   Philippine Cobra, *Naia naia samarensis*.   Numerous cobras in the Philippine Islands show traces of spectacle markings, but this form is uniform brown or black with no hood pattern.   Its general scalation, however, points to nothing more than an island race of the common Asiatic cobra.

PLATE 38   Dangerously Poisonous Snakes

King Cobra, *Naia hannah*. Largest of the cobras, in fact longest of the world's poisonous snakes. The record measurement is eighteen feet, although the usual length for adult examples is twelve feet. Its closest Old World rival is the Giant Brown Snake, *Oxyuranus maclennani* of northern Australia, which attains a length slightly in excess of ten feet, and also is a member of the *Elapidae*. In the New World tropics the Bushmaster, *Lachesis muta*—a pit viper—grows to a length of twelve feet.

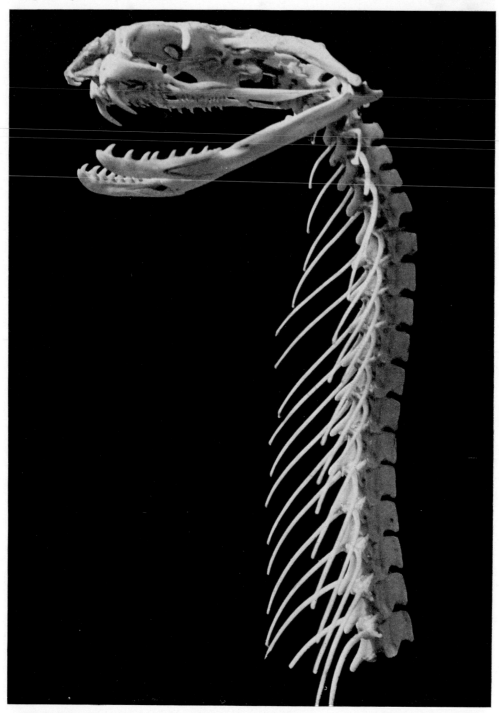

Skull of King Cobra, *Naia hannah*. The fangs are comparatively short, and rigidly erect, as is the case with all the *Elapidae*. They are, however, with this preparation from a twelve-foot specimen, half an inch in length when measured along the curve. The poison of cobras is particularly powerful, attacks the nerve centers and does not need to be deeply injected. The dangerous nature of this giant of its kind may thus be surmised. When it bites, it retains the grip and by chewing motions imbeds its fangs a number of times.

PLATE 40   Dangerously Poisonous Snakes

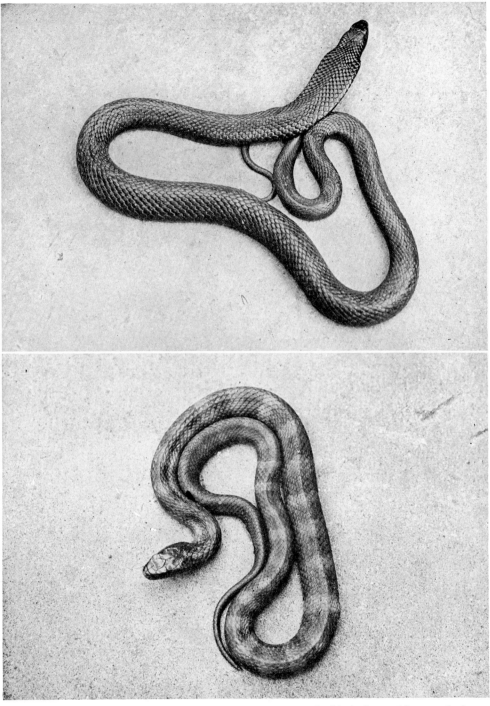

(Upper). Australian Black Snake, *Pseudechis porphyriacus.* Blue-black above, with a row of crimson scales along the side. Australia differs from other countries in having the majority of snakes poisonous, and these related to the cobras and kraits. A number spread the neck although they rear but moderately from the ground.

(Lower). Australian Tiger Snake, *Notechis scutatus.* Quickly stirred to anger this is one of the most dreaded of Australian reptiles. The venom, drop for drop, appears to be the most powerful of any Old World serpent. Fortunately, the amount of poison expended at a bite is comparatively small.

(*Upper*).   Death Adder, *Acanthophis antarcticus*.   Australia's most deadly snake.   Its poison is not so powerful as that of the dreaded Tiger Snake, but its large fangs inject a much larger quantity of the lethal neurotoxin.   The term "adder" has been applied owing to the thick-set body.   It is a member of the same family as the serpents on the opposite plate.

(*Lower*).   Sea Snake, *Laticauda colubrina*.   The marine serpents have an oar-like tail.   They are related to the cobras and kraits, inhabit the Indian and Pacific Oceans, although but a single species extends eastward to the shores of tropical America.

PLATE 42   Dangerously Poisonous Snakes

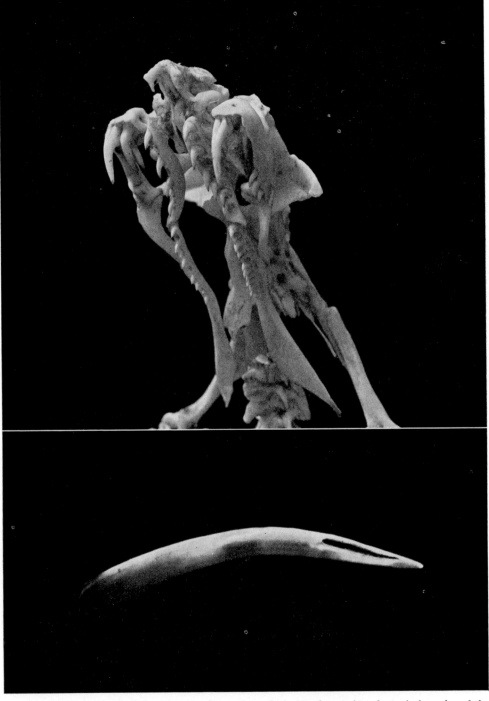

Fangs of Poisonous Snakes.   The *upper* figure shows the inside of upper jaw of a typical member of the *Elapidae*, the family to which the cobras, mambas and coral snakes belong.   The fangs are comparatively short and rigidly attached.   The venom of such serpents is of neurotoxic action.

(*Lower*).   Enlarged Fang of a Rattlesnake (typical of the *Crotalidae* and *Viperidae*).   The attachment of such fangs to the upper jaw may be noted with skulls on opposite plate.   Fangs of the viperine snakes are nothing more or less than hypodermic needles.

Skulls of Viperine Snakes. The *upper* skull is that of an African Puff Adder—member of the *Viperidae* or typical vipers.   With viperine snakes the fangs are of such length they are attached to movable bones and fold backward inside the mouth when the jaws are closed.

The *lower* skull is that of a rattlesnake—a pit viper or member of the *Crotalidae*. Note the cavernous indentation in the movable bone carrying the fang. This represents the pit, which *internally* expands to much larger size than noted outside the head of a living serpent.

PLATE 44   Dangerously Poisonous Snakes

(Upper). Common Viper or Adder; Kreuzotter, *Vipera berus.* Europe and the British Isles. The average length is between fifteen and twenty inches. A common reptile in many parts of Europe, where half a dozen species of small vipers occur—the only European poisonous snakes.

(Lower). Orsini's Viper; Meadow Viper, *Vipera orsinii.* Contrary to the general habits of poisonous snakes, this little species of Austria, Hungary and Italy is so gentle that in areas where it is common accidents are practically unknown, although the country children frequently pick it up and freely handle it.

(*Upper*). Long-nosed Viper; Sand Natter, *Vipera ammodytes*. Largest of European vipers although the maximum length is under a yard. Common in Austria, Hungary and the Balkan Peninsula. While the European vipers are rather monotonously similar in form and markings this reptile may be readily distinguished by the development of the snout.

(*Lower*). Tic Polonga; Russell Viper, *Vipera russellii*. Four to five feet long, this deadly viper of India and Malaysia is in strong contrast to the small species of its genus in adjoining illustrations. This viper, together with the cobra and kraits, combines to produce the high mortality from snake bites in India.

PLATE 46   Dangerously Poisonous Snakes

(Upper). Puff Adder, *Bitis arietans.* Africa forms the headquarters of the larger members of the *Viperidae,* and of these the present species has the most extensive range—from the region south of the deserts (and Arabia) to the Cape. It receives its name from loudly hissing when angry.

(Lower). Puff Adder Hiding. The blotched pattern tends to break the creature's outlines, rendering it difficult to detect. Three and a half feet is about the maximum length, but one this size would be three inches in diameter. The poison fangs are enormously developed. Small animals when struck die almost instantly.

(Upper). Gaboon Viper, *Bitis gabonica.* Of all serpents this representative of Africa's excessively stout vipers is the most sinister. It is as dangerous as it looks, having fangs in excess of an inch in length and glands with great storage of a venom both haemotoxic and neurotoxic in action.

(Lower). Gaboon Viper, *Bitis gabonica.* Combined with weird and fearsome outlines, the pattern of this snake is extremely bizarre. The hues are a mixture of pale tan, purplish and dark red. Yet among the leaves and debris of the forest floor the coil of this creature is difficult to see.

PLATE 48   Dangerously Poisonous Snakes

(*Upper*).   Egyptian Sand Viper, *Cerastes cornuta* (*Left Figure*).   A desert type of pallid hue which varies according to the hues of sandy surface in different areas.   The *right* figure is that of the Common Sand Viper, *Cerastes vipera*.   Both inhabit the regions bordering the northern Sahara—the former extending into Palestine and Arabia.

(*Lower*).   Sand Viper hiding.   These specialized desert snakes progress by a movement known as "side-winding", or throwing lateral loops forward.   Such locomotion is also used by a desert rattlesnake of the southwestern United States.   Sand vipers hide by flattening the body and with the edges shoveling sand over the back.

Comparison of Heads—a typical Viper and a Pit Viper.   The *upper* figure shows the head of the Gaboon Viper, *Bitis gabonica*, of Africa.   The *lower* portrays the Mano de Piedra or Jumping Viper, *Bothrops num-mifera*, of Central America.   With both, as is the case in general among the *Viperidae* (typical vipers) and the *Crotalidae* (pit vipers), the eye has an elliptical pupil.   With each serpent the pupil is contracted from the strong light in which they were photographed.   Note the pit, between the eye and nostril, of the lower figure, then compare this with the skull on Plate 43.

PLATE 50   Dangerously Poisonous Snakes

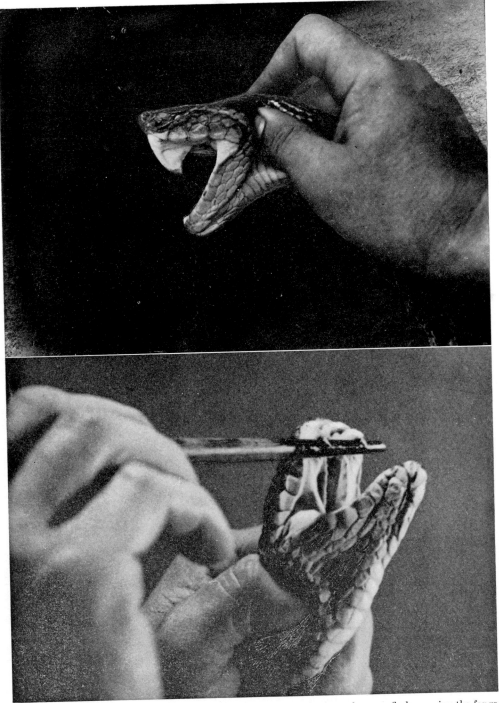

(*Upper*).   Head of Fer-de-lance, *Bothrops atrox*.   The sheath of membranous flesh covering the fangs thus normally extends nearly to the tips of the venom-conducting teeth unless instantaneously pushed back as the serpent bites.   This snake is a pit viper and all the remaining illustrations relate to the *Crotalidae*.

(*Lower*).   Head of Water Moccasin, *Agkistrodon piscivorus*.   The fangs are disclosed by the operator pushing back the sheath.   This North American reptile has proportionately shorter fangs than the tropical species shown above.   Fang length varies considerably among viperine snakes—even among species of the same genus.

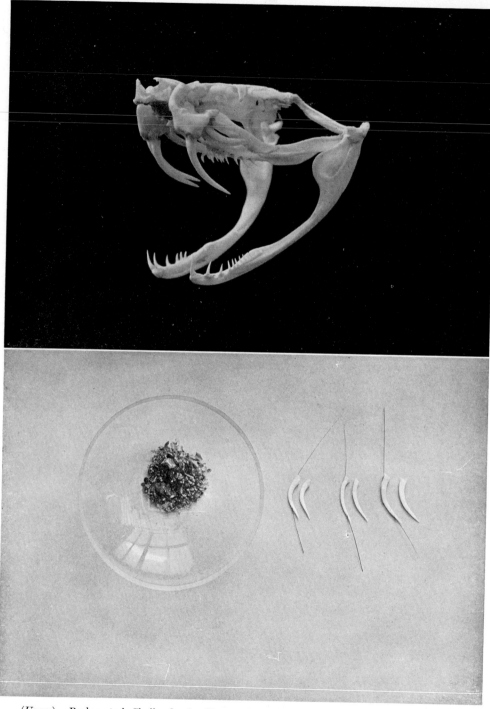

(*Upper*). Bushmaster's Skull—showing Reserve Fangs. The fangs of this great tropical American pit viper are proportionately very long. (See Plate 70.) All poisonous snakes frequently renew and shed the fangs. There is a row of these, from developing points to full size, behind the functioning fangs. A new member attaches outside the fang in use pushing it inward and loose from its base. It is afterward imbedded in a bitten animal and swallowed along with the prey.

(*Lower*). Amber-hued particles of dried snake poison. Also fangs of Diamond-back Rattlesnake, Fer-de-lance and Bushmaster.

PLATE 52   Dangerously Poisonous Snakes

(Upper). Copperhead Snake; Highland Moccasin; Chunkhead; Pilot Snake, *Agkistrodon mokasen.*
Widely distributed in the eastern United States. Its maximum length is slightly over four feet, but an
example a yard long may be considered fairly large. It ranges from central Massachusetts to northern
Florida, westward to the Mississippi Valley and in the south into Oklahoma and Texas.

   (Lower). Copperhead Snake. The body hue is pale brown with darker brown blotches. When among
dried leaves this snake is very difficult to detect. It is not so poisonous as the eastern rattlesnake and while
accidents from its bites are quite frequent the percentage of fatalities is low.

(*Upper*). Water Moccasin; Cotton-mouth Snake, *Agkistrodon piscivorus*. This poisonous water snake does not range farther north than Virginia, hence the common practise of calling the harmless water snakes of the northern states "water moccasins" is improper and misleading.

(*Lower*). Where the Water Moccasin Abounds. A frequently flooded area in Illinois about fifty miles north of the convergence of the Ohio with the Mississippi. Several of the southern snakes follow the great valley northward beyond their areas to the east.

PLATE 54   Dangerously Poisonous Snakes

(*Upper*). Water Moccasin; Cotton-mouth Snake, *Agkistrodon piscivorus*. The genus *Agkistrodon* has three species in the New World—the Copperhead Snake of North America and the two species figured on this plate. There are eight species in Asia, but none appears to be particularly aquatic.

(*Lower*). Tropical Moccasin; Cantil, *Agkistrodon bilineatus*. In form and its selection of sluggish waterways this moccasin is similar to the North American "Cotton-mouth," although smaller. It is more dangerous, however, owing to its irritability, speed in striking and high toxicity of poison. It inhabits Mexico and Central America.

(*Upper*). Hog-nosed Viper; Chatilla; Tamagá, *Bothrops nasuta*. Central America and northerly South America. One of the smaller members of the extensive genus containing the deadly lance-head snakes. Is seldom thicker than a finger and eighteen to twenty inches long.

(*Lower*). Godman's Viper, *Bothrops godmani*. Another small Central American species. The coloration is pale brown or gray with darker markings—these varying in form. Some specimens look somewhat like the North American copperhead snake. Despite its small size bites from this snake are highly dangerous.

PLATE 56   Dangerously Poisonous Snakes

Jumping Viper; Mano de Piedra; Timba; Toboba Chinga, *Bothrops nummifera*. Less than a yard in length this Central American species is grotesque in being the proportionately stoutest viper of the American tropics. It is also the most vigorous in biting as it makes a striking jump when irritated that may carry the body a full two feet forward, or to a greater distance if the snake strikes from the side of a log or bank where there is purchase to lurch its coils.

(*Upper*). Jumping Viper, *Bothrops nummifera*. The scales are peculiar in being exceedingly rough, like those of the bushmaster. Mutilated specimens have led some observers to the supposition that they had found young bushmasters north of the normal range of that imposing species.

(*Lower*). Jumping Viper, *Bothrops nummifera*. Receives one of its common names of "Mano de Piedra" from its resemblance in form to a native implement used in crushing corn. This series of young examples shows the variation in pattern—even among specimens in the same litter.

PLATE 58   Dangerously Poisonous Snakes

(*Upper*). Cotiarinha, *Bothrops itapetiningae*. A small brownish viper of southern Brazil. It is rather rare. Snakes like this when prowling near human habitation are liable to hide in trash heaps. Careless workers are inclined to handle and transport such material with bare hands. This is a common source of accidents.

(*Lower*). Jararaca; Maximilian's Viper, *Bothrops neuweidii boliviana*. This snake is of the "fer-de-lance" type and like it, is also called the jararaca. It is one of the most widespread of the South American pit vipers. The subspecies figured has the blotches crowded and vividly defined. Note how the dorsal blotches alternate anteriorly and fuse on the posterior part.

(*Upper*). Jararaca; Maximilian's Viper, *Bothrops neuweidii pauloensis*. A subspecies occurring in the state of São Paulo.

(*Lower*). Jararaca; Maximilian's Viper, *Bothrops neuweidii meridionalis*. One of the northerly subspecies named by Amaral. The difference between this snake and the pattern of the fer-de-lance is that with the latter, the large triangular blotches extend from the center of the back to the lower sides, the apex of the markings directed upward. (See Plates 60 and 61.)

PLATE 60   Dangerously Poisonous Snakes

(*Upper*). Fer-de-lance; Barba Amarilla; Jararaca; Terciopélo, *Bothrops atrox*. The more familiar name (meaning resemblance of the head to the shape of an iron lance) originated among the French-speaking population on the islands of Martinique and St. Lucia, where this serpent was once abundant, but is now rather rare. On the tropical mainland it is common from southern Mexico, through the Central American countries and over a great area in South America. In Central America it is more frequently called Barba Amarilla (Yellow Beard), and in Brazil, Jararaca (from the arrow-shaped head).

(*Lower*). Honduran Specimen of Barba Amarilla, *Bothrops atrox*.

(*Upper*). The Fer-de-lance, Barba Amarilla or Jararaca varies in hues and pattern. The example above and those on the opposite plate demonstrate this condition. The body hue is most frequently gray, or greenish-gray, with darker, pale-edged blotches. Occasional specimens are brownish. The blotches are sometimes irregular and reduced in size.

(*Lower*). A Day-old Litter of Fer-de-lance. There are over fifty young serpents here, each twelve inches long—from a six-foot mother. They have fangs and poison at birth and can inflict dangerous wounds. The litters of three Honduran specimens were 64, 65 and 71—hence the abundance of this formidable species.

PLATE 62

Dangerously Poisonous Snakes

(*Upper*). Jararaca, *Bothrops jararaca*. A Brazilian species not extending north of the Equator. It will be noted that the name "Jararacá"—the accent on the last syllable, in the country districts—is commonly used among the closely related and similarly marked snakes of the fer-de-lance type.

(*Lower*). Jararacucú, *Bothrops jararacussu*. Thicker-bodied than the more widely distributed kinds called "Jararaca." It is mostly confined to southerly Brazil. The markings are angular and the light borders of the blotches form a connected chain.

(*Upper*). Jararacucú, *Bothrops jararacussu*. The chain-like effect of yellow markings is clearly shown. Body hues are gray-green or olive, with blackish blotches. This snake is seldom over five feet long, but its proportionately large head and enormously developed fangs render it one of the most dangerous in South America.

(*Lower*) Jararacucú, *Bothrops jararacussu*. These snakes deceptively blend with vegetation, but fortunately have a habit of warning of their presence by vibrating the tail, which produces a sharp rasping among leaves. Brazil has long conducted a campaign in inducing native workers to wear protective leggings.

A Big Fer-de-lance. This particularly large example was captured in Honduras where it is called Barba Amarilla, meaning the Yellow Beard, owing to the yellowish tint of the chin and throat. The specimen is eight feet long, its impressive dimensions being clearly brought out by the height of Douglas March, a "six-footer" and expert in extracting the venom of serpents. March was bitten by a four-foot specimen and rendered almost blind and helpless within a half hour. His life **was** saved by the administration of neutralizing serum.

(Upper). Island Tree Viper, *Bothrops insularis.* Unique among South American serpents in restricted *habitat.* It occurs on an island of less than a square mile of surface forty miles from Santos, Brazil. Its food consists of birds and requiring an exceptionally active poison to quickly kill such elusive prey, it is rated as the most venomous of its genus.

(Lower). Urutú, *Bothrops alternatus.* Southern Brazil, Paraguay, Argentina and Uruguay. Attains a length of five feet, is quite heavy in body and may be rated as the most handsomely marked member of the genus *Bothrops.*

PLATE 66   Dangerously Poisonous Snakes

Heads of South American Pit Vipers.   The *upper* figure shows the Urutú, *Bothrops alternatus*, of southern Brazil and the *lower* the Jararacucú, *Bothrops jararacussu*, of the same region.   The latter is of the "fer-de-lance" type, there being several species of similar outlines.   With these the head is javelin or arrow-shaped, the upper surface from the nostrils to the eyes having a sharply defined edge and accentuating the lance-like aspect.   Hence the common names for these snakes of "lance-head," "fer-de-lance" (head of an iron lance) and "jararaca" (arrow or javelin-shaped).

Horned Palm Viper; Eye-Lash Viper; Bocaracá, *Bothrops schlegelii*. There is no mistaking the evil outlines of this head, characteristic of palm vipers, and these small arboreal snakes are as dangerous as they look. They have proportionately large fangs and the poison glands occupy the greater part of the temporal area. These reptiles blend with their surroundings and prospectors should be wary about going through thick, brushy places. Under such conditions men have been bitten on the hands and face. A trail gang, cutting through the jungle in Honduras had such accidents, several of them terminating fatally.

PLATE 68   Dangerously Poisonous Snakes

(*Upper*).   Horned Palm Viper; Eye-Lash Viper; Bocaracá, *Bothrops schlegelii*.   The palm vipers form a group of slender, rather small species—seldom over a yard long.   They are arboreal, have a particularly wide head and are characterized by a prehensile tail, which, as a rule is kept twisted around some projection.

(*Lower*).   Home of the Palm Viper.   A jungle area in Honduras.   The luxuriant and varied flora forms a scene of great beauty.   Single leaves of the coroza palms grow to a length of twenty-five feet, while pendant lianas hang from the larger trees at great heights and sweep the ground.

(*Upper*). Black-spotted Palm Viper, *Bothrops nigroviridis marchi*. Coloration is leaf-green, each scale tipped or delicately "smoked" with black. The *habitat* of the typical form is southerly Central America, but the subspecies shown was recently discovered in Honduras. It is distinct in arrangement of its scalation.

(*Lower*). Palm Viper Area. Tropical American tree vipers show a liking for tightly coiling just where the base of palm stems join the trunk, the latter forming a good avenue for their travel and enabling them to seek various elevations or cross to encroaching branches of other kinds.

PLATE 70   Dangerously Poisonous Snakes

(*Upper*). Bushmaster; Surucucú; La Cascabela Muda, *Lachesis muta*. Growing to a length of twelve feet, this spectacular species of the American tropics may justly be rated as the king of the world's viperine snakes. It ranges from southern Central America throughout equatorial South America, but is everywhere rather rarely seen.

(*Lower*). Head of the Bushmaster. Drop for drop the venom of this great pit viper is not so deadly as that of some other New World species, but great fang length and large amount of poison injected at a bite render it the most formidable of the New World poisonous reptiles.

(*Upper*). Massasauga, *Sistrurus catenatus*. There are three species in the genus *Sistrurus*. The top of the head has large, symmetrical shields. This genus of small rattlesnakes indicates relationship to the moccasins. The Massasauga inhabits the central states in North America. It usually frequents swampy places.

(*Lower*). Green Rattlesnake, *Crotalus lepidus*. One of the smallest species in the typical rattlesnake genus. This example was captured in Ramsay Canyon in the Huachuca Mountains of Arizona, by Dr. A. H. Wright of Cornell University. This rattler is greenish gray with rings of black. It occurs only in the Southwest.

(*Upper*). Horned Rattlesnake; Sidewinder, *Crotalus cerastes*. Southwestern United States. Characteristic from a horn-like development over each eye. Living on yielding sand it progresses by throwing lateral loops of the body forward, causing it to move at an oblique direction to that in which the head is pointing.

(*Lower*). Home of the Sidewinder. With the exception of spring and fall the desert rattlers are seldom seen abroad during the day. There are other kinds, but the Sidewinder is particularly fitted for a life in such places. Its locomotion is precisely like the small vipers of the Sahara.

(Upper). Horned Rattlesnake or Sidewinder, *Crotalus cerastes*. The horns are produced by vertical elongation of the large plate over each eye. This is a small species, of pallid hues.

(Lower). White Rattlesnake; Bleached Rattlesnake, *Crotalus mitchellii*. Deserts of Arizona, southern California and Lower California. The arid Southwest forms headquarters of the rattlesnakes. Over a dozen species occur in that region. Elsewhere, there is no such grouping, two to three species being the maximum number overlapping in distribution.

PLATE 74

Dangerously Poisonous Snakes

(*Upper*).   Prairie Rattlesnake, *Crotalus confluentus*. (Typical form.)   The common rattler of the plains.   Combining its races, or subspecies, *confluentus* has the widest range of North American rattlers. The typical prairie form has quite symmetrical, rounded dorsal blotches edged with yellow or dull white.

(*Lower*).   Great Basin Rattlesnake, *Crotalus confluentus lutosus*.   The Plateau Region from the Rockies to the Sierras.   The head markings, while faded, are similar to the typical form—particularly the marks across the supraocular plates (the plates over the eyes).   The dorsal blotches are smaller and become ring-like toward the tail.

(*Upper*).   Panamint Rattlesnake, *Crotalus confluentus stephensi*.   A pallid, desert form, recorded from Nevada and eastern California.   Rattlers from desert areas vary in hue according to the colors of the sandy districts in which they occur.   They may be gray, pallid tan, pinkish or distinctly red.

(*Lower*).   Grand Canyon Rattlesnake, *Crotalus confluentus abyssus*.   Distinguished by its vermilion or salmon coloration and almost complete absence of pattern when adult.   Observed only in the Grand Canyon of the Colorado in Arizona and named by Laurence M. Klauber, Curator of Reptiles of the San Diego Zoological Society.

PLATE 76   Dangerously Poisonous Snakes

(Upper). Pacific Rattlesnake, *Crotalus confluentus oreganus.* Except in the southerly portion of the Pacific Region of the United States, this is the only species of rattlesnake—in fact the only kind of poisonous snake.   It is abundant in many sections and occurs under various conditions, in the flat country near the coast and the high Sierras to elevations of fully 5,000 feet.

(Lower). Pacific Rattlesnake—Black Phase. There is much variation in color. A tendency toward suffusion with black is commonly noted, a similar condition to the timber rattlesnake in the eastern states. Black examples, with a chain of paler markings indicating the margins of the dorsal blotches, are often called " Diamond-backs."

(*Upper*). Tiger Rattlesnake, *Crotalus tigris*. Deserts of Arizona and Northern Mexico. It prefers the higher slopes among the rocks. Receives its name from the tawny body hue with darker markings of ring-like pattern.

(*Lower*). Willard's Rattlesnake, *Crotalus willardi*. Apparently the smallest rattlesnake and of rare occurrence. The length appears to be not more than fifteen inches. It is recorded from Arizona and northern Mexico. The curious arrangement of the white stripes on the head render it distinct from any other species of *Crotalus*.

PLATE 78   Dangerously Poisonous Snakes

(*Upper*). Timber Rattlesnake; Banded Rattlesnake, *Crotalus horridus*. The common rattler of the eastern United States. Abundant in the mountain areas. Frequents ledgy slopes and congregates during the Autumn near specific crevices which are the hibernating "dens." As a rule it is not savage and records of bites are comparatively rare.

(*Lower*). A Rattlesnake "Den." A shattered limestone ledge in the Ozark Mountains of southern Illinois. Crevices under the larger rocks lead deeply inward and downward beyond chance of penetration by frost. Female rattlesnakes return to the dens in late Summer and the young are born in these places.

(*Upper*). Timber Rattlesnake; Banded Rattlesnake, *Crotalus horridus*. (Black phase.) The common coloration is yellow or tan with dark cross-bands. Frequent specimens are suffused with black and some are almost entirely black. A southern variety (the canebrake rattlesnake) is gray, with black cross-bands and a reddish stripe on the back.

(*Lower*). Black-tailed Rattlesnake, *Crotalus molossus*. Inhabits the boundary region of the United States from Texas to Arizona inclusive and ranges well into Mexico. This is a powerful and handsome rattlesnake and appears to be closely related to the tropical species found southward.

PLATE 80   Dangerously Poisonous Snakes

(*Upper*).   Red Diamond Rattlesnake, *Crotalus ruber*.   On this and the adjoining Plate, also Plates 82 and 83 are illustrations of rattlesnakes which may be grouped as "Diamond-backs" in simplifying identification.   All have a rather symmetrical chain of "diamond" or rhomb-shaped markings.   The species above is a rather common and large rattler of southern California and the Lower Californian peninsula.

(*Lower*).   Mohave Diamond Rattlesnake, *Crotalus scutulatus*.   Recognized by the enlarged scales on the top of the head.   Inhabits the arid Southwest of the United States and extends into Mexico.

(*Upper*). Western Diamond Rattlesnake; Texas Diamond-back, *Crotalus atrox*. Second largest rattler of North America.   It reaches a length of six to seven feet.   The range is from Texas to California. Owing to its abundance and inclination to quickly strike, it holds first rank in the number of fatalities from bites.   Specimens from desert areas are of pallid hues.

(*Lower*).   Striking Coil of a Texas Diamond-back.   Ordinarily, rattlesnakes do not thus arch the neck, but strike from a laterally bunched loop.   Rattlers of tropical America, however, rear in even more spectacular fashion, over a foot from the ground.

PLATE 82   Dangerously Poisonous Snakes

(*Upper*).   Eastern Diamond-back Rattlesnake, *Crotalus adamanteus*. Southeastern United States.
Largest of North American rattlers.   Reaches a length of eight feet and its fangs are proportionately longer
than among other rattlesnakes north of the tropics.   It should be rated as among the most deadly serpents
of the world.

(*Lower*).   Mexican Diamond-back Rattlesnake, *Crotalus terrificus basiliscus*. This subspecies of the
tropical rattlesnake inhabits the southerly arid region of Mexico. It differs from the Central American and
typical form in having no bands on the neck—a difference to be noted in comparison with the illustrations
on opposite plate.

(*Upper*). Tropical Rattlesnake; Cascabel (Spanish), *Crotalus terrificus durissus*. Long neck bands, in vivid contrast to the body hue characterize examples from Central America and northern South America. *Terrificus* is the most poisonous of the rattlesnakes.   Its venom differs in having a largely neurotoxic action and being nearly colorless.

(*Lower*). Tropical Rattlesnake; Cascavel (Portuguese), *Crotalus terrificus*. (Typical form). Occurs on the higher ground.   This is the only known rattlesnake (including its two northerly races shown on these plates) inhabiting the entire area from Central America to Argentina.

PLATE 84   Dangerously Poisonous Snakes

A Costa Rican Rattler
Photographed in threatening pose, by Dr. C. Picado, of San José

By

RAYMOND L. DITMARS

—

REPTILES OF THE WORLD
SNAKES OF THE WORLD

SNAKES OF THE WORLD